It's Amazing What *You Can Still* Accomplish with *Only Half a Brain*

My story of my life, stroke, and perseverance

BY JACK BOUSQUET

DORRANCE
PUBLISHING CO
EST. 1920
PITTSBURGH, PENNSYLVANIA 15238

Dorrance Publishing Co
585 Alpha Drive
Suite 103
Pittsburgh, PA 15238
Visit our website at *www.dorrancebookstore.com*

ISBN: 978-1-6853-7109-8
ESIBN: 978-1-6853-7954-4

IT'S AMAZING WHAT
You Can Still
ACCOMPLISH WITH
Only Half a Brain

My story of my life, stroke, and perseverance

INTRODUCTION

At first, I was confused and scared… actually a little angry and most definitely lost. On September 27, 2002, I suffered a massive stroke. I lost 40% of my brain; I had to learn to control my left leg to be able to walk again. I attended speech therapy to speak correctly. I found myself in the dark, in a foreign and obscure place. I was so alone, I was without a connection, I felt distant, and I was different.

I found everything, absolutely each and every thing, previously believed to be simple or commonplace was now confusing and beyond my reach. For example, I had to relearn how to tie my shoes. This one was really crazy—no matter how many times I tried to put on my pants both legs ended up in the left side. Long division, well… I saw something that looked like half of a rectangle…. I knew the smaller number went on the outside and the larger number on the inside. That said I did not know what to do next. I did not realize this was math. My mind had failed me… parts of my body I no longer had command of. I felt distant from family and friends. I felt distant from myself. I was no longer Jack.

I only went about 100 or so feet that day but more important, I walked. Sure, they were still holding straps at my side, but YEP, I did it. I knew I was going to be all right. The nurses pulled tight on the straps again, and the nice nurse relocated my wheelchair. I eased into the chair with a huge smile on my face. Everything to do with coming back from my stroke was baby steps, lots of little things that seem insignificant on their own, but when you combine all the little things together… well, I began to get confidence and believe in myself again. One always needs hope and I had hope and now confidence that I can push farther. Everything you want in life is on the other side of hard.

I was searching for hope I was searching to find others and their stories who suffered a stroke or possibly another debilitating illness to see and understand how others approached the fight to find their journey back to recovery. I wondered, do other stroke victims have similar problems, how did they cope, what they did to recover, did they recover, did they return back to the working world? My most difficult and pressing issue…? I was no longer myself. I wondered if other stroke survivors feel this way?

When I left the hospital, I went to several bookstores. In addition, I searched the internet. I was looking for books about hope, the journey to recovery, someone's story to fight through the issues to not quit and give up. Unfortunately, I merely found several books articulating the stroke and not the journey nothing about one's recovery. I believe my story can provide huge value for others who have suffered from a debilitating stroke.

I requested views and opinions from family and friends. I also began to take notes to document my thoughts and progress as I wanted to tell my story … **never ever give up.** When you are down with little hope and uncertain of your future, you must never give in or quit. Work at your shortcomings and practice over and over again what you can each and every day to invest in yourself.

I was hopeful to write a book. I am not an accomplished writer; I am not even a good writer… actually, I have always struggled with writing.

Unfortunately, I stopped writing soon after I began. Yep, it appears I quit. That is until I met Pamela Nye and Chuck Foster. They asked me to be a keynote speaker at their first event. So, I began to think maybe I can, hell … just do it, Jack.

I overcame so much I did not give in or give up. I can beat this failing; it cannot be that hard to write as well. I will overcome this misfortune. Yes, I will tell my story. **Never ever give up.**

Chuck Foster with Operation Scrubs March 25, 2019 for Pamela Nye's Operation Scrubs event May 6, 2019

The keynote survivor speaker is **Jack Bousquet**, the man responsible for $4 billion dollars of real estate development before his massive stroke, then 2 billion more after his recovery. Bousquet will share his amazing road-to-recovery story with the uplifting message: *"It's amazing what you can accomplish with only half-a-brain."*

Nye/Bousquet will be available for TV/radio appearances interviews throughout National Nurses Week. Nye will also be talking about stroke, stroke awareness, what to do when a stroke is observed or experienced, stroke prevention and stroke recovery. Bousquet will focus his talk and questions about stroke recovery.

Pamela Nye/Chuck Foster with Operation Scrubs, see a nurse thank a nurse hand out May 6, 2019

Stroke survivor, Jack Bousquet: will share details about his massive stroke and accomplishing $6 billion dollars in real estate development—$2 billion occurred after his stroke— also the challenges he still faces today, and why he believes, "It's Amazing What You Can Do with Only Half-A-Brain!"

Pamela Nye- RN, MS, CNS-BC, CNRN, and SCRN/Assistant Professor at UCLA School of Nursing. Effective February 15, 2019: retirement as Stroke coordinator/Clinical Nurse Specialist at UCLA Medical Center/Santa Monica

CONTENTS

Introduction v

1 room 224 [2002] 1

2 Orange Curtain Truck [2002] 5

3 I have a roommate [2002] 15

4 It's my birthday I'm having a stroke [2002] 21

5 Early years [1953] 29

6 He saved my life; I meet Dr. Dhanda [2002] 49

7 From my mom [2002] 53

8 Get it, what if I can't recover [2002] 57

9 Last Day of speech therapy [2002] 59

10 Pixie dust [1991] 65

11 Dermatomyositis [1997] 77

12 Driver's license [2002] 97

13 Time to move on [2003] 101

14 Finding my way after the stroke [2004] 109

15 Find ways to compensate [2003] 123

16 Kor Group early days [2004] 139

17 Frank Faranda [1995] 157

18 It's Linda's birthday I'm having a seizure [2004] 181

19 That lovely lady I live with [1968] 187

20 Georgia Tech [1975–1978] 209

21 That night I will never forget [1983] 225

22 I let him go, I said goodbye...early Anguilla days [2004] 237

23 Excited to have a project in Hawaii [2007] 255

24 Oh my gosh cancer it is [2008] 265

25 The other Frank called me [2009] 271

26 The lean years [2010–12] 285

27 Back to the beginning [2013] 295

28 Not again, the C-word [2018] 337

29 Next [2021] 351

30 A look back [2001] 357

CHAPTER 1
ROOM 224 [2002]

I wake and someone is talking to me. I don't understand … where in the hell am I? Who is his guy? Why is he here?

My head hurts so very bad it is difficult to see. I have no idea what is going on. I don't know where I am. So, I try to sit up. Oops that's not working, why can't I sit up? I find it impossible to sit up. What the hell. Disoriented, confused, and yes scared, I can't sit up. Why? Who is this guy? Where am I? … I start looking around. I did not know where I was, how I got here, or what happened.

OH crap … I am in a hospital bed. I am at the hospital. A strange man is standing next to my bed and he was talking to me. I could not understand him at first. This was very confusing.

I find out later that Dr. Shultz is a neurologist… my neurologist.

Pay attention Jack … look at me! *This guy knows me. He knows my name; who in the hell is he? I am so confused. What the hell? My head is killing me, and the pain is intense.*

Dr. Shultz shakes his head; I can see the concern and worry on his face. Dr. Shultz stares at me, odd smile on his face; he keeps speaking my name Jack, Jack, Jack… I am scared. I am so very confused. *Think, Jack, come on think. He is talking to you … why? I must pay attention… I know I am in a hospital room. This guy is wearing a doctor's coat. Yep, he must be a doctor. Crap, there is a nurse, and yep, she definitely is a nurse standing behind him. I don't know why I am here. I keep talking to myself, come on, Jack, focus, how in the hell did we get here? What*

1

happened? Can I remember ... *come on think*; it is difficult; just small images pop up?

Well, I remember an ambulance ride ... yes, there was motion. I recall paramedics talking about my daughter. I think I saw a sign on the doors from when the door to my ambulance opened: EMERGENCY? Yep, I must be at our town hospital. Why? Think, Jack. I do not remember an accident, actually I do not remember. My head feels like someone split it open, intense pain.

Dr. Shultz keeps calling my name, over and over. Jack, Jack, Jack, Jack ... focus Jack stay with me, please! I look back at him. He says, I want you to smile for me, Jack. That's right, smile. Keep smiling; you can do it. Come on, Jack. Good job, please keep trying to smile, Jack. My head hurts. *I think I am smiling. Why does he want me to smile? This is odd. This is silly. This is stupid.* I am so confused; my head hurts so very bad. Dr. Shultz nods his head, tries to smile; however, I think I am smiling better than this guy. He looks at the nurse and the concern on his face heightens, but he says, Jack, good job. I am thinking Linda always says I smile funny for photos. It's hard to smile when someone says smile.

He then took a pen from his shirt pocket and held it out in front of me. Take this pen, he said. I reached for it with my right hand. To my surprise the doctor slapped my hand and pushed it back. Noooo! He demanded, not with your right hand. I said take it with your left hand. *Okay, this guy is grumpy; left hand it is.* It's not moving. I keep looking as my left hand and arm remain still. What the hell? I am sure I tried and did everything possible to move my left hand. No matter how hard I tried, it would not move, not even my arm. Not a bit. However, my right arm keeps lurching in an effort to grab the pen. Now I am afraid; actually scared. *Why can't I move my arm, what is wrong with me?*

Okay, Jack, let's try something different. Now move your left foot. It doesn't move, but my right foot lifts up. I am getting what I call a storm in my head. His voice keeps getting louder, everyone talking at the same time. It is so loud, I can't understand with all this noise, and things are moving slowly. Everything is in slow motion.

Can you lift your left foot, Jack? What the hell I am thinking what is going on? I can't sit up and I cannot move my left arm, left leg, I can't move the left side of my body. My head hurts so badly. The concern and worry on Dr. Shultz face deepens he keeps looking back at the nurse and they are talking. He turns to face me again, Jack can you wiggle your toes? *Nope that doesn't work either,* I try they don't move however, my right toes are moving. He then pokes the underside of my left foot with his pen.

Can you feel this, Jack?

I reply, Yes, I can.

He says, Jack, I want you to close your eyes and see if you feel the pen touch the underside of your foot again. Tell me when you feel it, okay, Jack? So, I close my eyes and shortly after I feel the pen poking my foot, I feel it, yep and you just did it again. To my surprise he runs the pen back and forth on the underside of my left foot, I tell him it is ticklish and I pull my right foot back. Dr. Shultz nods and says, well, that is a start.

Dr. Shultz holds a miniature flashlight directly at my eyes. He moves his upright finger back and forth and says, Please follow my finger with your eye. He looks at each eye one at a time. This makes my head hurt even more and the storm gets stronger. I have a huge storm going on in my head, confusion, and fear. Pay attention, Jack. I am so tired I can't focus. I am falling asleep again. Pay attention, Jack, Dr. Shultz says. Please focus; I am going to say something, he repeats. This is important I want— I am falling asleep. I can't concentrate. I can't hear well. I can't move my left leg. Where is Linda? There she is behind Dr. Schultz and the nurse.

I remember the paramedic guys saying this guy (me?) Hmm, was having a stroke. I can't move my left arm to grasp the pen. It's impossible to move my left leg. Oh my gosh, I am having a stroke? I black out again. Sleep... everyone knew I was having a stroke. It took me a while to see for myself.

I wake and am not certain, but I think it is a different time of day? Is it just minutes later or hours? I have no idea. I hear Linda's voice and the voice of Dr. Shultz. I see a nurse. I hear my dear friend Jon Yudin, although I can't see him. The storm is gone, but my head is killing me, the pain is so very strong. I am out again. Sleep ... I was later advised that my friend Jon told the nurses that he was my brother as only family could visit me. To my surprise, tough, old, hard Jon either visited or called me every day for two months after I left the hospital.

Chapter 2
Orange Curtain Truck [2002]

I wake … Linda is telling me to focus, pay attention to what the doctor is telling you. JACK … there he is. It is Dr. Shultz again … he always asks me to smile. He is doing exercises with my arms and legs. This is odd. It is the same exercises that Dr. Klashman, my rheumatologist performs for dermatomyositis tests. I don't understand … for sure they know that I have dermatomyositis (I will talk about dermatomyositis later). He has me place my hand right next to my left hand facing upward, touching his hand and he asks that I push as hard as I can. Jack, can you push your left hand harder? No strength here at all. Next, he puts one of his hands on my ankle and asks me to raise my leg. The right leg lifts up. The left leg moves up ever so slightly. No strength here either. Dr. Schultz smiles and says to the nurse, this is good. See his right leg is remaining still. We need to work at this, Jack.

I have something to tell you, Jack … you must remember this; I want you to say—orange curtain truck—whenever I say what is important. JACK say it. JACK. Come on, JACK what is important? JACK, orange, curtain truck. … Okay, I will remember orange curtain truck, orange curtain truck. JACK, look at me. WHAT IS IMPORTANT?

I reply, Orange curtain truck.

For the rest of the week with multiple visits Dr. Shultz would be talking and in midsentence he would ask what's important, Jack? I would respond orange, curtain, truck….

Dr. Shultz would stop by my room while making his rounds; he did not have a particular schedule. He was pleased with my progress. We would mainly

5

talk and in the middle of conversation Dr. Shultz would add what is important, Jack? I would always respond ORANGE, CURTAIN, TRUCK. I saw him for a couple of years.

Each visit with Dr. Shultz he would ask simple questions to begin, like what is your name who is our president and where are you? However, on one visit, Dr. Shultz asked me Jack, what word doesn't belong here? And he said, buzzer, bell, and light. I said they all go together; you have a buzzer a bell and flashing lights with the type 1 high-rise life safety code. He said, no don't you see the light isn't a sound? Well, yes, I responded, however they all work together if you consider the high-rise life safety code. He laughed and said let's stick with what is important, and I responded, orange curtain truck.

What happened next, I found intriguing and as the years passed, I smile when I find another word that has three meanings. There are so many, I had no idea. Dr. Shultz said, let's see what you can do with this, Jack. Tell me as many words as you can that have three meanings. Hot and cold came to mind immediately, so I said, Hot, the temperature is hot outside, the man was hot meaning angry, the girl is hot; I am sure you understand that meaning.

Yes, very good. Do you have another? How about cold?

I responded, the temperature is cold outside; she is cold and indifferent, and I do not feel well; I think I have a cold.

Do you have another? I thought for a while and nothing popped into my head, but I said yes and surprised myself … Fast, he ran fast, she was fast, meaning an easy girl, and the clock was fast or ahead of time. It took me a while to get that third one. Dr. Shultz began clapping. This is great you are coming back, Jack; good job. I think things are going to work for you; your brain is working again. I have to run, Jack. Keep practicing at lifting your left leg. I will see you tomorrow.

One day Dr. Shultz arrived with another doctor. I thought this is odd, he always comes alone. I thought maybe he has an assistant or intern? He introduced me to a psychiatrist. I was surprised. Immediately I began to wonder why. I thought I was doing well, coming back, making quick progress. Hell, I don't need a shrink. I don't want a shrink. He was a nice guy. That said, our conversation was a bit awkward. Looking back on this now, I imagine I was definitely the cause for the awkward conversation and then out of nowhere, he looks me straight in the eye and he asked me if I was depressed. Okay, I thought he is quick to the point. So, I responded hell no. I am not depressed. I am happy and lucky, very lucky ... nervous about my future for sure ... what if I can't provide for my family. I do not know when or if I can return to work and actually make a living, provide for my family. I am not depressed, hell no.

I make rich people richer. I have worked for large corporations, small businesses, and rich people who want to create new hotels. Real estate development is similar to a film development.... The owner takes the role as the producer, and the development manager the role as director. The cast and crew are made up of the entire consulting and contracting team. I take responsibility for directing the cast and crew toward the timely and cost-effective completion based on the goal of the producer. I only hope and pray that I can still be a force in the real estate development world. Only time will tell? I think I can, nope, I will be back.

We talked awhile longer. He gave me a prescription for depression pills and recommended I join a stroke support group. He said they meet near the hospital and I could find safety there. I was reluctant concerning the pills, however. I thought he must know best. I took the pills for maybe a week. I did not like the feeling, and you see, I felt out of touch, slow, and distant. So ... yep, I tossed the pills and missed my next appointment. We had that one meeting. I am not certain I did the right thing. That said, for me, I needed to focus on recovery and getting back to work. I was afraid I would be overthinking the depression thing; I had to clear my thoughts of that, put it down, and not look back. Regarding the support group invitation, well now, I never joined any support group for dermatomyositis. I did not believe sitting with a bunch of sick people would help me; actually, I was afraid it would hold me back. I know to a trained medical staff this belief must make me sound foolish, maybe even stupid?

Once when I was recovering from dermatomyositis, Dr. Klashman said to me, Jack, you pretend to be better and then you get better; very odd however this seems to work for you.

So, it appears I preferred to be on my own, enough double-thinking on my part when I visit a doctor. I always second-guess my progress, no need to have others with similar condition ask me to also second-guessing my progress. So, I felt more confident to fight the sick battles on my own. That said, I always confided, well maybe not confide, I would talk with Linda. Interest-

7

ing, she would most always say, I am not a doctor, and Jack you are not a doctor either. Every time I got the same response from Linda. I think I just liked saying how I felt out loud to her? It gave me a chance to believe I was fine or at least on the mend. You see, I believe I am making progress, and then it must be true. I was afraid to let myself think anything even the smallest doubt, which was not positive.

After my seizure, I saw Dr. Shultz every month again. About ten months after my seizure, I had an appointment with Dr. Shultz. He wanted to run an electroencephalogram. I wasn't certain what it was. He said it will take a couple of hours and it won't hurt. I will be asking you many questions. I want to see if I can map how your brain responds to my questions. My appointment was in the afternoon, so I drove in from my office in Hollywood. When I walked into Dr. Shultz's office, he was in a very good mood, smiling and saying how he was looking forward to my visit. He usually is not a happy smiling guy. We talked for a while and he explained that he would be placing many electrodes on my head. He will be using the electrodes to map and monitor my brain activity. I was sitting on a chair that reclined. Make yourself comfortable Jack, this may take a while.

He began asking me simple questions similar to when I was in the hospital; then the questions became more difficult and focused. His questions bounced around concerning several categories, for example, math, history, music, a bit of art, current events.... He asked me a couple of spelling questions. I told him I could not spell before the stroke. I joked that I had difficulty spelling complicated words like the. So that ended the spelling bee.

I was curious to find how I was doing. I asked a couple of times and Dr. Shultz's reply was you are doing fine, Jack. Please stick to my questions. So, as you can imagine, I became worried that things might not be going well. Some of the questions were very complicated to solve. I had to concentrate to find the answer. I had to overcome my short-term memory issue, so sometimes I asked for the question again. Other times, for example, when he gave me a math-word question, I tried to separate what was important and what wasn't necessary to solve the problem.

Then, without a pause, he stood up from his chair and said, we are done. Let's get these electrodes off your head. Sorry that the gel got all over you. There are so many electrodes. You can clean up over here. You already know I am impatient. I asked how I did before I began to get out of the chair.

Dr. Shultz looked at me and smiled. You are lucky and fortunate your brain is formulating messages by taking many circuitous routes through your head. It is bouncing around all over the place like a BB in a bottle taking some crazy routes, but it is getting to where it needs to. You do not need to see me anymore, if you have a problem or something else goes wrong, definitely another seizure please call me immediately. I don't believe you will have another seizure. You are good to go, Jack.

This was a great moment. I felt like I'd just won the final game at the World Series. I did the best I could to clean up my hair; I decided to take a shower when I got home. I thanked Dr. Shultz and shook his hand.

That was the last time I saw him. That said, when I returned to California after my five-year project in Texas. I was originally scheduled to have my tongue cancer surgery in the same medical office building. The surgery center was on the ground floor near the back door. I walked up the stairs and down the hall to his office. I wasn't sure if he would remember me. I wasn't close or have the relationship to him like I did with Dr. Klashman or Dr. Dhanda. I thought I would stop in and say hello. Tell him he did good, thank you, and all is well with Jack. Unfortunately, the office was closed, his name no longer on the door.

Dr. Dhanda

First thing each and every morning, Dr. Dhanda would make his rounds and stop in. He isn't much of a talker, however, I enjoy his visits and he has provided huge value for my recovery. Dr. Dhanda believes I am doing well and he is pleased with my recovery.

We began occupational, physical, and speech therapy. The initial sessions were a bit daunting. That said I relearn old tasks quickly.

I still have a problem with my left hand and left side of my face. What is really odd and at first alarming…actually the first time I panicked with terrible fear…you see, I could not understand what was going on. I get and they still continue to this day, sharp intense severe pain in my left hand and arm. It feels like a truck is parked on my arm, fortunately the pain usually only continues for fifteen to twenty seconds. I have found that when I am sick, for example, during the time I have, say, the flu, the pain happens often, say, four to five times a day. Where normally it occurs once or maybe twice a week. The pain comes from nowhere.

At first, I was worried. That said, I believe however, I have no idea if this is correct … I believe it isn't really happening. It is in my head, so I just wait for the pain to pass. I always look at my hand and touch it with my right hand. Starting with my thumb, I hold and slightly pull one finger at a time I learned this from reflexology. It is comforting fortunately it always passes. However, when I am with people, say, in a meeting or at a restaurant and this occurs, I can't look at my hand as it causes odd attention and I definitely can't make a sound of pain. I do the reflexology and no one notices same. Just looks like I am massaging my hand. It is like what my friend Sandra Richardson who worked on our team in Anguilla always said all storms pass. I know she meant something very different; it just comes to mind when the pain begins. I believe it isn't there and it will always pass.

When my insurance ran out for therapy, I found a woman who worked exclusively with people who have issues with their hands. I paid her fee directly. It was well worth it as she helped me to understand what was going on and she gave me several exercises that helped me to get better control of my hand.

My hand craved touch. I told her how during speech therapy, when I got confused, Elizabeth would hold my hand and I became calm and things appeared clear. To this day my hand seeks touch; it is always numb and feels odd. I believe she looked forward to my time with her and I was a challenge for her as most of her patients were experiencing carpal tunnel issues. I definitely had something far more complicated going on. For me, in addition to the occasional severe pain, I also had issues with my left hand. For example, it would often crush whatever I was holding or break off a control device. For example, I was thirsty and went to the water cooler. I turned the knob only to find the device in my hand with water continuing to pour on the floor.

Unfortunately, this happened more times than one. I cannot hold a Styrofoam or paper cup as I always crush it. Also, not always but more often than I would care to admit, if I hand something like a glass or say a pen to someone with my left hand, well that hand has a mind of his own and he doesn't release my grip. This is embarrassing and creates an awkward situation. So, I usually make a joke, say something stupid and pull my fingers back with my right hand. I do my best to try and remember to never use my left hand when giving someone something. When I slip up, I want to kick myself hard.

At home to continue exercising and developing feeling in my left hand, she had me put several coins, small objects, and trinkets in a bucket filled with rice. I would spend hours and hours feeling through the rice to find an object and do my best to identify the object by feel. It never ever got better. After six weeks, I dumped out the rice in the trash and put the bucket away.

One day seventeen years later, I was at Dr. Klashman's office, and just when we were saying goodbye, he asked me to close my eyes and hold out my left hand. Twice he placed a coin on my palm. I knew it was a coin. That was easy; however, I got both wrong. I could not feel the difference between a dime or quarter, nickel, or quarter.

Occupational therapy initially was my greatest challenge. For example, I had difficulty reading maps or balancing a checkbook. I found it difficult to do well at most everything. To my surprise, I discovered I could not follow simple reading instructions to solve various questions. That was when I learned I had a short-term memory problem. So, by underlining or providing a circle around key data allowed me to look back at what I believed previously was important to complete the task and respond correctly to the particular question. This worked, and I began to excel and my occupational therapy came to a close a couple of weeks later. I continued the same strategy at work, definitely in meetings. With pen in hand to mark up what I read, I can solve any question. Unfortunately, without pen and paper I am most often lost.

One day while at occupational therapy, I was doing some simple math, and when I got to long division, I didn't have a clue. I knew the smaller number went here and the larger number inside a half rectangle over there, unfortunately that was all I could remember. I had nothing. It was like being in a black hole. Long division did not make any sense to me and I was totally frustrated and I became angry. Yep, I guess I was a bit scared. I reached for a small calculator on the table and one of the nurses said, we want you to do this without the use of a calculator, Jack. So, yep, I was frustrated and I lost my temper and tossed the calculator. It flew away and landed on the floor. I didn't know Dr. Dhanda was behind me walking through the room. He picked up the calculator and walked to my table and he placed it down on the table.

He said, Jack, you had a massive stroke. I want you to look around this room, you are recovering quickly, and I know you are working at it. Many of the others ... well, their stroke was not as severe. However, they are not coming back the way you are. So, stop being angry and concentrate on making yourself better. Figure out what you now need to do to compensate when something goes wrong and you find it now to be a challenge. He walked away, and I thought about what he said. I was certain now more than ever that I would make Dr. Dhanda my doctor. He remains my doctor today. I love the man. He is smart and he saved my life; but not much of a bedside manner. For example, when I returned from working in Houston, Texas being away for five years, I was excited to see him. I actually stopped by his new office while picking up a prescription on the lower floor. I asked his office manager, Sheri, if Dr. Dhanda was in. A moment later, without her finding him, Dr. Dhanda happened to walk around the corner to the front desk.

I said, Hello, Dr. Dhanda, it is great to see you. Well, he just acted like his old self and said, good to see you. So, are you living here again? With that he turned and walked out of the room back down the hallway. I get bronchitis a couple times each year, it happens quickly. I call his office and always get an appointment for that day. Dr. Dhanda takes great care of his patients. Dr. Dhanda took great care of me.

That night my wife Linda taught me how to do long division. She explained the process to me step by step like she was teaching one of our children and surprisingly she was very patient with me. It all came back very fast. Before the stroke, I could do math in my head very quickly in business. I could keep the numbers in my head while giving direction or arguing my approach to solve a problem. Now to compensate whenever I am at work, I always have my calculator an HP 12-C (I have had it for over thirty-five years, definitely a relic) close in my suit coat pocket. I do the math first as fast as I can, next begin my argument or discussion. I believe most in the room don't notice I'm using my calculator. Having precise information at hand and quickly gives one an advantage in any discussion.

The therapy room is large and mostly occupied by physical therapy functions. At one end of the room, the hospital located a couple of tables for occupational therapy. I would sit at the tables doing my best to solve the latest task they gave me while watching others doing their best to recover. Physical therapy was actually easy for me now that I could walk again. This therapy did not last very long.

Watching others

So, some of the people in the room were fascinating to watch and an interest to me to find how they were or were not recovering. I believe they, as well as many others who I met along the journey back, all took a significant part in my recovery.

For example, a Hispanic man who looked to be in his late twenties or early thirties was in a terrible accident where a car pinned him between the car and a wall, crushing his legs. I watched him work so very hard learning to move his legs and try to walk again. I liked seeing his progress, determination, and how he was gaining strength. He would walk on a platform holding on to rails on either side. The rails also provided support when he would fall. The last time I saw him, he had improved immensely. That said walking with braces still remained a huge struggle for him. I hope he mastered walking. I never saw someone fall so many times, get up, and keep trying day after day.

He was always alone. I am certain someone had to transport him to the hospital. I would wish someone family or friend would be there to support him. That said I knew we were all on our own here. For example, concerning me, Linda would always drive me to therapy and be there at the main door waiting in her car to drive me back home. That said this guy had a mountain to climb that was far more difficult than all in the room. It just seemed right for someone to be there for him as he had too much to deal with alone. I think he helped me to get better; he definitely helped me to stay positive and never give up.

There was a very pretty young woman who also suffered from a stroke, someone told me her stroke was caused by diet pills. She was always well dressed and was accompanied by a Hispanic woman who attended to her every need and kept her safe. This woman was the only patient to have someone with her. Most often she remained strapped in her wheelchair and the other lady would maneuver her around, get things for her from her purse or usually a large cloth designer bag that hung from the handles of the wheelchair. I do not know what I do not know about her condition. I only saw her from afar. That said the pretty young woman could not sit in a chair without falling forward. The therapists worked day after day with her doing their best to reteach her how to sit, trying so many options. They even tried chairs with arms and had her wrap her arm around the chair's arm. Unfortunately, nothing seemed to work.

There was a guy who also suffered a stroke and now he could not wear a shirt, the material bothered him. His wife tried silk shirts, however, she said, silk only worked for a limited time. Everything else about him appeared fine and normal. I would imagine it would be difficult to go to a restaurant or out in public when a shirt makes one so uncomfortable.

While waiting for speech therapy, I met another stroke survivor who appeared to be on a similar schedule to mine. We got talking one day. I told him I can't play the guitar anymore as my left hand's fingers do not feel the stings. And to my surprise it is now impossible for me to sing. He laughed and said, so what, I can't read. Oh my gosh, I thought. What do you mean you can't read? All the letters run together. I don't see words anymore. What do I miss the most? I miss reading the sports page, he said. There was a newspaper on an adjacent table. I walked over and found the sports page. I then located a pen or pencil and began to draw vertical lines at the space between each word. After marking up a small section, I placed the paper in front of him. He smiled, and then to my surprise, he began to read out loud … we both started laughing.

So, when I found we were scheduled near the same time, I would grab the sports pages and mark them up. One sad day came, and I never saw him again. I guess he recovered and moved on. You see, I never knew what would be my last day, so I assumed the same for the others. It would have been nice to know. Maybe we could have said goodbye or even provided contact information?

I never ever attended support groups for my stroke or even the dermatomyositis. I didn't believe it was for me, I like being on my own, I guess?

CHAPTER 3
I HAVE A ROOMMATE [2002]

My first night at the hospital, it must be night; everything is quiet. I do not see nurses walking in the hall by my room. Linda, where are you? What is going on? I can't tell if it is day or night. I think it is night? I reach for the phone. This is not an easy task. Yeah, that's it. The right hand still works. I try to call our home number. The phone doesn't work. I keep losing control. Did I do it right? Maybe this stupid thing doesn't work? Hmm ... The hell with this phone.

Earlier someone brought me a tray of food. I stared at the plate for a long time. I wanted to throw the plate at the wall. I believe my right arm could handle this request. What does that say? What should I do? I don't like being here. I am afraid, scared, and very unsure of my future. *Why not do it, Jack? Toss the plate as hard as you can.* Well, I did not toss the plate. I wanted to, but I could not give in, that would be giving up. Anyway, that was my logic. I will never forget what happened next.

There is a young boy beyond the curtain in the bed next to me. I can hear two voices talking. One voice is older and the other young. Sad, somber, concerned, and devastated ... angry. He isn't twenty-one years old yet. A Hispanic boy with a heart problem. A boxer. He is crying. His father is crying. The boy will be okay; however, he can't box anymore. I had a good life. A full life. I feel for the boy. He lost the opportunity to pursue his dream. His dad kisses him goodbye and leaves the room.

I can't move the left side of my body. My head hurts so bad. Did I have a stroke? Will I die? I don't want to die here. Oh God, don't let me die here. I

15

got to go home. I want to go home. If I can get home, I will be all right. Oh my God, does my head hurt. I need the Benadryl and Tylenol. Where in the hell is Linda? I need you to bring Benadryl and Tylenol from home to me. That poor boy. Sleep. It was so hard to stay awake. Yep, I fell asleep.

There was never ever a threat of death. I was just scared, very confused and my brain was failing me.

My new roommate, he was a very unfortunate old man. The young boxer was my roommate for only a day or two. One afternoon after a failed attempt of trying to learn again how to walk, a nurse pushed me in a wheelchair back to my room. When we arrived at my room, I needed her assistance to me get back in bed? I am concerned and beginning to panic. Anxiety heightens. No matter how many times I try, I find it impossible to move my left leg. Each and every time I tried to walk, I would do fine with my right leg, however, I could only drag my left leg. What if I can't walk again? What if my left arm merely hangs from my body? How can I live? Most important how can I work?

So, after the nurse left, I was trying to move my left leg over and over again. I kept this up all the while looking at my right leg and saying out loud, Don't you dare move, stay still. When, on the other side of the curtain, the sounds of crying and moaning began to fill the room.

This was a different voice, an old tired voice. Oh my gosh, I have a new roommate. I hope he is okay, sure doesn't sound like it. I asked him, You on the other side of the curtain, are you all right? What is wrong, are you in pain? He didn't respond his moaning and crying kept up for a long time. When a nurse came in to check on me, I asked her who was in the other bed. She responded, He is very old and sick. He wants to join his wife. He wants to go.

Linda arrived later in the day. She brought me a dry shaving kit and a razor, dry shampoo, and she did her best to give me a shave and clean me up.

Linda was surprised to hear the crying; pointing to the curtain that separated beds she said, I see you have a new roommate; is he okay? I responded that he cries all the time when he isn't sleeping. She walked over to the curtain, moved it aside, and looked in on the old man.

Linda tried to find me another room, talked to the nurses to see if we could make a change, but there were no open beds. So, I learned to tune out his crying and moaning. Such a sad man who merely wants to die. Fortunately, he sleeps most of the time.

Auspiciously, because we never talked and he basically stayed to himself when the hallway would go quiet and I believed it was nighttime, I would ask the attending nurse to please close the door to the hallway. This gave me privacy. Alone time.

With all quiet around me, well ... relatively as my roommate slept most of the night, I would slide down to the bottom of my bed; this was a difficult and interesting task as I had to exercise all efforts to make this happen. I found it was difficult, very hard, getting back in bed was even a greater challenge. Next, I would get my feet to the floor, stand up while holding on to the bed and trying to navigate to another suitable object so I can hold on and steady myself with my right hand. I would practice and practice trying to move my left foot and leg. I fell twice; fortunately, I did not hurt myself. I found it was difficult to stand again. I used everything I had to get back up. I was fearful someone heard the noise when I fell. I waited and prayed the door would remain closed and no one would come to my aid. If they knew what I was doing I was certain they would keep the door open and make sure I remained in my bed.

On the second night, I made a little progress. My leg actually moved forward, slightly. But, yes, it was a baby step in the right direction. The next day the nurses who were holding me up while I tried to walk were amazed and pleased to find I was making progress. You moved your foot, Jack. That is awesome. That night I practiced in my room again. I did not fall this time.

The next morning, three nurses—the nice nurse and two male nurses—arrived at my room like clockwork, just like the other days about an hour or so after Dr. Dhanda leaves, Dr. Shultz did not adhere to a schedule. Sometimes he would see me midday or midafternoon. It is time to practice walking, Jack, said the nice nurse. You are making great progress. You are surprising us. Let's see what you can do today.

I respond that I want to go home. She said, Honey, remember the doctor said he believes you can go home when you can walk to the end of the hall, go up one flight of stairs, turn around, go back down, and return to your room.

I practiced again the night before and actually surprised myself. I was able to move my leg and make the turn to get back to my bed. Please be mindful, my right hand made certain I did not hit the floor. I had such a small space to practice walking and I had to keep my right hand within reach of furniture and walls in the event I would fall. The turnaround was the most difficult task. I was feeling very confident. I knew I would be able to walk again; I was no longer scared or angry.

One of the male nurses helped me get out of bed; he put me in a wheelchair and pushed me to the hallway. He helped me stand. Next, they would place a belt around my waist at both sides a strap would hang down about 2.5 feet. The nurses would stand at each side and hold on to the strap. The first time we tried this, I couldn't' move my left leg. This was very frustrating. I would get scared and angry. At first both nurses would drag me along. Then I learned timing and I could keep in step with my right leg. That said, the nurse on my left side would pull up on the strap he was holding and walk in unison with me and the nurse to my right. My leg acted dead and would merely be dragged along. This was extremely frustrating for me. The previous day during this exercise I was able with total concentration to slightly step with my left leg.

Last night I kept practicing moving my left leg. I was actually taking baby steps. I even began laughing at one point and was fearful I had alerted the night nurse. Fortunately, not, as the door remained closed.

So, I was excited and looking forward to showing them today that I can do it. We made our way out of my room and the four of us took position in the hallway, the nice nurse standing about twenty to twenty-five feet in front of us with the male nurses at my sides. Okay, Jack said the nurse to my left on three let's go. ONE, TWO, Three and we are off…. At first my left leg did not want to participate. I said to myself, come on Jack what in the hell are you doing? The nurse on my left began to drag his side again and pull up on his strap, just like the previous times. After about five feet, I began to smile as my left leg got in sync. Please be mindful, I was taking very small baby steps.

I was walking again. Yep, you can do it, I said to myself. The nice nurse was smiling and began to clap and she spun herself around in a circle. The nurses on each side were cheering me on, look at Jack go, you are walking man you can do it, congratulations. They eased up on the belt straps and I continued along. Unfortunately, I got very tired. Are you all right, Jack? asked one of the male nurses. I am fine just a bit worn out. This was so much more exhausting than walking short distances in my room at night.

I only went about 100 or so feet that day but more importantly, I walked. Sure, they were still holding straps at my side, but YEP, I did it. I knew I was going to be all right. The nurses pulled tight on the straps again. The nice nurse relocated my wheelchair. I eased into the chair with a huge smile on my face. Everything to do with coming back from my stroke was baby steps, lots of little things that seem insignificant on their own, but when you combine all the little things together, well, I began to get confidence and believe in myself again. One always needs hope and I had hope and now confidence that I can push further. I googled strokes often on my phone and found article after article that advised the first ninety days is key. One has to force a comeback early.

Two days later, I walked down the hallway, up and down the stairs, and back to my room. I went home the next afternoon after a couple of tests and discussions concerning speech therapy, occupational therapy, and more physical therapy.

I was very happy to leave the hospital, and I was certain I would progress faster at home. I wanted to be with my family. I sat in my wheelchair with my daughter, Ashley, pushing my wheelchair quickly down the hallway to the exit door. I kept saying, Faster, faster I want to go home, baby. Linda drove her car to the main door and was waiting for us. Ashley was laughing and mimicked me saying, Oh my, I want to get out of here and go home. Linda already had parked her car near the main door. It was great to be outside, a wonderful drive home. I believe I can get better faster now. My family will help me.

Later that day, my first day home—we live on the side of a small mountain—I stepped out to my backyard to enjoy the view of the valley below and have the sun on my face and foolishly I decided to walk around my pool. Yep … you knew this was coming, I fell in. Fortunately, it was at the low end. Definitely cold and humbling, I needed to be more careful. How in the hell did that happen?

CHAPTER 4

IT'S MY BIRTHDAY;
I AM HAVING A STROKE [2002]

September 27, 2002 – My birthday.... Today I am forty-nine years old. Oh my God—forty-nine years old and realizing I'll be fifty next year. Hell, I am old. Where has the time gone? I can remember saying, you can't trust anyone over thirty. Yes, I am a product of the '60s. My name is Jack. Actually, John Paul Bousquet, but everyone calls me Jack. When I was a young boy, everyone called me Jackie, my dad called me JP.

Nine years ago, I was diagnosed with dermatomyositis. Dermatomyositis is an autoimmune muscular disease and I'll tell you about how I was diagnosed and how I overcame the effects of the disease later on.

Today is my second day of treatment for the dermatomyositis. My first two years were hit and miss, difficult and most frustrating as nothing helped much until, that is, Dr. Klashman tried IVIG; this procedure gave me my life back. Each month I receive an intravenous immunoglobulin (IVIG) treatment. I have been receiving the IVIG for about seven years. When the treatments began, I would go to the hospital as an outpatient. Living in Los Angeles, I either went to UCLA or to Cedars-Sinai Medical Center. Each day I receive a liter bag of IVIG, a slow drip the process lasts about six to seven hours and I went for two consecutive days every month.

I sit in a room with cancer patients who are receiving chemotherapy. At first, I would talk with the other patients in the room, that said, I would miss a patient for a couple subsequent treatments and ask the nurse how he or she was doing only to learn they lost the cancer battle and were no longer with us.

So … I found it best to read a book or watch TV and most important keep to myself and remain quiet. It was too hard to make an acquaintance, definitely not worth it. I did, though, one day a year or so later meet a young boy who was ten or eleven. He wasn't getting treatment. However, we met in the waiting room. His disease, juvenile myositis was even rarer than mine. He was brave and his mom even braver. I can't imagine what the boy is going through at such a very young age.

I don't like being the sick guy. I wear a medical bracelet I added another gold bracelet on my right arm, one of Linda's. You see, I wear the gold bracelet to disguise my medical bracelet as I do not want to look like the sick guy. I have been given information concerning dermatomyositis support groups. That said, I don't want to meet and talk with a bunch of sick people. I did join an online dermatomyositis group. I found from reading about these people I am doing fantastic by comparison, there are thirteen people that I could find living in California who have dermatomyositis.

My doctor, Dr. Klashman, a talented doctor who brought me back from this rare debilitating autoimmune disease was a professor at UCLA and one of his professors was the head of rheumatology department at Cedar-Sinai. The treatments are difficult to arrange and I need it, I desperately need a seat in the room. His old professor at Cedar-Sinai had more pull than Dr. Klashman, so most of my treatments were at Cedar-Sinai.

After a few years, I became a test patient for Dr. Klashman and the first to receive IVIG at home, under the supervision of a nurse. That is how I met Patty. She is my nurse for the past four years. I know I was the first to receive IVIG at home in Los Angeles. I believe I am the first for all of California as well?

Today, the second day of treatment, I woke with a severe headache. IVIG treatments will cause terrible headaches. For me the headaches began during the first day of treatment and then would last for three or four days. My nurse, Patty, knew this and had me try a combination of Tylenol and Benadryl. These combinations worked well and allowed me to soften the pain and sleep off the headache. I always scheduled my treatments for a Thursday and Friday. Doing this gave me the weekend to recover from the headache, and I would be in good shape, just a slight headache, when I returned to work on Monday morning.

To control the day's headache, I took the Tylenol and Benadryl mix, took a long shower, and went downstairs to have breakfast. My typical raisin toast and Coke. Yes, Coke. The breakfast of champions. It's a southern thing. I studied at Georgia Tech in Atlanta and the Coca-Cola headquarters are across the street from the campus. I found several students as well as a couple of professors enjoyed a Coke during breakfast. My wife, Linda, believes that I should change my eating habits. I am not a coffee drinker. I hate coffee. I have tried to drink that stuff black, with cream, no sugar, tons of sugar. No matter how I try it, I hate coffee. So, Coke it was. I also eat way too many fried foods, hamburgers, hot dogs, and steak. Linda is always trying her best to get me to eat better.

So, this morning as I was enjoying raisin toast and Coke, the phone rang. It was Nancy Bell. Nancy Vincellette is her married name. Nancy and I grew up together in a little New England town called Clinton. A little summer town on the shore in Connecticut. There are fewer than 10,000 people living in Clinton. Nancy and I were childhood friends and we share the same birthday. Every year since we graduated high school, I have called Nancy to wish her a Happy Birthday. On this day, Nancy called me. It was such a nice surprise. I know it sounds silly, but this ritual of calling on our birthdays is something we enjoy still. Most often we never actually get to talk. Typically, it is a message left on an answering machine. This day, we spoke.

After breakfast, I made my way back to the kitchen, opened the refrigerator and took out the treatment package that Patty had prepared on the previous day. The doorbell rang and Patty entered our home ready to begin today's work together. I sat at the kitchen table while Patty checked my temperature, blood pressure and she placed the IV in my arm. She recorded various notes in her log, always lots of paperwork for Patty. She was in her late thirties, an attractive woman, tall and thin. Patty was very sweet and kind. She was single and on occasion she would talk about an older man whom she dated, plans for the weekend, and other small talk.

We used a lamp in the family room to hang the IV bag, the lamp switch was at the ideal height and the lamp was strong enough to support a full bag of IVIG…. The bag held about one liter of IVIG ($10,000 worth). The use of the lamp let me sit or lie down on the couch and Patty always sat on the adjacent love seat and we would watch TV or movies on the VCR as the IVIG slowly dripped into my body for six or seven hours. When Patty had to catch up on more paperwork, she would sit at our kitchen table.

Our home like most in southern California has an open floor plan. The family room is divided from the kitchen by a counter. We settled in to watch a movie while the IVIG dripped into me. We began watching a movie, The Sweetest Thing. The morning seemed routine enough and after a couple of hours, my daughter, Ashley, arrived home. She was attending Cal State Northridge at the time, which is just a short drive to our home. It was my 49th birthday and Ashley came over to have lunch with me. (YEP, I had a stroke on my birthday; isn't that special?) As Ashley arrived, I sat up to say hello and the rest of the day is a bit foggy. I will do my best to recall what happened next.

As I remember it and with input from all in the room ... I was sitting on the sofa. Ashley was sitting next to me. Patty was sitting on the love seat adjacent to us and Linda was making meatball sandwiches for lunch in the kitchen at the countertop. So, where she was standing Linda could also watch the TV and she had a clear view of all in the family room.

I was thirsty, so I reached for a glass of water, which was sitting on the coffee table in front of Ashley and me. When, to my surprise and shock, Ashley put her arms around me slamming me back. She was yelling at me, asking if I was all right. Ashley kept yelling, Dad, Dad, Dad. Responding that I was fine, I thought to myself, *What the hell is the matter with her? What is Ash doing?*

Later I learned that I had been falling forward and Ashley moved quickly and caught me from crashing on the coffee table. As I brought the glass toward me, it dropped on my chest. I do not recall the glass hitting the floor. I also do not believe I felt wet, although the glass must have dropped to the floor and I was certainly wet .... I also learned that although I thought I was speaking clearly, Ashley could not understand a word that I was saying. My mind was clearly thinking words, but strange sounds were coming out of my mouth. I was a bit confused and totally disoriented.

The movie ... remember there was a movie on. Not the best of movies to watch with one's daughter or nurse. An awkward part in the movie ... the women were dancing in line, singing he is too big for here, too big for here, and too big for here. Well, the volume kept getting louder and louder. Patty, my nurse, continually asked me if I was all right. She came right over to me; her voice was loud, and well ... everything was so loud I couldn't understand anything. I thought I was fine and asked, what is wrong with you guys? But Patty couldn't understand me as only unintelligible sounds were coming from my mouth.

There was a strong smell of burning popcorn a horrible pungent sickening odor. My head hurt like someone hit me with a hammer…so much confusion, loud noises, and people moving slowly. This was the first time I experienced a storm. You see, I call this a storm in my head. The storm has occurred many times over the years. That said, only one additional time did the popcorn odor return, about a year later when I had a seizure. Everything around me was slow, very slow and the room kept getting louder. The popcorn smell was awful. Way too much for my head, my brain starts to overload and nothing absolutely nothing makes sense. The storm makes my brain feel as if it is being squeezed; my brain stops working. I was confused and the storm was taking over.

I knew something was wrong, but what? Ashley and Patty were acting crazy; they were so loud, talking at the same time and slow. So … what came to mind during this irrational moment was the emergency plan we had. I am thinking maybe it is my heart, but my chest doesn't hurt. In the event of an emergency with my heart the doctor/hospital had given us an adrenaline kit. In it was this huge needle that was to be pushed right into my heart. Remember the scene from Pulp Fiction? My heart was fine, though in my mind I was fearful that Patty was going to sit on me and stick me with that huge needle. I had a head full of images of a needle stuck into my heart. I was confused, but I did know something was wrong. I didn't realize that horrible sounds were coming from my mouth and no one could understand me. I find it so very difficult to stay awake. I keep falling asleep.

I found out later that Linda called 911. The telephone was right next to her at hand's reach in the kitchen (no one has a land line telephone anymore) and she requested an ambulance seconds after she saw me drop the glass and when Ashley pulled me back, she saw my face drooping, hearing slurred words Linda's quick thinking most likely made the difference for me to recover. Linda still complains that Patty did nothing; Patty just kept saying Jack are you all right?

The room felt out of control. Suddenly it got worse. The room was occupied with two paramedics. Men moving in slow motion as if in a time-lapse movie. I was dumbfounded. *What in the hell are they doing here?* The TV was so loud. I have experienced this storm in my head several times since then. A storm can occur at a crowded restaurant or at a party when all appear to be talking at the same moment. When the room slows down now and I get a storm, I find it best to remove myself from the people, find a quiet place, and the storm will pass quickly.

BAD smell of burnt popcorn, slow motion, and a violent storm in my head. I could see myself and the others in the room as if I were watching this crazy scene from far away; Patty, Ashley, Linda, Jack, and the paramedics. Where was I? What was happening? I was very confused, but I was not afraid. I didn't know why I was so calm. I am watching myself and there is chaos. I am so confused; *why am I calm?*

The storm is gone, but I can't stay awake. My head hurts, however, no more or less than it did earlier that day or than it has hurt at any time I have had the IVIG treatment. Paramedics walking in time lapse, I watch myself and wonder why no one responds when I talk to them, not even Linda. This is very bizarre. I am frustrated and angry. *What is going on? Answer me damn it.*

I wake again and find myself strapped down. I can't move. *Oh my God, I can't move.* I don't like this and begin to panic trashing back and forth. I cannot get loose. I open my eyes to discover there is motion; yep, I am in an ambulance ... it must be an ambulance. There are two men standing over me talking with each other. *What the hell is going on? I can't move and I try to speak.* I try to break loose, but it is imposable. Now I am scared and I begin to panic. The men pay no attention to my questions. I yell Where am I? Why am I here? Who the hell called you? I have something on my mouth and I can't reach it with my hands. I again try to break loose to move it. *I can't, I can't, I hate this, what in the hell is going on?*

The paramedics are talking with each other about my daughter. One asked the other if he thought my daughter was hot. The response was yes very hot and the nurse was hot also although she has some miles on her ... I am confused. *Why am I here and I can't believe they're talking about Ashley right in front of me?* I start yelling at them, how dare you. That is my daughter! They ignore me.

The conversation shifts. They begin discussing me with one paramedic asking the other if all that oxygen is good for this guy. Could it hurt his eyes and make him blind? The answer frightened me. Hell, this man is having a massive stroke and he needs to suck on that oxygen. STROKE—what in the hell are they talking about? I am not having a stroke. I am not having a stroke. I hate being tied down. I keep trying to ask who called them. Why am I here in an ambulance? Like the scene in the family room earlier, I can see them. I can see me. Everything is moving in slow motion. The storm returns with that awful smell of burnt popcorn, however, far more intense this time.

Finally, they look at me. Who called you? I ask. One guy removes what is on my mouth? I keep saying who called you? They say WHAT is he saying? I keep repeating the question. I try speaking slowly one word at a time. When the smaller guy says, Your wife called. I think, no she didn't. I am thinking. We would have discussed it; she wouldn't just call. My head hurts so bad, it keeps getting worse. I am watching the scene with me lying on my back in an ambulance. I can't stay awake.

The ambulance stops and the doors open, I can see an EMERGENCY sign. I have been to the emergency room several times with my two sons who like many boys do crazy stupid things and get hurt. I realize where I am and that they are taking me to the Henry Mayo Hospital. But why? I don't know why.

I think I fell asleep again. The storm is so violent. More confusion. Lots of people talking. Voices coming from all directions. 360 degrees around me and I am in the middle of the circle. I do not see myself now and I no longer smell burnt popcorn. Actually, I don't see anyone around me, I only hear voices, loud voices and the voices are arguing. Give him alteplase (a clot buster drug) we are going to lose him. It is a massive stroke. They are arguing. They want to give me the drug to break up a clot. I hear the sound of mylar moving. In the confusion, the arguing reminded me of my design team meetings. Engineers often have varied approaches and solutions to solve design problems. Listening to the doctors argue brought me back to my meetings.

Then a quiet, kind voice with a strong Indian accent, with a little bit of laughter in his voice, spoke from my right side. I felt someone pulling on the bracelet on my arm. My medical bracelet ... this doctor was reading it. Quietly he said we can't give the clot buster to this man. This drug will kill him. He has dermatomyositis. I studied this disease in college. (I found out later he actually wrote a paper on dermatomyositis while he was studying medicine). This drug will cause massive bleeding in his brain; if we give it to him, he will die. I say we give him aspirin and wait.

I found the argument very exciting. The storm was strong. I said, If I have a vote, I am all for the aspirin, guys. They are not paying any attention to me or what I was saying. I blacked out again and woke to find I was in a hospital bed in room #224.

CHAPTER 5
EARLY YEARS [1953]

I enjoyed a wonderful and happy childhood. Most notably I always knew I was loved. I was fortunate to have a blessed and caring childhood. A mom who held me close and a dad who made me the man I am today. He taught me to do the right thing because it is the right thing to do. A man is only as good as his word.

One afternoon during the spring of 1992 while I was attending a business seminar, the speaker asked the audience a question. To provoke an open discussion with the audience the speaker led off with this question: If you could go back in time by say some sort of magic would you want to live your life all over again? To be clear he continued you would go back to your beginning maybe starting off as a young child of six or seven years old? The conference center immediately became a buzz of voices and activity. Some called out hell no; others shook their heads and said those were difficult times, no way would I want to be a child again. I thought for just a short time not even ten seconds. I replied, Absolutely, I enjoyed my time as a young boy. Several called out, Are you crazy? I was sitting close to the front maybe only three or four rows from his podium. The speaker paused and turned his attention my way, pointing at me, "What is your name? he asked. Could you be so kind to stand? Can someone get this guy a microphone? Seconds later someone approached me from behind and handed me a microphone.

Could you tell us your name?

Jack Bousquet, I responded.

Okay, Jack, he persisted, all your childhood days were fun you never had a bad day? Can you say that, Jack? He went on to ask before I could respond to his initial question, So you do not have any regrets?

I responded is there something I may want to change? Several in the room called out you are crazy who would want to be a child once more, not me nope I could never go back to those days. He responded, Yes, Jack is there anything you would want to change?

I answered; I don't believe I would change anything as that might change me. I enjoyed my childhood. Yes, I would live it again. The room was a clamor, the speakers asked are you certain, and so can we assume you are from a wealthy family, Jack? I took a couple of steps forward and replied, no, I am not from a wealthy family. My dad is a teacher at our town's high school, a very small town Clinton, Connecticut. I am the oldest of five children. My dad had to work a second job to support our family. I was his helper insulating homes. I am lucky, I knew I was loved; I grew up with a strong work ethic, our family was very close and we remain close today. Hell, yes, I would gladly do it all over again, I had fun and I would have even more fun. You see, I know that sixth grade History test, the one I failed, well … I know it doesn't mean anything. Family is everything. Those days shaped me to who I am today. What I think, what I desire, most certainly who I am. My childhood was definitely a wonderful journey.

My mother, Patricia Ann Michaud, a young woman of only eighteen wanted to marry. Due to her age, she required her parents Laura Michaud and Lucien Michaud's approval and her father's signature to marry John Malinowski. They married October 1952. I never knew the date. My mother would say she can't remember the date, then look to the side and back to me and say it isn't important, Jack. I always believed she remembered. How could you not recall your wedding day? Her birthday is October 11, 1934. So, yes, she was very young reaching eighteen years by a day or so before marriage, I imagine her to be impetuous … most likely naive, definitely inexperienced when it comes to life's decisions.

My mother always loved the name Michael. She wanted to name me Michael, and give me my middle name after my grandfather her father Lucien Paulen Cyril Michaud. All knew my grandfather fondly as Frenchie as a child as well as to the day he died, I nevertheless I called him Pop Pop.

Michael Paul Malinowski was my name for a short moment, until John Malinowski, her husband, told the nun who was also a nurse to change my name. He chose John Paul Malinowski for the name to be listed on my birth certificate. Yes, I was named after him. My mother learned my name to be

John only later when she saw the birth certificate. Today I wish Lucien to be my middle name as I prefer that to Paul, I guess because Lucien is my grandfather's first name and Lucien to me sounded mysterious and like no other. The choice naming me Frenchie would have been odd. That said everyone knew me as Jackie. Later in life the one who gave me his last name called me JP as well as Jackie. I call him my dad.

I came into the world on September 27, 1953 at Catholic Providence Hospital in Holyoke, Massachusetts. The next day a nun came to see my mother. She took a moment to talk with her as the nun was worried and concerned. The nun sat next to my mom and began to advise her that her husband does not want the birth announcement to be in the newspaper. The nun was doing her best to tell my mother something was wrong. Now, remember my mother at this moment to be very young, and please be mindful, my mom was naive and trusting. My mother told the nun who also was her nurse, we live in a different town from where John is employed, so maybe he is concerned as he works for the town that he could lose his job. I know her response doesn't hold water. It doesn't make sense.

I do not know this woman, she is foreign to me, and she is not my mother. You see, my mother is strong, confident, and assured. Everyone knows what Pat Bousquet is thinking. My mother speaks her mind; she does not hold anything back. At times she can be so outspoken that some could find her hurtful and curt. I guess she changed; it appears my mom grew from an innocent young girl to become a domineering confident outspoken woman with definite points of view. I am glad. You see, I believe she gave me as well as my sisters and brother the tools to be strong and confident like her.

A couple months later, my mother would learn the gravity of the nun's concern as well as come to know what the nun was desperately trying to tell her.

My mother and John drove to Silver Springs, Florida for their honeymoon. Upon returning home, she assumed they would find an apartment. I believe it odd that she never talked with John regarding where they would live.

They began a future at John's parents' home, taking residence in the Malinowski front bedroom. My mother talked about how she did not like living there and how she was ever so lonely as John worked long hours and often was not home at night. My mother was saddened and forlorn. My mother's parents asked Grace my grandmother's sister to search for an apartment. Grace and her husband Homer lived in Granby, Massachusetts. The same town as the Malinowski's and knew the area well.

One afternoon my mother's world stopped spinning. The moment began with a knock at her apartment door. She opened the third level apartment door to find a young woman named Lilian, who advised my mother that she was John's girlfriend. Lilian went on to tell my mom that she was engaged to John and they plan to marry soon. Me, a baby of two months was lying on the sofa. While Lilian was talking with my mother I fell to the floor. My mother ran and took me in her arms. I stopped crying immediately. When she turned to face the door, she found Lilian gone.

John did not return home that night. Imagine if you will the thoughts and anguish for a young mother alone in the world with a two-month-old baby. The afternoon of the second day, after her encounter with Lilian, my mother put me in a stroller and walked to the pay phone a few blocks from their apartment. She called her mother doing her best to hold back her tears. My mother's Uncle Paul, her mother's brother, picked us up that afternoon and we moved into my grandparents' home.

Now remember, we are Catholic and this was 1953. So, my mother and I returned to the apartment the next day.

That night, well … John was in a bad car accident. He needed time at the hospital to recover.

My Pop Pop (grandfather) went to his church to talk with the priest. Yes, our family is very religious; my mother remains a strong Catholic to this day. He articulated the unfortunate story of his daughter's short marriage. The priest advised marriage is a sacrament; he was not certain what my grandfather expected from him. With that, the priest said he will be making rounds at the hospital in the morning and plans to see John at that time.

No one knows the priest's conversation with John. That said, the priest called and asked my grandfather to see him at the rectory the next afternoon. The priest told my grandfather to get his daughter away from John; if she stays, John will destroy his daughter. Let her go. She cannot stay there. We moved back to my grandparents' home that night. My grandfather found an attorney to help my mom. My mother and I lived at my grandparents' home for the next four and a half years.

About a week after we moved in with my grandparents, my mother with help from her grandmother (meme) and Aunt Laura returned to the apartment to get our things. They chose a time when they thought John would be at work. While they were on the street placing our clothes and belongings in the car, my mother noticed John's car parked across the street. She could see a woman sitting in the car, my mom is not certain if the woman was Lilian…the woman who knocked on her door that dreadful day when my mother's world stopped spinning…or someone else as her view was such that she could only see the woman from behind. My mother crossed the street to approach the car. John quickly stepped out of the car and he and my mom began yelling an argument ensued in the street. My mother kept advancing towards John's car with that John quickly retreated back to his car and started the engine and began to drive away.

Well now my mother saw a large rock sitting on the ground beneath where she was standing. She took the rock in her hand and threw the rock at John's car. That rock smashed his back seat side view window. I believe that was the moment my mother got her spunk … the exact instant my mom gained her confidence and strength. The moment she became more like her mother. The moment my mother became the woman I know and love; the woman who our family and friends look to when times are tough and difficult situations threaten.

The home of my grandparents was located in an extremely modest neighborhood on 71 States Street, Willimansett, Massachusetts. Residents included my Pop Pop (grandfather) who worked as an oiler on a crane. Every Christmas from age two to four, I would go to work with him to watch the erection of the Christmas tree in Springfield. My Nana worked at Johnson's bookstore. My mother was a secretary at Spaulding. Her office was at the intersection of our street. Many of the women who also lived on our street…and I assume also on the adjacent streets in the area…did piece work for Spaulding. The ladies sewed baseballs. They all worked from home.

My uncle Don, who is seven years older than me., So for me he is more like a brother.

Most important were the old ladies living with my grandparents they were the ones who looked after me. My Memere (great-grandmother) every Friday baked all the bread, pies, and cookies for the upcoming week. She always made certain to save some of the ingredients to bake me a couple of mini pies. Her sister, my great-aunt Laura did most of the cleaning. The old ladies loved me.

I spent most of my time with them. I could not go outside until afternoon. I had no idea what afternoon was. That said I knew afternoon came after we had lunch and when the Art Linkletter Show ended.

My Pop Pop never yelled at me. I gave him good cause for same many times. For example, when I was two, my Pop Pop found a bicycle at the dump one day. He spray-painted the bike black; he made it look like new by purchasing a couple of new tires and a new seat. He also added some streamers that attached to the handlebar grips. For the final touch, he attached a bell to the handlebars and training wheels. I was so small and I could not reach the pedals so my Pop Pop attached wooden blocks to the pedals to shorten my reach. My first bike was a beauty and I loved it.

His house had a long driveway, which provided lots of room for me to practice riding. When I was three, the wooden blocks and training wheels were removed. Let's get on with the story. When I was four, I rode my bike into the garage and ended my ride with one of my famous skid outs. Unfortunately, the rear tire collided with a stack of storm windows my Pop Pop had purchased and planned to place on his home. The impact from my bike caused the storm windows to go down like dominos falling with several of the windows' glass breaking to pieces.

My Nana (grandmother) well she yelled often. Of the two, my Nana assumed the role of disciplinarian. When we would go to the city, my Nana and I traveled by bus. I would wander away. She said I moved so quickly. Can you believe she purchased a dog leash and attached it to my pants?

Please be mindful, everyone around me was old. I did have a friend, one person who was not part of our family, a lovely old lady who lived next door, Mrs. Petersen. Hell, she was older than my great-grandmother and great-aunt Laura. I would go next door to see Mrs. Petersen and we would talk. I do not believe Mrs. Petersen ever got out of her chair. I was to learn later in life that my friend Mrs. Petersen suffered from dementia.

My friend Sam

At the age of four, I invented an imaginary friend named Sam. He was a good ally, through thick and thin, my good friend Sam was always with me. Sam even had his own place at the dinner table. Unfortunately, Sam became a problem. One afternoon when I was four, while my Nana and I were returning home on the bus from the city, a big black woman sat down next to me.... Well, now, you see, she sat on Sam. I screamed, You are hurting him! Get off of Sam! He can't breathe! My Nana was so embarrassed; she did her best to explain to the woman why her grandson was being so irrational and absurd. The lady took another seat; many on the bus laughed and smile.

The next morning, I was surprised to find no chair, also no place setting for Sam at our breakfast table. His chair and dish were always next to me, but not this morning. So, I asked. Where did Sam go? Is he coming back? Why would he leave? My Nana got out of her chair and walked towards me, she said, Jackie, Sam is gone. He will not be back.

Whyyyyy! I yelled. My Nana said, because I killed him. Sam is gone, Jackie. You do not need him anymore. I never saw my friend Sam again.

Years later, while attending my Nana's funeral, all of her grandchildren had a story a fond memory of her, to share. Our cousin Amy was chosen to tell each story on behalf of all the grandchildren standing in front of the church. My contribution was how Nana convinced my friend Sam to leave. Picture if you will, Amy telling my memory and when she read the line Because I killed him, the priest who was standing close to Amy actually started to laugh. He did his best to cover his face; however, he could not stop laughing. My Nana loved me. We all are fortunate to have a bit of her strength in us. My grandparents kept close with their extended family. The home was constantly filled with aunts, uncles, cousins, and most often distant relatives that only my Nana could explain.

I have a dad

A friend of my mother's set her up on a blind date; the night included a show at the Student Prince, at the time a popular night club in Springfield, Massachusetts. The entertainment included a comedian and band, which is how she met Norman. He is my dad. Norman Henry Bousquet. An ex-Marine who recently returned from the Korean War who now was attending American International College on the G.I. bill, dated my mom for almost four years.

Norman ate dinner each and every night at my grandparent's home. He would pick me up in the afternoon after class. He gave me a lot of his time. His family had issues with my mom as well as me as you could imagine lots of tension, which became the impetus for their first fight. My mother wanted to get away so she and I took a trip to visit her sister Gail who lived in Wisconsin. This was my first time on an airplane. My only memory is of the pilot giving me silver wings while he sat in the cockpit, a badge for my shirt.

While playing outside at my Aunt Gail's home, I started to push a stroller down the sidewalk. Shortly after I got lost. A police car drove by. The police officer took notice; I guess I looked out of place walking alone at just four years old. He asked me where I lived, and when I answered 71 States Street, Willimansett, Massachusetts, he was surprised. My aunt's purse was hanging on the stroller. The policeman found her driver's license and saw her address was just a street away; this was my first ride in a police car. With a knock on the door, my aunt and mother were surprised to find the policeman and me standing on the step.

When we returned home, Norman asked my mom for her hand. His graduation was the following Saturday. They decided to marry the following week.

Norman was from a large family, six brothers and a sister. Only Raymond, his closest brother who just a year prior finished a tour with the Army—can you believe Raymond had a previous tour with the Navy—attended their wedding. Richard and Robert at the time were away at basic training becoming Marines. His parents, sister, and three other brothers refused to attend. Please be mindful, the time was 1950s one did not marry a woman who previously married let alone a woman who came with a son. They were married June 21, 1958.

My mother did not have an engagement ring; they each have matching wedding rings. The wedding was modest with a reception at my grandparents' basement. I was at their wedding. I even got a ring. My ring came from a Cracker Jack box. This was a huge day for me. You see, I had a dad now, a new beginning. Patricia and Norman left for Niagara Falls. With the wedding over, I took sips from several discarded drinks. Yep, I was drunk.

Raymond was my dad's closest brother growing up. Raymond married my aunt Jackie, who was pregnant at the time. Their daughter, my cousin Nancy and I became very close. We were the two outcasts of the Buskey/Bousquet family. However, Nancy is sweet. Everyone liked Nancy.

I was so excited when my mom and dad returned from their honeymoon. At first it appeared our new family would be living in an apartment a couple of streets away from my grandparents. I remember my mom, her mother, and the elders (old ladies) scrubbing the apartment walls with Lestoil. The apartments were originally constructed to house servicemen and their families at the conclusion of the Second World War. Over time the apartments housed low-income families. What people refer to as the projects.

We never moved in. My dad had previously applied for a teaching position in Clinton, Connecticut, a little town located on the shoreline just an hour and a half from his hometown Chicopee, Massachusetts. He held a degree in economics, and the town was searching for a teacher to take a position in the business department and the town wanted to offer an economics class.

We moved to Clinton, and my parents found residence in one of the two upstairs apartments on the second floor of a huge home owned by the Dressing family who lived on the main level below us. They had four children Tommy, Billy, Betsy, and Cathy. The youngest, Cathy, was the same age as me. We started kindergarten together.

In Massachusetts everyone knew my dad as Normand. However, when we moved to Connecticut, all called him Hank. You see, when he joined the Marines, the corps could not find records for a Norman Henry Bousquet. So, he said, ya know what, how about trying to see if you can find Henry Norman Bousquet. So that was that. He never knew his middle name was actually his first name until that moment. With all in order, now he became a Marine. A couple months later, he shipped off to the Korean War.

Hank, as well as the remainder of his siblings, was born at home. Buskey was his parents' last name as well as three of his brothers, while my dad's last name as well as the remainder of his family is Bousquet. I know what you are thinking. WHAT? No need to read it again, just look below.

This will sound crazy, but when his parents moved to Chicopee, Massachusetts from Montreal in the late 1940s, they took residence in a Polish neighborhood. Finding neighbors with names like Jabinski, Kowalski, and Nowicki, they wanted to fit in and have an American-sounding name, so they chose Buskey. Yes, that sounded better, that sounds American. All seven children were born at home. I guess the paperwork for the birth certificates was handled at the home as well. Marcel, the first born and oldest brother, as well as the youngest, the twins, Richard and Robert, received the Americanized last name Buskey. Lucile, Rene, Gerald, Raymond, and Norman (Henry) were given the correct or original name Bousquet.

My parents were excited for me to start kindergarten. However, a new issue was on the horizon. My dad retained an attorney; he wanted to give me his last name. The process was complicated, the court must be held in Massachusetts, and we lived in Connecticut. As strange as this may sound, my mother also was required to adopt me, a bizarre and antiquated 1950s legal process. My dad was concerned the adoption process was long and slow. You see, when I start school, it would be impossible for the adoption to be finalized.

My dad was concerned about my name changing and what affect that would cause. Please be mindful, this was the 1950s, a divorced woman remarrying was definitely not commonplace. Hank met with the Clinton, Connecticut school system superintendent Board of Education. Hank explained the situation to the superintendent and requested that I would be allowed to start school with Bousquet in lieu of Malinowski as my last name. Today that most certainly would not be allowed. That said, in the 1950s, our world was a more forgiving and simpler place.

That was the easy part. My parents also were required to obtain John's approval for the adoption. So, my mother called John to explain that Hank wanted to adopt Jackie. Arrangements were made for John to meet my mother and Hank at my grandparents' home on a Saturday. I can't imagine for a minute this meeting could be awkward! Can you? Hell, yeah. It was a circus.

That day in 1957 was the last time I saw John. I believe this day to also be the first I saw him, as I cannot recall anything previously. I remember the moment; however, it is impossible to recall his face. He pulled up in his car while my parents were standing on the front lawn. I was playing with my Nana in the driveway, riding my bike. We were about twenty-five feet away.

John drove up to my grandparents' home and parked on the street. He stepped from his car and immediately became aggressive. With that my Nana lifted me from my bike. She took me by my hand and said, It's time to go inside, Jackie, would you like some popcorn? As we began to enter my grandparents' home my Pop Pop, who I assume saw or heard the commotion in the front yard, passed us on his way out to join my parents and John.

My great-grandmother (meme) and my Nana with concurrence from my mom made certain I never heard a discouraging word about John. They did not talk him up. However, they made certain John was never talked down. Actually, they all never talked about John, at least not in front of me. They were fearful and cared to protect my well-being. So, most of what I am telling you, I learned in my teenage years after my family learned John passed from a heart attack late spring of 1971. The second time I saw him, yep, was at his funeral. (I will tell you about that day later).

So, John and my parents continued to argue on my grandparents' front lawn. The conversation turned darker when John advised he would show up in court to contest the adoption; that is unless Hank paid him a couple thousand dollars. John yelled, Give me the money for the kid. Hank said, What in the hell is wrong with you? John, you are trying to sell your son? Just think about what you are saying. Are you insane? John became angry and made a move to hit Hank. John was looking for a fight. Hank stepped back, pulled a knife, a switch blade from his pocket with the knife in hand Hank stopped he made a stance, he stepped toward John … John backed down. After some pushing and shoving a lot of screaming and yelling John retreated to his car, with the window down John drove away yelling, I will see you in court, the adoption will not happen. The knife, always in Hank's possession, was discarded later that evening never to be seen again.

I am fortunate to have an impeccable memory much stronger than most; this has been a great tool for me in business. I have always been fortunate to recall information, dates, numbers, and most important memories, I actually can see them.

I was adopted on February 4, 1960. An easy day for me to remember as February 4th every year we had a birthday celebration. This date is also my great-aunt Laura's birthday.

John did not show up at court as he had threatened, so the day is remembered as calm and happy. My memory, what I can see … the judge asked Hank to place me on the bench next to him. The judge asked me what I wanted. The judge said, Jackie, do you want this man to be your dad? That day is our beginning. I have a dad.

However, driving home in the car, I was disappointed. You see, they told me my name would be changed. Please be mindful, I at the time only five and understand at the time I already thought my name was Bousquet. So, I believed when they said my name would be changed, I assumed I would no longer be called Jackie. I thought my new name would be Hank, like him, my dad.

My mother told me it never occurred to her to change my first name until that very moment. My dad said, No, you will always be called Jackie. Today the three of us have the same last name Bousquet. I am little, not thinking, just going with the flow, everyone was happy so I was happy as well. Life is good.

Looking back now as an old man myself with children and grandchildren of my own, I have an appreciation. You see, I can imagine how difficult it must have been for my meme, great-aunt Laura, my Nana and Pop Pop to have me move away from their home and live separately from them. I was fortunate my family foundation was built strong; they loved me and took great care of me. They all have passed on and I miss them dearly.

Clinton Connecticut

When I was eight or nine, we moved to 28 Bluff Ave. a three-bedroom ranch style new track home development in Clinton, Connecticut. I have three sisters and a brother. My sister Jill, (yes, my parents have a sense of humor) I have a sister named Jill. They told me I got to choose her name. She was born when we lived at the apartment, Bonnie, Robin, and our brother Gary he is the baby of the family became part of our family on Bluff Ave.

Family is everything; we are a happy and we are a close family. We were like a TV family with emotional ups sometimes passionate downs often a financial struggle, however our love our trust galvanized the family strength, we always came through we rose above…. together.

Our parents made certain we always knew we were loved. My dad would joke that he married our mother to be my dad; he chose me the others just showed up It is merely a joke however I believe partial truth, and yet not all is understood. Despite our considerable efforts, there remained essential facets of our family universe that we simply do not know how to explain. Perhaps the most famous of these mysteries is that to me and I believe as well from my brother and sisters Hank was our dad, Hank was my dad. Measurements have determined the amount of love in our family universe to be very high.

Our mother was a stay-at-home mom looking after five children; however, for a short time when the wallet was thin, she worked nights on the assembly line for Ponds, a factory at the time located in Clinton. If my recollection is correct, I believe she worked nights for less than six months. I hated her working.

Our dad attended classes at Wesleyan College each and every summer achieving a Master's in Business Administration. You see our dad was a school teacher at The Morgan High School he started teaching 1958 in time becoming head of the Business Department. He also was retained as an associate professor, teaching night classes in economics at Yale in New Haven for a couple of years. In an effort to make financial ends meet at the conclusion of his two-year agreement our dad elected to forgo his contract with Yale and not extend the agreement.

He took on a second job, a construction position insulating homes this paid far more than an associate professor position. This did the trick to help our family manage. My dad worked hard; however, now he could make ends meet. Our family was better off. I was his helper working with my dad each day in the summer and on occasion during the school year. He would pick me up after school and we would work until dark however most often setting up lights to finish the job that day.

Without a DOUBT my dad's favorite place was a bar called the Jug Inn. This establishment is long gone now, unfortunately, I think it was lost to a fire. However, at the time the Jug Inn a bar the local watering hole located about a half of a mile from our home.

With five kids, like I said above he had to insulate homes for a second job. I helped him in the summer on new ground ups and after school we would insulate the crawl space under the beach homes. Many homes along the Connecticut shore line are raised slightly a couple of feet above grade. He would insulate the underside of these homes. I was a skinny kid and I so enjoyed working for and with my dad. In the summer we always ended the day at the Jug Inn.

As a little kid, this is where I learned to play pool ... a beer for my dad, soda for me. We held the table forever, or until my mom would start to worry. I have such fond memories there.

One summer night my mom actually walked into the Jug Inn and, upon entering, spotted us. Without saying a single word, she walked to a small table next to the place we were playing pool, then placed a plate of hot dogs and baked beans on the table, and walked out. My dad turned to me and said, I think we should let these guys have the table. Tomorrow we can see if they could keep it. Let's go home, JP.

So, with that, we said our goodbyes. My dad picked up the plate and he and I started for home. My mom was standing next to our car in the parking lot. My dad gave her a kiss, said something like that was special; she smiled returned his kiss and we drove home.

I always wondered who the dinner was for. My mom placed just one dinner plate on that table. Was the dinner meant for me or for my dad? As I grew and became wiser, I realized the plate was symbolic. A message placed and point taken with nothing more. However, I so enjoyed telling that story. Actually, when we lost our dad to cancer in 1990, that was the first story I shared to all who ended the day at my parents' home after the funeral.

For years prior I was naive. I did not know we were struggling financially until I went to college. In 1978 at Georgia Tech, I met so many from various backgrounds who had so much more than I. Many were given cars, most parents paid for their education and several had parents who gave them the gift to travel and see the world. That said, what I gained from my background was a strong work ethic, the importance of a family's bond. Believe in yourself however most important do what is right because it I the right thing to do. My dad taught me a man is only as good as his word. If you do not believe in yourself, no one else will.

He also taught me how to fight. I could hit him anywhere; he would not hit me in the face. We had some good battles. Many times, say, after a Hercules or possibly a Robin Hood movie, we would battle using yard sticks for swords and hold pot covers for shields while fighting throughout the house. This all ended one afternoon when I being much older twelve or thirteen at the time, we began to wrestle. Somehow, I picked my dad up holding him with his feet off the ground, I fell backwards we landed on the living room coffee table. We found the table smashed and flatten below us. My mother came running into the room and she went crazy screaming and yelling at us. This has to stop look what you did to my table, he is too big now, if you have to do this go outside, and then she cried. Well, the fun was gone, that incident became our final battle.

Yankee fan

I come from a family of Red Sox fans. I loved baseball, as strange as it might sound it was my mother who was the one who taught me how to hit and catch and actually play the game. She would be there even when I was older for practice to hit me ground balls in the back yard before a try out.

When I was only seven or eight, I attended my first time at a tryout hopeful to be selected for a team. I was standing in the outfield with many other boys on each side waiting our turn to catch pop flies hit from one of the coaches. On my left hand was a sad excuse for a baseball glove. It is what I would call a baby's glove. The other kids had real baseball gloves and most showed up carrying their own baseball bat. I rode my bike to the tryout. I rode my bike everywhere. While standing there in the field, I heard my dad calling JP. I turned to see him on the sideline standing behind a low fence. I ran to him and when I got close, maybe just ten feet away, he tossed me a new baseball glove. I caught the glove, placed it on my left hand, and I cried out, Thanks, Dad.

He said, Show them who you are. Now go out there and get them, JP.

Like I said I come from a family of Red Sox fans. That said, when I was a kid Mickey Mantle was my favorite. I was a Yankee's fan. They, my family, cousins, aunts, and all my uncles thought I was disrespectful.

Playing Little League, I was fortunate to be the first on my team to pick my number. So, of course, I chose number nine. Oh my gosh, was I so surprised and disappointed when I peddled my bike home, I ran into our house. I could not wait to show my dad my baseball jersey. I found him sitting on his chair in the living room reading Time magazine. He asked, You chose number nine? I thought you would choose seven as Mickey is your favorite player. I see you chose Roger's number. So that moment of disappointment touched me. So, I can't take it back. Well nine has always been my number this continued later in life for example in Florida and Virginia softball and California playing softball for a Disney team, Virginia and New York playing basketball, number nine was displayed proudly on my dirt bike … always nine I never wore another number.

One night I was with my grandson Knox and Rachel his mother we were attending a pizza dinner at a restaurant to meet the coach. The baseball coach was selecting numbers for his kids. Knox was seven at the time, when his name came up the coach said what number do you want Knox? I stood up and asked if number nine had been selected yet. The answer was no, hell I was happy to see that old number nine show up on my grandson's back.

While working on my first development—a small office building for the Life Insurance Company of Southwest in Dallas—I met my hero Mickey Mantle. You see the president of the insurance company knew Mickey; I told him how I picked his number and foolishly chose Roger's. He laughed.

Mr. Redfield

The summer of seventy-one with high school days behind me I wanted a car. I owned a motorcycle however I wanted something that was more appropriate to drive in the rain as well as the cold and snowy Connecticut winters. The faster I would ride during the winter the colder I would get. It was so cold during the winter months I would place newspapers under my shirt and inside my pants legs to help insulate as well as break the blistering cold. This helped, that said, just a little. You cannot believe how difficult it is to ride a motorcycle on a snow laden road.

My first car was the car of my dreams a 1967 MGB British green roadster. I asked my dad if he would cosign a car loan for me. He said, How can you get a car loan, you do not have a job; you do not have a down payment. Sure, I will cosign ... no one will be stupid enough to give you a loan.

So ... the next day I got a job selling educational books (encyclopedias, however don't you think educational books sounds like a more important position)

I went to our little Clinton National Bank and asked to speak to the president; I advised I am hopeful to secure a car loan. To my surprise the lady I was talking with said I believe he is on the phone now however please take a seat I will tell him you are waiting. He could have let me sit there for a long time. That said, in a matter of minutes, Mr. Redfield greeted me.

Sturge Redfield was the President of the bank. Mr. Redfield was a down to earth kind of guy for example he could be found each and every morning sweeping the bank's sidewalks, yes in his suit. His first task before opening his bank for the day!

When we met, I introduced myself. He said, I have been watching you play baseball in the Summer League caught a game just last week. Jack, weren't you also in the Morgan school play, Carousel last fall? Clinton is a small town. That said I was surprised he knew who I was. I am just a kid, a nobody. I thought to myself. Oh my. Maybe I will get a loan maybe this will actually work.

We talked for a while about baseball with the small talk conversation touching our little town. When he next asked if I had a job, I replied, Yes, I sell educational books.

He replied, Encyclopedias?

I said, Yes, sir, encyclopedias. I start next week. He was writing something. However, I could not see when he put down his pen, looked over the top of his glasses at me and asked will your dad co-sign the loan? I replied absolutely.

How much is the car? he asked. I replied, $1,500, a British sports car.

So ... he responded, I'm not going to give you a car loan, what you should do is take a personal loan for $1,800. Keep the extra $300 safe in the event you run short sometimes. But I have one request ... after you buy the car you must come back to the bank so I can see your new car.

You see ... Clinton is really Mayberry RFD. Got to love small towns and a simpler time. Mr. Redfield was a good man he went on to lecture me how important good credit is and how this loan was my first step to show the world that I am trustworthy. I learned from him that afternoon, important notions that helped me later in life.

So next on to see my dad for his signature. I will never forget the moment. My father was doing some paperwork in his office at the high school. Actually, a small room in the back of his economics classroom; I believe what once was a large closet.

Walking in, I said, Hello, Dad. Look what I got, and I placed the loan papers on his desk. He took the papers in hand and began to read same, then looked up at the ceiling. Has the world gone insane? laughed. Who gave you a loan?

The president of the Clinton Bank, Mr. Redfield, I responded.

What is your down payment?

You know I don't have any money.

So, he loaned you $1,500 without a down payment?

No ... $1,800.

You asked to meet with the president of the bank and he actually met with you. Mr. Redfield gave you a loan. This is insane, absolutely insane. He went on while saying a few words out loud shaking his head all the while (not swear words he never used those) as he co-signed my very first loan. This is serious, JP. Don't default. Be smart. I can't afford another car payment.

I said, Thank you, Dad, and gave him a hug. He patted my head and smiled. As I walked out, my dad continued talking out loud to himself ... I can't believe he had the balls to speak to the President of the bank.

The next morning, I drove to the bank, parking my car at the corner right outside the main bank doors. Mr. Redfield was delighted to see my MGB. I paid the loan off almost a year early.

So, the next Monday I began training for my new job. Our class to sell encyclopedias was scheduled for two weeks of training. The instructors would film you and one could watch the replay on a TV to learn as well as see our mistakes.

We were a class of about twelve; it was so easy from previously being in plays Carousel and The Boyfriend. I could memorize the lines quickly. I was the first to conclude training, in just half of the expected time; I finished in a single week, actually just four days.

I worked the phones the next day and secured two appointments, one for that night.

Well on your first sell it is required that your boss tags along with you to ensure you have it all down.

I went to an apartment in New Haven on the east side. I walked in with my sales support stuff in a large briefcase to find a very poor black family with five small children. The mother was cleaning up after dinner, the children were running around screaming and playing the father did his best to follow my presentation, finally the mother sat by his side. The home was absolute chaos and squalor.

After just thirty minutes, I sold them the encyclopedias, including the bookcase also the children's sets of books and a dictionary. I sold everything we had to offer. (A $35 commission) my lines and timing were spot on. For example, saying things like ... it's merely 87 cents a day or don't you want a better future for your children?

I don't know what happened next ... they both had already signed the agreement, when I said, don't do this. Let me explain how much you just purchased and with the finance charges you will be paying this debt for the next —— years.

I told them there was a library just a block away from their apartment. Take your children there. The father tore up the agreement, and I was immediately fired. I had to leave my sales stuff behind.

I drove home in my new MGB with the top down, I might add. Thank God Surge gave me an extra $300.

Chapter 6
He saved my life;
I meet Dr. Dhanda [2002]

I share a room and I am closest to the door, unfortunately I can't see the window. It is always dark. I hate the dark wish I could see sunlight. Usually, my door to the hallway remains open I can see a short wall beyond the hallway and sometimes the back of a nurse's head. There is usually a lot noise and I can see people, mostly nurses passing by my door. The curtain that separates me from my roommate is always closed. I know there must be a window for my roommate, he can see the sunlight. I know building department codes require same. I wish I could see outside it is always dark here. I think it is night when the hallway is quiet?

It was difficult to sleep so one of the nurses (I wish I could remember her name) gave me a sleeping pill, she is sweet and has been very helpful. I still can't move my left arm and leg. I can't even think about getting out of bed, so when I need a bed pan or anything... well, she responds quickly and I don't feel awkward when she is on duty. I can speak although with a bit of trouble. She always smiles and talks to me; she has a kind voice. I don't believe it was that long ago that she gave me the sleeping pill ... and now a woman's voice ... yes, it is her voice calling my name. Jack, Jack, Jack, wake up the doctor is here. I hear two women's voices the other is complaining that she didn't have time for her morning coffee. The kind nurse keeps calling my name. So, I am thinking, it must be early morning, I think it was only moments ago I couldn't sleep?

I open my eyes to find two nurses at my side and a doctor standing near the foot of my bed. The doctor is reading my chart. The nurse who was calling my name touches my face and smiles, so sorry to wake you Jack, Dr. ——- (I can't understand what she said his name is. Da something?) Dr. ——— is here to see you. The doctor starts a slow walk towards me and says with a strong Indian accent … you appear to be doing better. I understand you are having difficulties sleeping?

Jack, smile for me, that's much better he says and begins to write in my chart. After a minute or so, he takes my arm, the right one places his hand on mine with both of our fingers pointing upward and he says push as hard as you can. Right, he says and adds, now let's do the same thing with your left hand. The doctor lifts my left am and places his hand to mine. I try to push but do not have much strength. He places by arm back on the bed. The doctor shakes his head and sits down and begins to write on my chart again.

He asks several questions: what year is it? Who is our president? What is your wife's name? Laughs and asks what is your last name? Where are you? How do you feel? He tries to smile and shakes his head and continues to write again. I can't read his face, is he worried, am I doing well? So hard to find what this doctor is thinking. He stands and begins to walk towards the door. As he approaches the door to the hallway he says, you can speak again that is good however, you have some difficulty, you will need help we can take care of that with speech therapy, I also want to schedule you for occupational as well as physical therapy to start once you can walk again. He isn't much of a talker, his manner is very deliberate. That said I am excited that I can move my arm even if it is ever so slightly. It is difficult, but yes, I can move it. He shakes his head and tries to smile. As the doctor walks away into the hallway he says without looking back at me, I will return tomorrow morning, sorry to wake you. The nurse who missed her morning coffee walks out after the doctor.

I can't remember her name. I wish I could. There have been so many nurses; they let me know when their shift ends. They write the name of the next shift's nurse on a marker board hanging on the wall at the foot of my bed. She is talking about how she is looking forward to going home. She walks to the white board, erases her name, and writes another.

She turns and walks back towards me, smiling as she says goodbye, Jack.

I ask her how many Indian doctors work here? She replies are you asking about your doctor? She says Dr. Dhanda. This time I hear his last name.

I made Dr. Dhanda my doctor. He isn't much of a talker, no bedside manner, however, he is smart, very kind, and he saved my life. Most important I like him; I believe he is a great doctor.

I told Dr. Dhanda my story of hearing his voice when I arrived at the hospital. How I recalled the argument the doctors were having concerning the clot buster pill. Give him alteplase (a clot buster drug) we are going to lose him. It is a massive stroke. They are arguing. They want to give me the drug to break up a clot. How he read my medical bracelet and I said if I have a vote, I am all for the aspirin. You and the other doctors were not paying any attention to me or what I was saying. To my astonishment Dr. Dhanda said, You were talking? Maybe you thought you were talking? Jack, only barking sounds came from your mouth that day. I was shocked; I asked again, you could not understand me? Just a lot of loud barking? Dr. Dhanda smiled and said, Yes, Jack.

Having a stroke for me …. Well, I did not think I was actually having a stroke. You see, I had no idea what was happening.

CHAPTER 7

FROM MY MOM ... HOW THEY, MY CONNECTICUT FAMILY LEARNED OF MY STROKE [2002]

Written in my Journal October 10, 2002 Pat Bousquet

What a terrible two weeks. I drove myself to Cape Cod in Massachusetts, on Friday the 27th of September. My friends, the Negellis, Scanlons, Gagnons, Dowies, Phil Jackson, my daughter Jill, and her husband, Bob, were also there. We were all invited to our friend Joe Regan's daughter's wedding. We were all having such a grand time congregating in our hotel rooms, before the wedding, when I received a few telephone calls. It seemed that Jack possibly had had a stroke and was being brought to the emergency room in a hospital in California. It was also his forty-ninth birthday.

He had been receiving his IVIG treatment and apparently had the stroke while he was getting the treatment. The stroke was on the right side of his brain. His nurse (who was administering the IVIG, called the paramedics right away). They gave him 100% oxygen, which I think turned out to be a good thing.

I stayed at the Cape, attended the wedding, then went home, very early, Sunday morning. I made arrangements and by Monday, I was on a plane flying to California. I was terribly worried about Jack and also worried about what condition I would find him in. I knew that a stroke could mean many different things. I went directly to the hospital from the airport. (Linda had a friend of hers meet me at the airport) I was so nervous about what I was going to find when I got there. The whole trip, I was pretty much sick to my stomach.

When I entered the hospital room, I was happy to see him sitting up in his bed. His family all there around him. He was happy to see me, and he made a comment, now I know you really do love me. His voice sounded to me, with intonation, like a young child. The left side of Jack's face was drooping. He had trouble with his left hand, and foot. He had no feeling on the left side at all. He was so intent upon going home that he was driving everyone crazy. Well, he finally went home. He is having physical therapy and occupational therapy. And is progressing a little bit. I stayed until the following Monday, then I flew home. How I hated leaving him!!!!

Dr. Klashman his IVIG doctor seems to think that the stroke was caused by the treatment. He will no longer be getting the IVIG. What else?

They did another MRI to see if the disease is back. Pray Jesus I hope not!!

Talked with him a couple of times, his voice sounds better, not so childlike.

Questions???? Will he be able to run his company? How will the family live? I am scared for them.

> **Oct. 15, '02** I've been talking to Jack at least once a day. He is beginning to sound better. Today his secretary will drive him into work and bring him home. He will stay maybe an hour or two. Hopefully, all will go well. I can't believe that this is happening to him. I cry every time I think about it. It is so sad.

> **Oct. 16, '02** Jack went to work for a couple of hours yesterday. He couldn't do some easy tests, like putting a paper clip, rubber band, penny, etc., under a towel, telling him to take out the paper clip. He could not tell which was which. He can do the logic problems very well, but he was quite dismayed because he couldn't do these simple tasks.

> **Oct. 18, '02** Today he was training to teach his left side to do things and to have more memory. It is very difficult for him.

> **Oct. 19, '02** we are still talking on the phone every day. He had a very bad weekend.

The OT people gave him some simple tasks to do and he was unable to do them. He was very down. I told him to just keep on trying. I know that he can do it. I also know and thank God, every day, when I open my eyes, that not only is he alive, but he can walk and talk also. Thank you, thank you. I also know that it is going to take time. He can't close his eyes and tell you what is in his left hand. They are retraining his brain. It will come I know it….

> **Nov. 4, '02** Jack is doing a bit better. Linda let him drive the Porsche yesterday. She said he did well. He is supposed to take a test ($450) to see if he can drive on Wed. They are now rethinking the test. The doctors didn't take his license away, she did. I think if she feels happy with his driving, then it will be okay.
>
> **Dec. 12, '02** Jack took a simulated driving test., it lasted 4 hrs. He said that he was nervous. He passed the test and now can drive his own car.
>
> **Jan. 27, '03** Robin, Bonnie, and I flew to CA to see Jack.
>
> **Mar 9, '03** Bob, Jill, Carolyn, and I flew to CA to see Jack. He is so much better. I am very happy. I think he has also lost self-confidence. But Thank God he is alive. He is working very hard to keep his company together. He has secured a few small jobs. (At least he thinks they are small jobs.)

Remembering

When I was in California, the first week that Jack was home from the hospital. He was so much like a little boy. His voice, his intonation, his actions. It reminded me of him being somewhere between four and six years old.

One day he came up the stairs into the family room, calling for Linda. He had put both of his legs into one hole of his under shorts, and was unable to figure out what was wrong. Linda guided him into the bathroom and helped him. I was sad.

Jack, Linda, and I drove to a pharmacy to pick up his meds. Jack was in the back seat. Linda left the car running because it was so hot out, and she had the air-conditioner on. Jack got impatient waiting for her. He got out of the car and was going to drive he said. I took the keys out of the ignition and hid them in my hand. When he got into the car, he could not figure out what was wrong. He just sat there. I took him for a walk to find Linda. Then I secretly handed her the keys. I was sad again!

He broke the faucet from the water dispenser. He dropped plates and glasses.

We went to Home Depot, while there we discovered Jack had his shoes on the wrong feet.

CHAPTER 8

GET IT LINDA,
WHAT IF I CAN'T RECOVER [2002]

The morning after my stroke Linda arrived at the hospital early to see me. My speech was better although I was still having difficulties talking; fortunately, we were able to communicate. I have no memory of this moment, unfortunately Linda has a very poor memory she cannot provide any details until that is when she called Lee and Michelle arrived. Linda remembers our conversation regrettably nothing more.

Hollywood & Highland opened to the public November 11th, 2001. My team and I remained working for Trizec-Hahn closing contracts finalizing loose ends until May 2002. Kevin Dennis and Laura Doerges, my close friends and colleagues who have worked together well over ten years started our real estate consultant business Bousquet Dennis & Associates.

My title VP Design and Construction when hired by Trizec. A year later while all the Trizec employees attended a team building effort in Vegas I was promoted to SRVP in addition my contract revised to include a sizable completion bonus. I requested the bonus to also be available for my staff, with that I shared 50% of the bonus prize with my team. The bonus based on a complicated mathematical structure considering costs saved and schedule made.

Wednesday the 25th two days prior to my stroke Kevin Dennis and I were meeting with Lee Wagman President with Trizec to finalize the team bonus. A sizable issue in the bonus total was apparent due to additional fees charged by the insurance company. Owner Controlled Insurance Policy (OCIP) costs much higher than thought as the insurance company at projects end levied addition fees based on construction change orders. We decided to wait get our arms around the insurance issue and finalize the bonus total at a later date.

The morning after my stroke, I was not sure I could recover; nervous, I was uncertain for our future. I told Linda to call Lee tell him I suffered a stroke most importantly advise I agree to the bonus total, my bonus $500K. Michelle Kling Lee's assistant arrived at the hospital later that morning with my check. By use of a wheel chair Linda and I met Michelle in the hospital lobby for me to sign the bonus agreement.

CHAPTER 9
LAST DAY OF SPEECH THERAPY, I GO BACK TO WORK THE NEXT DAY [2002]

There were so many nurses who helped me; I could have never made the recovery without them. They taught me how to walk again and how to talk again, hell they helped when I was at my worst to relearn some basic everyday simple functions, like tying my shoes or buttoning my shirt.

There was one who stands out among her peers; to me she is a princess among nurses. She played an important and most significant role in my recovery.

Her name is Elizabeth she is young, kind and I found her very talented. I would see Elizabeth twice a week for about two and a half months. I had a difficult time with my speech. You see my problem was twofold I mixed up words and I also could not make certain sounds … S and L and W sounds were impossible. We talked about most everything during our time together. She understood the problem with my left hand, you see I can't feel it and my hand longs for touch. So, when I was struggling, she would hold my left hand and say come on, Jack, you can do it, try again. Odd as it sounds, it helped. I don't know why? To this day my left hand still longs for touch. Sometimes I wish I could reach out and feel touch. When someone touches my hand, it is an odd feeling as my hand is numb; however, I like the touch and always wish it would feel like my other hand. It is calming, doesn't matter if the touch is by a man or woman; I know this will not make any sense to you. Not certain it does for me?

In addition to my speech therapy Elizabeth would throw in mind puzzles, I found this fascinating and most helpful. One that comes to mind and it turned a corner for me was about five people the puzzle was extremely difficult to solve and when I solved same it gave me renewed confidence.

You see I brought it home and asked some family and friends to have a chance, well they found it too hard, I know they also didn't need to prove anything to their self so they gave up way too quickly. I need to prove to myself that I can think again. You see I was scared to death that I couldn't provide for my family. What would happen to us if I can't think, if I can't work, if I can't provide for my family? Elizabeth gave me a page or two and from the clues in what I read about the five people she asked me to tell her what was their job, what sport did they play, and what language other than English did they speak?

On this day, my final day of speech therapy I entered her office pulled up a chair and we began talking … just simple small talk when she asked what does Attila the Hun and Mickey the Mouse have in common? So, knowing from all the puzzles previously, I learned not to overthink just relax and search for the direct and simple solution. Please be mindful, in my previously lifetime I worked for the Mouse for over nine years the best years were as Director of Design and Development for Disney Development Company, (Disney's real estate arm.) so I thought about it for a few seconds, absolutely no one calls Mickey Mouse - Mickey the mouse. I smiled and I responded with - they both have the same middle name, (the). Elizabeth's face light up and she laughed. Jack, she said, I ran out of puzzles for you weeks ago. I have been going to the town library searching to find more for you. This is our last session; your speech is back. Your mind is sharp. I do not believe I can give you any more. It was a pleasure to help you. I believe I am going to miss working with you, Jack.

The next day I went back to work. Bousquet, Dennis & Associates. It's my business and I had two partners Kevin and Laura. Please be mindful, for the past couple of weeks I would go to work for an hour or two, but I really didn't do much. The drive in and just being there was an accomplishment for me. That day was a huge step for me to get my life back; I was nervous but also very excited. I found Laura was going on an interview the next day. To remodel two hotels, LAX Sheraton at the airport and Four Points Sheraton in Santa Monica. I told them that I would join Laura at the interview. Laura asked if I was up for it; she and Kevin thought I should pass. I replied that I was fine and I will attend; Laura will certainly take the lead.

The next day Laura drove us to the interview at the LAX Sheraton we met in one of the hotel meeting rooms. The interview lasted about two hours there were five or six people interviewing us. One of the interviewers was their banker. He talked about how his bank wanted more muscle as the previous Kor Group projects were always behind schedule and way over budget. Laura and I have worked together for over ten years. She is very smart and a great project manager. We work well together; I have a lot of trust in her abilities. So, we talked about how to manage a successful project and I told stories about our previous life time and how we delivered on time and on budget over and over again. An hour into the interview I was confident that we would win the prize and have a new contract. The presentation was going great Laura and I held their interest. As the discussion continued, I was more than certain our firm would win the role as the Development Manager.

A development manager assembles the team, creates a work plan, and ensures that the different team members (architects, consultants, attorneys, contractors, subcontractors, and governmental agencies) are working toward specific common goals, communicating thoroughly, and being as efficient with time and money as possible.

I am okay; yep, I did not give up and call it quits. The stroke was massive and it left me with issues that I have to overcome even to this day. I beat the stroke. I can still run a development like no other. Yippee ki-yay.

This was a lunch meeting there was so much food. Everyone enjoyed the hospitality. That is with the exception of me. You see I can't feel my left hand but most important I can't feel the left side of my face. I was afraid to eat that maybe I would get food on my face and embarrass myself. You see I was fearful that they would find out I had a STROKE. Only a handful of people are aware I suffered a stroke, my family, my partners, and close friends.

At the conclusion of the interview, we won the prize. Life is good, I am back.

What the hell.

Laura drove us back to the office and I experienced my first panic attack. It came from nowhere. This had never happened to me before. She drove back a different way, and we ended up on the 105 interchange. This is the same interchange from the famous bus jump scene from the movie SPEED. So, the ramp is extremely high and as we were approaching the top, I got a panic attack. Terrible fear I couldn't understand why this was happening to me? I was also nervous that now I have another issue to deal with, come on haven't I gone through enough? Previously I had a slight fear of heights however this was full panic. This fear of heights became a new obstacle it was definitely a common problem for me and something I had to deal with as it kept reoccurring in my future. At this moment, well I kept the fear to myself; Laura never knew I had a panic attack. I also learned that when we got to an acceptable elevation on the way down the ramp my panic disappeared.

In the future I learned to tell myself, Jack you can endure anything for ten to fifteen minutes. Stop it get a grip stupid. This fear of heights remains today. I absolutely cannot drive on a mountain road. When I get to a situation where I have to drive up or down through a mountainous pass, I ask Linda to drive and I pull over and change positions with her. I know to you it doesn't make any sense, well now it doesn't make sense to me either. My mind doesn't see or handle views of terrain as it should. Please be mindful, it doesn't get much better when Linda is doing the driving, she scares me to death. We usually or should I say more than often we get in an argument, as I will say we can get there ten minutes later please slow down. My mind gets confused I just can't deal with the heights. The most severe issue is going downhill with a turn to the left.

Bridges also are huge issue I get nervous as I approach and then the panic grips me as I start the climb. Atriums in buildings cause a similar panic. I am scared to death on roof tops. I do my best to try and avoid these situations. Can you imagine how difficult it is for me to tour or see the progress of one of my construction sites?

Our office was on Hollywood Blvd. over the El Capitan Theater. Hollywood and Highland, a project from my previous lifetime that I lead while working for Trizec-Hahn is across the street. So, when Laura went up to our office I walked across the street and walked up to the third floor where we developed several restaurants and I entered Wolfgang Puck Vert Brasserie. Carl Schuster at the time managed Wolfgang 'catering and restaurants. I had developed a respect for Carl a very likable manager and a smart business man. Carl was sitting at a table talking to a couple of his employees. Carl saw me walk in and he excused his self from his team, I walked over and shook his hand, nice to see you again Carl and I asked if I could purchase a gift certificate. I bought a gift certificate for $100.

The very next morning I drove to Henry Mayo Hospital. I did not take long to find Elizabeth. I told her the story of the previous day's interview. I thanked her for teaching me how to talk again. I told her the challenging mind puzzles gave me confidence. No one suspected that I had a stroke, we got the contract ... thank you Elizabeth. I gave her a hug and spun her around. Elizabeth smiled and gave me a kiss on the cheek. Fortunately ... the (me too) campaign would not occur for many years.

I am glad that I could show my gratitude and emotion, I also believe she welcomed the hug. I will never forget you, thank you. As I was walking away, Elisabeth said, About you not eating, your fear of getting food on your face. Well, now the next time you find yourself in a similar situation, eat with the others and use your napkin. It doesn't matter how many times you place the napkin to your face. No one will notice. Another lesson that I took to heart as I always make certain I have a napkin, if I don't, well, I refrain from eating.

I am back

Three months later the LAX and Four Points Sheraton projects are proceeding nicely. We have a new request from our client to make significant new scope modifications to the Ball Room he hoped to add additional area. After exhausting any and all efforts we were able to convenience our client that this was an ill-conceived notion. The cost would be heroic and the added value insignificant. Foolish notions that provide little or no value can kill a budget and cause the schedule to be delayed. Fortunately, Brad listened and took our advice.

On a positive note, we also picked up a couple of additional projects. Two adaptive reuse developments converting industrial storage space to loft condos and the converting a multi-level department store to high end condos.

One day about a month or so after the height panic incident Laura and I were returning to our office from a meeting downtown for a new school. We took the train from Hollywood while on the way back we came across an outdoor escalator narrow and extremely steep. Please be mindful that I had been on this escalator several times before, and I didn't like it. That said it wasn't an issue. However, on this day, I found it to be a very different experience for me. As we were on our way down, I had my second panic attack. This time I could not disguise my fear. It was daunting the fear gripped me. Laura knew immediately that something was wrong. I held on so very tight that my shirt sleeves got dirty from the handrail rubbing through the shirt cloth. I was fine as soon as I got to the bottom. Fear; shortness of breath and a surge of heat that made me sweaty in seconds. It was awful and embarrassing.

When I left my office in Hollywood to go home that day, I first crossed Hollywood Blvd. entered Hollywood and Highland complex and I forced myself to ride the escalators up and down for about thirty minutes. These escalators are steep and one can see several levels below. Not as difficult for me as the open-air escalator, which was very steep, however a close second. The next day was a Saturday so I had to conquer this silly escalator problem I drove into work we had monthly parking pass at the bottom of Hollywood and Highland. I must have looked foolish as I spent the next hour riding the escalators.

It did not help, however, when I am at an airport. Still to this day, I have problems with escalators. I just have to say stop it, Jack; you can do anything for five to ten minutes. Like I said, I have similar problems while driving through mountains or on high ramps and most definitely problems crossing high bridges. For a while I would drive ten to fifteen miles out of my way to avoid ramps that scared the hell out of me. I still struggle with heights and driving over bridges and through mountain roads today.

For example, we drove to Ojai for Mother's Day brunch 2019 I had to pull over and have Linda drive through the mountain pass. I know this doesn't make sense definitely isn't logical. I have gripping fear that takes control of my brain. I believe I must work through this, just another issue to deal with caused by the stroke.

CHAPTER 10
PIXIE DUST [1991]

As a young boy our family enjoyed our time together you could find us in the living room every Sunday night looking at our little television watching The Wonderful World of Disney. I believed Walt to be so fascinating, his excitement for Disneyland beyond my immigration, it caused me to dream, maybe one day I can walk along Main Street, Adventureland, and my favorite Tomorrow Land.

I was eleven in the summer of 1965. Our family did not go on vacation; I did not go to summer camp. My parents would say, Your vacation is right in front of you, Jackie, your backyard, your neighborhood, and we are just minutes from the beach. Life doesn't get any better.

Hammonasset Beach State Park was as far as we got. I loved spending the day there. When my grandparents visited us in the summer we always went to the beach. The family finding a spot for our blankets near the water, the old ladies my meme and Aunt Laura in full dresses sitting at the old pavilion with the shade of the roof over head. Returning home for a BBQ picnic in our back yard. No fences to separate the back yards no dogs on a leach. Our back yard touched our neighbor's grass the dogs ran free running with us kids from yard to yard.

I had a paper route I delivered the papers on my bike, my dog Freckles always with me. If I could not see her all I had to do is call out her name in seconds Freckles was running at my side while I peddled to the next street. Riding my bike with my dog running next to me this boy dreamed of Disneyland.

We were living in Chantilly, Virginia ... 1987. Linda pregnant with Drew at the time we planned a vacation for Geoff and Ashley a couple of days at the Beach in Sarasota, returning to our favorite beach and a week at Disney World for the kids. Disney World caught my immigration, it fascinating to see the expansion of the theme park the construction for new hotels. I started to dream, my thoughts occupied my days as a boy dreaming that one day I could walk in Disneyland, this vacation however I dreamed I could be responsible for creating hotels or great experiences for Disney.

Disney calls

I wish I could have met Walt. I was there during the Eisner days. Yes, Michael Eisner is an amazing guy I absolutely enjoyed the few meetings and time with him.

On a cold winter day in 1991, I got a call from a headhunter saying Disney wanted to interview me. I knew Disney took months to hire people. I was looking at the sports pages sitting on my desk I saw that the Lakers would be in town the following Friday. I wanted to see Magic play. So, I said I cannot make this week however I can next Friday. Unfortunately, I never made it to the game a wasted ticket. That said I went home with an offer a couple of months later I worked for the mouse.

When I got the first call from the head hunter, I advised I was not interested. About eight months prior, I started a new position in Syracuse. The company Pioneer Development provided a loan for me to purchase our home. Please be mindful, our home in Chantilly, VA sitting empty languishing on the market trying to find another family for purchase. The housing market dismal at the time. So, picture if you will my predicament—I own two homes one in Chantilly, Virginia that I cannot sell, the other in Syracuse, New York also tied me to a sizable company loan.

Minutes after my conversation with the head hunter my old friend from our Cadillac Fairview Urban Development (CFUD) days calls me. Paul advised Disney actually Disney Development Company (DDC) the group responsible for Disney's real estate development is putting together a team in Burbank, CA four previous Vice Presidents from our old CFUD days, including Paul from Atlanta and Kerry from Boston for development, Mark from

Dallas to head up financing and are looking at me from Washington, DC for design /construction. I knew Paul Stockwell from Houston we worked in the same office; I never worked with Mark or Kerry however I only knew them for CFUD officer meetings twice a year at our main office in Dallas. Well now Paul says, Jack come on at least come out here for a visit, you never know. Less than fifteen minutes later the head hunter called me a second time, this time I agree to make the trip to Burbank, California.

I make plans and travel to Burbank, California it is so cold in New York the Syracuse winters can be miserable; I look forward to my trip. I find my interview crazy. You see, they set me up in a room; interviewers arrive one at a time on a precise schedule. Can you believe I am interviewed by about twelve people at Disney? Then Paul finds me and he says, "Larry Murphy wants to interview you, he is third in the chain behind Eisner and Wells. If you get more than two minutes with him you are lucky and he isn't a nice guy; be careful."

So, I got a cab from the Disney Channel Building to Disney Studios. Can you imagine how exciting it was for me to be at Disney Studios? As I walked through the studio, I remembered dreaming about Disney when I just a young boy. When I arrived at Larry's office, his door was open. Larry was sitting at his desk and he had his back to me.

So, I knocked on the doorjamb, that got his attention however Larry did not turn to look at me, he said one annoying word, WHAT? I replied to the back of his head, hello, Mr. Murphy, I am Jack Bousquet. I believe you want to meet me? With that, Larry turned to face me and said, They told me you are some kind of construction, businessman whiz banger; you don't look like a construction guy to me! Larry turned his back on me again. So, I didn't think I would get hired anyway. How could I abandon my financial responsibilities, I need to provide for my family, hell I am here to see a basketball game.

What popped out of my mouth even surprised me. I said if I spit on the floor and scratched my balls and say how the fuck are you doing Larry, would that do it for you? Half an hour later I left with a verbal agreement; my contract arrived in the mail the following week, including stock options. Like I said above I did not make it to the Laker game that night, I had to wait for another night to see Magic play.

Should we go or should we stay

Linda and I talked about Disney, what should we do? Linda and our children did not like Syracuse it was so cold our children Geoff/Ashley had a tough time making friends. At the time Drew was just a baby. I believe mainly because they loved our life, they missed their friends back in Virginia. I was not thrilled with the work here in Syracuse. The projects neither as difficult nor exciting. To sum things up we missed our previous Chantilly, Virginia life. That said, financially the choice for Disney did not make any sense. If, say, we choose Disney, we have the two homes with demanding mortgages one Chantilly, the other Syracuse plus a $75K loan hanging over our heads to Pioneer Development Company. We decided to go or did I not listen sometimes I only hear what I want to hear.

I drove to work the next morning; I gave my resignation to the partners. The news was not taken lightly, the owner Mike Falcone being on vacation in Florida also created an awkward wrinkle. I was hired to lead the design and construction efforts for the development company a position I am very comfortable with a position I know like the back of my hand. In addition, I was also responsible and accountable to lead an in-house General Contractor construction group responsible for building all of our projects. Leading the General Contractor group was a new responsibility. Initially I was fearful that I may have difficulties in this position. However, once I took control, I found the role easy; straight forward no need for me to be nervous it was not difficult at all. However, on a secondary role I was retained to assist with the development of his sons Michael and Mark as his boys, young mid-twenties at the time, are the future for Pioneer.

Mike called me we talked by phone. You are making a mistake, Jack. You can be a rich man working here. Remember your partnership commences in a couple of months. Your salary is nothing compared to your equity position. I like what you're doing here; you're a strong leader, Jack. His team in Syracuse reinforced Mike. Yep, they convinced me to stay.

My mind is racing, so I believe I must go home I cannot wait until day's end to tell Linda we are not moving to California. Will Linda be relieved or will she be disappointed? This news defiantly is not a conversation one has by phone. The partners shake my hand, glad you are staying Jack, and we have an optimistic view for the future. I advise I will be back shortly I must talk with my wife as Linda thinks we are moving. I leave the office making the short drive home.

What happened next changed our life. This being one of those critical moments that define you, what you; consider being trust, the love a couple adores.

When I arrived home, Linda was in the kitchen. Please be mindful, although we talked and talked about leaving for Disney, incurring the financial daunting, we really never understood each other's position, or did we?

I told Linda I quit. I told her they convinced me to stay. I talked about my partnership how we could be wealthy. Our conversation opened thoughts and feelings that were not apparent earlier when Linda and Jack found themselves struggling with this important decision.

Somehow, we transitioned from the kitchen to the family room with the left-over bottle of wine from the night before with a couple of glasses, the fireplace already held a fire. We sat on the hearth, I lit her and my cigarette, and we talked. After a while it became clear for both Linda and Jack, they wanted to go... however this decision unnerving and most irresponsible. At one point Linda said, you can't go back and resign again. I replied I can do anything if that is what you want, I am certain they would see me as an ass, so what, I would never see them again, I can do it, if that is what you want.

I decided to stand, now looking down at Linda; I went on to say, the decision to go yes Linda is extremely irresponsible, baby we could lose everything. Two mortgages plus that huge loan may do us in, we might have to start over, our credit ruined we may not be able to own another house. I need to know that you are with me sweet baby no matter what; I need to know we are together on this direction. Say we lose everything say we must start over.... Well, that does not matter as long as we have each other. Linda I must know we share the same decision. If you want to go, if you are willing to take the financial risk stand up and kiss me.

Without hesitation I watched my wife stand, Linda with huge alligator tears running down her face, I took her in my arms we kissed we held each other. Linda whispered in my ear, I could never go back and quit a second time. That will be hard for you, JP. I took her face in my hands we kissed again.

So yes, the partners were not so pleased when I called them together in the conference room again.

We did however hold a family meeting that evening in our kitchen that same night. I asked our children do you want to stay here or do you want to move to California? They all with the exception of Drew cried yes. Drew who was just a little guy remained silent. Geoff, looking at Drew, asked, Do you want to stay here or do you want to see Mickey Mouse? Andrew yelled, Mickey Mouse! We all started laughing.

I drove to California in my 1988 rag top corvette arriving in Burbank March 30th to be in time for my first day at Disney April 1, 1991, yep April fool's day. A day later and my stock options would not be realized until November 1st. Along the way I stopped in Richmond, Indiana for a quick visit with Linda's parents. Disney made arrangements for a corporate apartment for my first 3 months.

Linda and I believed it best for Geoff and Ashley to finish the school year in Syracuse. Three school systems in a single year we believed may harm them. Geoff and Ashley however did come to California for a visit on their spring break. It was great to see them, I was lonely.

Two weeks before the semester was scheduled to end, Linda met with the elementary school principal. She requested paperwork for our children covering the full schoolyear term. The principal advised no problem I believe it wise to join your children with their father. Disney per my contract provided First Class airline tickets for Linda and our children to fly to California. I asked if it was possible to receive cash as my wife would like to give our children an adventure crossing the country. So, after Linda met with AAA, she sat with our children at our kitchen table mapping out their journey. Niagara Falls, St. Louis the gateway to the west, Petrified Forest, Grand Canyon, including local tourist spots in-between.

I found a rental home in Newhall, California in the Santa Clarita Valley just under an hour commute to Disney. The rental home included a swimming pool and Jacuzzi. Our family so happy for the pool and sunny weather, our children adjusted quickly, life was good. A month after our home in Chantilly sold, the equity just enough to pay the Pioneer $75K loan. After fourteen months of carrying our Syracuse mortgage that property finally sold, although for a sizable loss. Jack and Linda did not lose everything, we did however have to start over, and we could not afford to purchase a home for another three years. Our family was happy, life was good.

A silver pass entitled our family to visit Disneyland whenever we chose. We went to Disneyland often, usually for the day. That said, sometimes just to see the electric parade or watch Fantasmic after dinner. Ashley was fortunate for her birthday party celebration there. Linda escorting all the girls on rides me taking our boys Geoff and Drew to Tom Sawyer's Island. Our Bousquet family tradition—once we passed the gate leaving Disneyland, we would skip through the parking lot all the way to our car.

Linda started as an extra enjoying her acting adventure in the Hollywood movie business, eventually moving her way up getting lines, also becoming a stand-in for two Cheryl Ladd made-for-TV movies while earning her SAG status. Having the lead in a small budget movie and joining a local acting group performing at a theater in Burbank. Linda still holds her SAG card today. I found my work exciting; me responsible for California and New York City corporate developments also Pacific rim second generation corporate projects. (Tenant improvements for all the Disney leases)

What comes to mind as I find myself close to end of this Disney chapter is one of my favorite stories; I am compelled to tell you his one.

Where in the hell is Fred?

Shortly after I began my career with DDC, early in the evening after a long day of meeting at the main studio office building ...well the Seven Dwarfs building, the one where the nineteen-foot Dwarfs stand at the roof line...and my first meeting at Disney Studios, I was very excited and loving my new position while walking to my car I passed a couple of the soundstages. At the time only five stages existed at Disney Studios. I being so happy, so pleased with my great fortune came across an open door to one of the soundstages. Above the door was a lighted sign ON AIR NO LOOKY-LOOS. I, being Jack duty bound to see inside, stepped through the open doorway to find at least 100 people inside. Oh my, I am watching a Hollywood movie in the making; I was as cheerful as a little kid.

The crew in the process of filming a scene from the Marring Man. Yep, the movie where they met and after Alec Baldwin and Kim Basinger became a couple. I thought Kim to be gorgeous and oh my, there she is right over there. Watching, taking in my surroundings, I see commotion in the distance.

A security guard is angry. I see him escort two men to the exit, with the conversation obviously not being heard, I see him write something on his clipboard. He returns back to his original spot.

I watch him searching the crowd, he is looking for something. Oops, and when he locks his eyes on me and points, I panic. He begins a quick pace in my direction. So now I am worried the two he previously escorted out were dressed differently than everyone else. Oh crap, here I am in a suit and tie holding my briefcase. *Yep*, I say to myself, Jack you look out of place, like black man at a KKK meeting. I can't move I was certain he will track me down before I reach the door. Now I panic, he will ask me to leave, take my name, I will be embarrassed, and what if I get fired?

When the security guard was within three or four feet ... I said... Where in the hell is Fred? I am sick and tired of his shit. Find him and bring him back here. It wasn't planned; there was no thought whatsoever. The words just came out. I imagine fear can cause one to protect oneself. The words just flew from my mouth.

As I watched the security guard turn in retreat saying, Yes, sir, I will get Fred, well I began to smile. I was quite proud of myself. I remember thinking, Fred? How in the hell did you come up with this, Jack? When I believed him at a good distance, I found the exit, walked on to my car. I learned my lesson; I never ever entered a soundstage during filming again.

We lived life to the fullest. We never looked back. Linda and I were invited to the Mighty Ducks opening game, the Angels season opener game, to several exclusive parties—for example, the Academy Awards after party. I was at the opening on Broadway for *Beauty & the Beast*, and unfortunately, I missed the Broadway opening for *The Lion King* as dermatomyositis had the better of me at that time. Our children invited to test new Disneyland theme park rides prior to opening to the public. Disney Family Christmas parties at Disneyland each and every year. We frequented the beach often, enjoyed family roller blading and family bike rides through the Santa Clarita paseo. Life is good, yes, our family is happy. Would we have found happiness In Syracuse? Maybe, maybe not ... really doesn't matter, does it? I guess not.

CF [1981]

Cadillac Fairview my stepping stone to even greater things, 9.5 years '81–'90. The people smart the projects challenging, lessons learned, building a solid foundation for my future. For me it was like packing a bag with all the essential tools to allow my future to shine. So many firsts … My first VP title at thirty-four. Managing staff for two offices, skyscraper, and highway interchange, master plans, saving historical structures and this company where I met Paul Stockwell. He called to advise about DDC.

I will never forget the day I was hired at CF I was working for Brown & Root; Tom Robinson led all Halliburton real estate holdings a thirty-two-company conglomerate. Texas Eastern one of the companies under this umbrella assembled thirty-two adjoining blocks of downtown Houston. Tom's team was responsible for the first two skyscrapers. Texas Eastern believed it wise to joint venture with a developer, CF from Toronto won the prize gaining four blocks to initiate the challenge, develop one block another block would be added to CF's control.

So, Gulf Oil occupied a huge portion of Two Houston Center at a meager below market lease rate. The plan- for Gulf's ownership, a build to suit managed by CF creating a new tower 3HC, replace the lease area at 2HC with two other energy companies at the more respectable market lease rate.

Tom recommended me for the Construction Manager position. That morning as I was getting ready Linda who at the time pregnant for our second child Ashley said make sure they have good insurance.

My interview was awesome. Please be mindful, Jack a mere twenty-nine, yes; I did not know what I did not know. They showed me the opportunity at the time only a handful of images articulated 3HC, a 52-story skyscraper. Images included a three-dimensional drawing and less than ten additional graphic drawings. So, I joined the CF team at the skyscraper's concept beginning. During our meeting the regional EXVP asked me to join his CF team, I being ever so excited … this was a skyscraper, and this job, this position to manage design and construction for a tower beyond my dreams.

All was set my first day just two weeks away, I am so grateful Tom talked me up I have to thank him I can't wait to give the news. Tom Robinson was my mentor I received a background from Ga. Tech I learned the business from Tom….

While standing in the elevator lobby waiting for the elevator when another thought came to mind, geez Jack, Linda said make sure they have good insurance. We never talked about insurance; I am thinking holly crap we never talked about my salary. You are stupid Jack an excited little kid, how can you return home … Linda, I got the job.

Congratulations, honey. Tell me about the insurance, are you going to make more money, Jack?

I don't know Linda we never talked about that.

The elevator door opened. I did not get in; I turned around returning to the conference room. Fortunately, the three executives who interviewed me were still sitting as I left them. I knocked on the doorjamb stepped inside the conference room holding my hands out to my side. I said I believe we forgot to talk about my salary. As you can see, I am very excited to join your team. With that, they laughed and said, "We were wondering when you might return." My salary increased substantially and the insurance great.

I only saw CF people at our company Christmas party and sometimes meeting CF staff for a drink at the Columns bar in the 2HC tower that is where I met and became friends with Paul. Our office was located with the Gulf Oil staff this allowed us to develop a strong relationship with the Gulf oil people. Tom Malt SR. Design/Construction Manager my boss he also was from Tom Robinson's B&R group.

A huge success 3HC was completed ahead of schedule and under budget, other CF developments at the time missing the schedule and budget mark substantially.

At job's end, sitting with the same three who hired me receiving my first completion bonus, the men asked why was 3HC so successful? I so pleased for the bonus said do you want me to lie or tell you the truth? The EXVP smiled said Jack start with the truth. I told them no one from CF cared about 3HC all were preoccupied with other CF developments that I only saw you people at the Christmas parties. Tom Malt and I made decisions, with the concurrence of our client Gulf Oil. Looking back today maybe I might change some if I were to see that situation again. That said, what I learned no decision can be more harmful than a poor decision or a long wait for approval. We made timely decisions the project did well for same. So, Jack what is the lie? I responded, I am very smart and I worked hard. Yes, I was a smartass.

Gulf Oil wanted me to join their team, offered me a job. CF offered me a huge challenge relocating to Northern Virginia to create the Fairview Park development—340K plus acres, 3.6 M sf office, a 250 key hotel, 450 apartments units, three lakes, loop road, spine road, and design and build a four-leaf clover highway interchange.

A year later I also became responsible for the design and construction for all developments at our Washington, DC office. I split my time managing separate teams between the two offices, the next year promoted to VP Design and Construction.

So proud, I was lucky I had great teams, Fairview Park won the NAIOP award for best mixed-use development in the country, in addition received an award for finalizing the interchange a couple of years ahead of schedule we also were awarded eight regional awards and six state awards for our office buildings.

CHAPTER 11
DERMATOMYOSITIS [1997]

The rash that accompanies the symptoms of muscle weakness looks like patchy, bluish-purple discolorations on the face, neck, shoulders, upper chest, elbows, knees, knuckles, or back. Some people may also develop calcium deposits, which appear as hard bumps under the skin. Dermatomyositis is a chronic disease without a cure.

The most common symptom of dermatomyositis is muscle weakness, usually affecting the muscles that are closest to the trunk of the body. Some patients also have lung involvement, which can cause difficulty breathing.

Risk Group

People all over the world can suffer from dermatomyositis. Women are at least two times more likely to suffer from dermatomyositis than men.

Symptoms

- The gradual onset of weakness over weeks or months
- Difficulty rising from a low-seated chair or combing one's hair
- Torso or "core" weakness
- Difficulty swallowing (dysphagia)
- Pain or weakness in the joints
- Generalized fatigue

- Patchy, reddish rash on the eyelids, cheeks, bridge of the nose, back or upper chest, and joints. In some cases, the development of hardened bumps under the skin.

My mother who was worried and concerned wrote me a poem.

Sent Sunday February 2, 1997
Subject poetry for you
From PAB CT (my mom)
Date 97-02-02 09:24: 10 EST
To Duse WB (Linda)

A Long Scary Night

I saw you my son, looking so tired and in pain
I tried to hold you, make it all right again
Why is this happening to you, I don't know
I can't cure this illness, this thing, this bad blow

When you were little, I could hold you so tight
I love and protected you through a long scary night
Now that you've grown, and you are so far away
I can't even help you; there are no words I can say

I try and I try as hard as I can,
To remember the boy is now a grown man
I can't even baby my son anymore
Life does that I guess, it shuts the door

I know you will be strong take all you'll endure
You'll try very hard of this I am sure
But I sit here alone and I think of your plight,
And I need to be helping through a long scary night

Dermatomyositis

... Disease such a strange and foreign word or at least it should be.

Dr. Klashman told me I have a better chance of winning the lottery over contracting dermatomyositis. So, every time I go to a grocery store, I purchase a lottery ticket. Unfortunately, I find myself still waiting for the winning ticket.

There were a few key steps that lead to discovering what was wrong with me. Unfortunately, at the time we didn't understand or even see them. However, it is amazing that all the signs were there we just didn't recognize the symptoms or even comprehend.

It all started with a rash. Just before my 40th birthday I began having a rash shaped like a butterfly appears on my face and a similar rash without the shape on my chest and shoulders. I also had purple nodules appear on the top of my hands. So, I saw a dermatologist. He was clueless, prescribed a topical cream. As you can imagine the cream was not effective. I actually saw three different dermatologists.

Something is wrong

One summer afternoon weekend around August 1991, I was trimming the hedge in my front yard that separates my property from my neighbors. It was a hot California day and when I finished, I began to itch like never before. It was maddening. My scalp, arms, chest, and neck—it was like having ants crawling all over me.

I put the hedge clipper and extension cord away. I went upstairs and took a long shower. I even poured some Witch Hazel on my head and rubbed it in my scalp. I thought this might help the itching. At the moment this felt very good and soothing. I was certain the itching would pass. After the shower I was surprised that the itching remained and continued in the morning when I woke. I was working for the Mouse at Disney Development Company and at work I still suffered from the itching. I joked about it to some of my staff. I told them how after trimming my hedge I had a terrible itch that was uncontrollable, and I was doing my best not to scratch.

I thought maybe I got something from the hedge. I am very familiar with poison ivy. So, I knew that was not a possibility. There was no poison ivy or poison oak in sight at or near my hedge. That said, I thought maybe something from the hedge had caused a similar reaction?

When I was eleven or twelve, I was helping my dad, Uncle Richard, and my dad's friend Don Gustafson clear trees for the road to our property. We were creating an access road for our future homes. They would cut down trees and trim them. My job was to pull the brush into a pile and burn it. When it was lunchtime my mother and Aunt Sandy arrived with sandwiches, Kool-Aid for the children, and beer for the men, we all, including my sisters, brother, and cousin sat around the burning brush and enjoyed a break. Everyone with the exception of me due to the smoke from the brush that was entangled with poison ivy ended up covered with a bad poison ivy rash, even on their eyelids.

So, I was clueless as well, however at the time I was certain it was caused from trimming the hedge. It just seemed so logical.

A couple of weeks later, I climbed over a four-foot wrought-iron fence in my backyard to cut and trim plants on the other side that acted as stabilization material to keep the slope in place. I live on a small mountain; a sizable slope separates my backyard from my neighbors down the hillside. The fence is on flat ground on my side; however, the slope in grade is on a 60-degree angle at the other side of my fence.

I trimmed all the plants that were obstructing the view from my backyard of the Santa Clarita Valley in the distance. I tossed the cuttings and tools over the fence landing in my backyard. Next, I began to climb back over the fence. This time it was impossible for me to climb back to my property. No matter how I tried I did not have the strength to lift my body up and over. You see the grade on this side was steep, so the four-foot fence was at least a foot higher due to the grade change. This caused a challenge that was now impossible to meet. Please be mindful, I lifted myself up and over the fence several times previously.

I was thinking to myself, what the hell I am getting old? I am going to be forty soon. If this is what it feels like to be forty, well, then I can't imagine what my body will feel like when I turn fifty. I could not get back over the fence, so my only option was to navigate down the slope cross through my down hillside neighbor's property, walk down the street turn right at my street and walk up the small mountain a good fifteen- to twenty-minute journey. When I should have just hopped over the fence as I did the previous year.

I was already tired from the trimming work not to mention the repeated times I tried to get back over my fence. Walking up my hill on my street became a challenge. I have walked this street many times, but on this day, I was struggling badly. By the time I got to my home, which is located on the very top of the mountain. I was exhausted. Yep, I kept saying to myself I hate getting old.

When I arrived home, I walked down the steps that separate the front to the backyard. I have a three-story home. One enters at grade from the front, bedrooms at the level above, a game room and another bedroom with bath at the level below.

When I finally got to my backyard, I picked up the trimmings taking several bundles up the steps to the landscape trash container. Each time going up the steps became a greater challenge. My legs ached, I was tired and foolishly I believed this is due to becoming 40 soon. My body was failing me.

The following weekend our contractor for the new Feature Animation Building at Walt Disney Studios McCarthy Building Company Schedule a softball game for team building.

We all met at a park in Burbank to play softball. McCarthy batted first so we Disney and consultants took our place on the field. I usually prefer left field as many pop flies are hit there, however this day I decided to play third base you see I was fearful to run and chase down those pop flies. I took the field later than the others without a warm up. A ground ball was hit to me, an easy routine catch. I fielded the ball and took a step towards first base to throw the ball and get our first out of the inning. To my shock when I threw the ball to first base to make that easy out the ball traveled only four or five feet, the ball touched the ground way short. My arm did not hurt I was surprised that I could not make the out having no strength to throw the ball.

I took myself out of the game and made up a story that I wasn't feeling well. I gave my goodbyes, apologized walked to my Corvette and drove home. Driving home I was afraid, there has to be something more to this than just getting old. So many things wrong. Maybe I am sick?

I was getting weaker and my rash was getting worse and now the skins around my fingernails split and bleed. My fingers hurt. I found it difficult to button my shirt. I saw two additional dermatologists, both prescribed additional topical creams. I never put the rash and the loss of strength and muscle pain together. I kept thinking what the hell I hate getting old as I keep hurting myself for no apparent reason. Surprisingly the dermatologists were baffled. I was beginning to think something very wrong was happening to me, I didn't have a clue. Maybe I was sick in side, maybe I am just getting old and my body is falling apart?

I scheduled a team building event a paintball war between one of our contractors (McCarthy again) and my team Disney Development Company, our group included the consultants. I wasn't feeling well I was tired and my arms and legs ached so I stayed home the day before to rest and hopefully feel better. This actually worked, the next morning I felt great.

It did not take long to get to the battle site as the paintball war location was near my home. The location was a natural rustic terrain area in the hillside. I got there early to ensure all was set up for the day's activities. Coffee and donuts for breakfast, pizza's delivery midday for lunch.

The game is simple where each team has a flag and once the opponent's flag is captured the game is over. When you are hit with a paint ball you are immediately eliminated, no longer competing in the battle and must go to the dead people's area. So, our first battle was absolute chaos. Kevin was about to capture the McCarthy flag when he was inadvertently pelted by friendly fire from several teammates. This actually worked to my favor. We were humbled by the defeat. Our team was eager for direction; I laid out a plan and strategy organizing our team in small groups where each had a specific mission and strategy. We won the next three battles. I believe all had a great time and we began to become a team. By midafternoon I was in bad shape. My legs were killing me, I found it difficult to go up the hillside terrain, and I also couldn't understand why my arms ached. I sat out the last couple of battles.

A close group from both teams drove to my home after the battle; sitting at my kitchen table we drank a couple of beers and talked about the earlier battles as well as our project, the new Feature Animation building at Disney Studios in Burbank. When they left, I took a shower and told Linda I wasn't feeling well and going to bed early.

I can't walk

The next morning when I woke was an absolute shocker. I couldn't walk, my body was in pain and I also found it difficult to raise my arms. I remained in bed and slept most of the day and through the night.

Linda spent twelve-plus hours surfing the internet. Please be mindful, the internet was relatively new. She started by selecting key words she found from the three dermatologists reports. From what she was reading, led her to tie the muscle weakness issue. She came up with a small list of possible causes. One that she thought most likely was Lupus.

When I woke the next morning Linda advised we were going to the emergency room. Linda is a strong woman who definitely thinks on her own. However, if you ask her, she would adamantly tell you she is not strong. However, she will admit to being bossy and stubborn. So, with a stack of printouts from her earlier research she drove us to our local hospital.

When we arrived at the hospital, after telling my story of pain and weakness ...well they thought I was a hypochondriac, and I can't blame them. Picture this if you will, a little blonde woman talking about her husband's rash, skin open around his fingernails, he keeps getting weaker and weaker each and every day. And now he can only walk now about ten feet at a time without resting.

Fortunately, a doctor came out to the waiting room to talk with us, Dr. Brickman, He asked how I was feeling. I told him I feel fine just very tired, and when I walk, I can't go much farther than ten feet, but if I sit down for a minute or two, I can walk again however, only for another ten feet or so. He turned his conversation to Linda. They tell me you have quite a few print outs from the internet and you believe he has a muscle disease possibly Lupus? Linda showed him her stack of papers they talked for a minute or so when Dr. Brickman said I want Jack to take a blood test, we want to check his CPK levels.

After the nurse drew blood, we sat in the emergency waiting room and waited and waited sitting there for three or four hours.

Hearing the clamor of a loud noise behind us we turned to see the double doors to the hallway open with a couple of nurses and Dr. Brickman wheeling a bed, to my surprise they came to me. They told me to lie on the bed and he wheeled me back to the hallway.

He was impressed with Linda, how she tied the rash and muscle deterioration together. But most important that this led Dr. Brickman to request a CPK check. You see CPKs are a sort of enzyme that protects our muscles when they are in destress. Most have a normal CPK count of about 35, for me that day my CPKs were well over 2,300. He asked Linda if she was a nurse. She replied no I am a house wife who is scared to see what is happening to her husband. We talked for a while; they took my temperature and blood pressure. The nurse made certain I was okay.

At the time I did not have a family doctor, so if and when I had the flu or some minor issue, I would see Dr. Nordella at the clinic adjacent to where Henry Mayo Hospital is located.

Dr. Brickman advised that he would forward the CPK test results and his notes to Dr. Nordella and I should see him first thing in the morning. He believed that I may have some sort of an Autoimmune Muscular Disease. This all should make one a bit nervous and maybe scared, however just knowing what might be wrong with me I found welcoming. Dr. Brickman wasn't certain but please be mindful, for about a year I had the silly rashes and I kept getting weaker and weaker. So, for the first time I was hopeful to find an answer, a reason other than I am getting old. My friends are getting old and they do not get hurt for no apparent reason, they are not losing their strength or the ability to walk.

Linda called Dr. Nordella's office when we got home, and as it turns out they were waiting for her call and had already scheduled time in the morning for me to see Dr. Nordella.

My legs and arms were weaker than ever. I still had difficulty walking for the third day. The rash and loss of strength has been evolving for almost a year. That night I studied Linda's printouts and the list of possible diseases she imagined for same. I started to anticipate. Yes, I guess I mostly started to speculate what we would find; this is definitely a mistake, not a good thing to do. Linda kept saying let's just wait and see what the doctor thinks tomorrow.

The next morning, she drove us to Dr. Nordella's office. He was also impressed with Linda, how she tied the rash and muscle deterioration together. He talked about the high CPK results.

Dr. Nordella advised that he believes I have an autoimmune muscular disease. Dr. Nordella advised that he wanted me to see an old classmate of his Dr. David Klashman a rheumatologist at UCLA. He also advised he had already called so I could see Dr. Klashman the very next morning.

Linda and I woke early, it was so very hopeful to find what was wrong with my health I was always so tired and curious to find why I can't walk and what is causing my loss of strength. At this point the rash and itching seemed minor and I still wasn't certain it all tied together.

She drove us to the UCLA Medical Center about an hour and a half drive from our home. Located just off the Wilshire Blvd. exit on the 405. That is the freeway all of America has seen on the internet, over seven lanes in each direction and the traffic is absolutely daunting. That said, on this morning traffic was definitely not my concern. We pulled into the UCLA Medical Center parked in the below grade garage and made our way to the elevator and up to Dr. Klansman's office. Along the way I found a bench or planter to rest or a few moments. It was great to arrive at his office and take a seat in his waiting room. I did not have to walk anymore, I could relax. However, our wait was short, within a couple of minutes Dr. Klashman greeted us.

Dr. Klashman

I met a young doctor who appeared to be in his midthirties. He had a great bedside manner and I found Dr. Klashman to be well informed. He was very likable, well educated, and most important, he could explain and articulate his thoughts where I could actually comprehend and understand what he was saying. I was immediately impressed concerning the command of his knowledge. We talked for well over an hour. During the visit he examined the rash on my face, chest, hands, and the skin openings around my fingernails. He also had to perform various exercises, holding my hands over my head, pushing my hands against his and lifting my legs while laying on my back with his hand on an ankle. He was alarmed at my weakness. He also watched me walk, and already knew that after a mere say eight- to ten-foot distance I was spent, however with a short rest I would be good to go another short distance again.

Dr. Klashman, began to explain what he believed was causing my illness. He talked about a rare autoimmune muscular disease called Dermatomyositis advised that he believes there are three possibilities for my CPK count to be that high.

- I just ran a twenty-mile marathon crashed and hit the wall.
- I just died from a heart attack
- The final and more logical answer, I have this very rare disease called Dermatomyositis.

He went on to explain there is no cure for Dermatomyositis as it is a chronic disease. He advised that he will schedule a day surgery later in the week to remove a piece of the muscle in my shoulder to analysis and confirm dermatomyositis. He advised that the disease is sun sensitive and I must be extremely careful, wear sun screen and stay out of the sun. He also advised that exertion of the muscles accelerates the disease. Okay now finally this all began to finally made sense.

I told him about ten months ago when I was in Cabo Mexico on a fishing trip and was sunburned so badly and how I got a fever and the chills that night. I was in bed, soaking wet and freezing cold I also told him about the softball game when I couldn't throw the ball, getting stuck on the back side of my fence and the paint ball war, how the morning after the paintball war I couldn't walk. Things began to make sense. He articulated more how dermatomyositis is a chronic disease, no known cure and the medical society isn't certain how or why one contracts same. I asked if my children would inherit the disease? Dr. Klashman advised no. he said let me give you this example; it is like standing on the Santa Monica Beach in every direction you can see sand, now in your hand you hold a handful of sand, that is the odds for your children. He then said you have a better chance of winning the lottery than getting dermatomyositis. Each and every time I find myself at a grocery store, well I stop and purchase a lottery ticket. So far, I have been extremely unlucky as I have never held a winning ticket.

The most common symptoms of dermatomyositis include skin changes and muscle weakness. In most cases, the first symptom is a patchy and bluish-purple skin rash on the face, eyelids, chest, nail cuticle areas, knuckles, knees, or elbows. Then you may have muscle weakness starting in the neck, arms or hips, and the weakness can be felt on both sides of your body. And it may get worse over weeks or months.

Dermatomyositis is one of a group of acquired muscle diseases called inflammatory myopathies (disorder of muscle tissue or muscles), which are characterized by chronic muscle inflammation accompanied by muscle weakness. The cardinal symptom is a skin rash that precedes or accompanies progressive muscle weakness. Dermatomyositis may occur at any age, but is most common in adults; women usually show signs of Dermatomyositis in late teens and men around age 40. Interesting my rash and muscle weakness showed up just after my 40th birthday.

Two days later, I returned to UCLA for outpatient surgery. The muscle biopsy confirmed Dr. Klansman's diagnosis, Dermatomyositis.

Dr. Klashman initially prescribed prednisone, the dose was high to counter act the dermatomyositis. I had trouble sleeping and my head got huge like a basketball. I began to wear a medical bracelet. Actually, years later this bracelet helped save my life.

I'm weak

I went to the grocery store, Vons for Linda. It was good to get out of the house for a while. My legs hurt however holding on to the shopping cart helped. I will never forget this day and moment. I wanted a six pack of beer. No matter how many times I tried it was impossible for me to lift the beer in to the shopping cart. I found a carton that as torn and the beer cans were loose. Yes, that is exactly what I did; one can at a time until all six were in my cart.

If the beer debacle story wasn't bad enough, I have another that was even more humbling even a bit embarrassing. I asked my assistant my secretary Rachel Ybarra to bring some work to my home so I could keep up with the projects at DDC. Rachel is one hell of a secretary a great assistant who I cherished and valued. We became good friends I knew her family and she mine. Rachel had an important and significant role in our organization. Rachel put together a stack of papers for me, and on her way, she stopped at a restaurant and got us baby back ribs for lunch. Rachel arrived at our home gave me a hug said something like I am glad you are getting better every one misses you.

She caught me up on the office. We talked about the papers she brought and Rachel took a few notes. Rachel saw me struggling as it was impossible for me to cut the ribs. Can you believe I was that weak? Consequently, Rachel took my plate and slid it in front of her and began to cut the ribs for me. She is sweet years later we joked and laughed about that day the day I did not have the strength to cut my own meat.

I missed work I took a sick leave with Disney for a period just shy of 6 weeks. At the time I had several projects at Disney Studios, the Pacific Rim and three projects in New York City. Concerning the Pacific Rim, I devised a plan and strategy with my good friend and colleague Ted Chang with Turner Construction to use Turner staff in that area. Most of the work there was simple second-generation tenant improvements. This strategy worked well for the past two years. The work at Disney Studios was challenging, I was fortunate to have an awesome staff. Lucky for me the projects were local and easy for me to navigate. The New York projects were also challenging a different story concerning my traveling. I had difficulty and at times a daunting challenge navigating through the airport.

The prednisone dose initially was 100 ml each day. Dr. Klashman got it down to twenty-five or thirty my body was responding and I was doing better. I lost a little weight. My head was huge from the prednisone so to me I looked like I had gained weight. I actually had to purchase larger shirts so my collar could button.

I could walk about seventy-five feet now before I had to sit and rest. Best way to describe this, it is like doing stomach crunches, the pain is intense however if you just stop and rest for eight to ten seconds the pain disappears. I knew my limitations I would walk and continually search to find a place to sit averaged about every fifty feet or so and no more than 100 feet. At about seventy-five feet the pain in my legs was so intense I needed to rest. Airports were a challenge; I could walk the length of two gates before I needed to rest. Like I said resting was no longer than say ten seconds. That said the main challenge was obtaining my boarding pass. At the time automated ticketing had not been invented yet. So, my challenge was standing in line to get a boarding pass, just thinking about doing this while diving to the airport caused me anxiety.

While standing in line waiting for my turn my legs would hurt so badly and there was no place to sit. I had to bear through this. Once I got my boarding pass, I would find a place to sit immediately, a planter a short wall anything would do. While waiting in line I would canvas the area to find an emergency place to sit. I knew where all the elevators were located at the American and United terminals. I didn't want to get hung up in line for the escalator and some airports have steep escalators, well that is another issue, isn't it?

My next challenge was placing my suitcase in the overhead storage compartment on the plane. When I was traveling with Laura, she would always take my suitcase from me and lift it in place. That said traveling alone was a bit intimidating. I would ask a flight attendant to help me; the ladies always accommodated me and never ever made me feel bad. Although I was embarrassed that I needed assistance.

Take a taxi Jack

There was one situation during the winter of 1994 where I had to exercise all efforts. I traveled alone from Los Angeles to New York. I took the train and then subway to my hotel. When I got to Grand Central Station, I departed from my train at one of the lower levels. I could not find an elevator and the escalator was out of order. So, imagine this, with my legs hurting and my arms are weak, I have the strength of a twelve-year-old girl. Halfway up the escalator my body gave out. I no longer could carry my suitcase. I am in NY. I tried desperately to get someone, anyone to carry my suitcase the remaining distance. They were already angry that I was an obstacle in their path. I got to one side as far as possible and tried to develop a plan.

I had a long shoulder strap on my briefcase so that was easy. I thought about just leaving my suitcase behind. Well, after a second thought, I knew that wouldn't work as I was scheduled for meetings through the week and definitely needed my clothes. Exhausted and weak, I sat down to rest, yes on the escalator steps with my suitcase on the step below me. So, imagine me sitting there with many angry people shaking their head and complaining as they walked past me.

I thought to myself, come on you can do this, Jack. One step at a time, maybe two? With a plan in hand, I would lift my suitcase one stair at a time, and I took a seat on the metal escalator about every five steps to rest again. My strategy annoyed a lot of New Yorkers they were not pleased, they had no patients concerning my struggle. When I got to the top, I felt like I had just won a medal in the Olympics. Hell ... I wanted to cheer out loud, but as you can imagine, I didn't. Yep, I remained quiet maybe I cheered silently? Fortunately, the escalator to get to the next upper level was working. I never used the train again. I always found a cab. I was foolish to take the train. I made this trip every other week for about four years. Fortunately, most often Laura traveled with me.

Over the next year Dr. Klashman tried various options. In addition to the prednisone, we added Imuran. Nothing seemed to work that said, I did begin to recover. I could walk about 150 feet and my strength returned to my arms. We moved on to try methotrexate, yep that's right, you do not have to look up methotrexate it is chemotherapy.

I would see Dr. Klashman every Friday for about nine to ten months, and he would give me a shot 10 ml of methotrexate. I enjoyed talking with him. We became friends, well, as good of a friend in a doctor patient relationship. He talked about his three daughters. I also found he played guitar and owned a Gibson Les Paul. I have a 78 black custom Les Paul. His youngest daughter played softball on a traveling team. My youngest son, Drew, played baseball on a traveling team as well, a Pony Baseball in our Valley.

Not able to play catch

I no longer could play catch with my son, just didn't have the arm strength the best I could do is toss the ball back to Drew underhand the ball would find its way to Drew by rolling and bouncing on the ground. How does a dad continue to teach his son to play baseball when he can't even throw a ball? During the next fifteen months of visits Drew's travel team played in tournaments all over America and his Santa Clarita Hart Baseball tournament team were champions in the Pony Baseball World Series.

I like Dr. Klashman and found many things in common. I gave him tickets for his family to visit Disneyland and a Jimi Hendrix guitar music book. Often, I would bring Disney T-shirts for Loriana and Dr. Klashman. His nurse was Loriana a sweet lady who I also enjoyed talking with. While taking methotrexate I could no longer drink alcohol and I love beer. This was difficult especially at dinner business meetings. But I stayed on the wagon. Each month I took a blood test to monitor my CPK count. This medication strategy also wasn't working. So, we slowly backed off the methotrexate over the last four weeks. Funny the methotrexate did not cause a sick reaction when I as on the full dose. That said, while weening off the drug I did feel nauseous. Maybe I blocked it out when I knew I had to have it weekly and maybe it was in my head when I was getting it out of my system. I will never know.

Drew's travel baseball team, Santa Clarita Cougars had a weekend tournament in Costa Mesa. I was working in Burbank for Disney Development Company (DDC) at the time, a quick drive home; Linda had everything already packed in her Tahoe. We back tracked a bit traveling to Costa Mesa, we checked into a motel early Friday night. Most of the other families were already at the motel when we arrived. I was off the methotrexate for the required duration and was a told I could enjoy beer again. So, to my delight, I actually smiled and began clapping I must have looked silly standing on the steps to the second level of the motel walkway? You see I noticed that directly across the street from our motel I saw a package store. I walked down the motel stairs, crossed the street, and purchased a small Styrofoam cooler and a twelve-pack of Coors light.

This was another small victory; yep, I guess it was a very small victory to not let sickness control my life. For me, well it is important to not have the dermatomyositis define me. I want to be defined by my family, my children and work. I was disappointed to find the package store did not carry cold beer. That said, I made the purchase and was looking forward to the weekend. Watching my son Drew play ball, with our family and returning later to our room with beer on ice. It does not get any better for a dad. I walked back across the street and returned to my room. Where I quickly located the ice machine, added ice to the cooler. I am impatient, so yes, I couldn't wait long enough for the beer to chill. My first beer was awful as it was still very warm it tasted like moose piss. That said, later that evening I enjoyed a couple of ice-cold beers. It was great to enjoy the simple things in life, definitely nice to have a cold beer in my hand again and Drew's team won their first two games the next day.

IVIG

Dr. Klashman talked about IVIG he explained the process and strategy; he thought it might work for me? Simply put, what I heard is, Jack your immune system is compromised the Dermatomyositis is confusing your white blood corpuscles. You have two groups; one group will plant a flag at a sick or damaged cell and the other finds the marker and destroys the cell. The dermatomyositis was confusing the group planting flags; they were placing flags everywhere at good as well as bad cells. Unfortunately, the disease was causing my immune system to actually eat holes in my muscles like Swiss cheese. If the IVIG works for you the first groups will no longer plant any flags. If we can stop them from planting flags the next group will no longer cause you harm. You will have some other issues that we have to watch carefully as your immune system will be depressed. Let's run a test dose and see if we can find if IVIG works for you. Jack, if this works, you would receive about a liter two days in a row every month. You will be receiving about a drop the size of your small fingernail from thousands of people. All these drops combined and merged together may be our answer.

The IVIG worked, my CPK levels went down, not to where they were before however at a manageable level. I got my life back. Well, my strength is that of a twelve-year-old girl. I began to get my strength back, and the rash all but disappeared. It is fine and I am happy to live with some strength.

Lost DDC position

Disney removed me from my position at DDC- Director of Development and Design, my new tile Director of Construction with Imagineering. I lost my team now working alone special projects assignments from Ken Wong.

Previously one of my responsibilities, I lead the preconstruction effort for Angels Stadium. I led the design effort to completion finalized the construction contracts allowing the project to commence construction.

A rather odd man very disagreeable that I did not care for, Timor Galan became responsible for Angels Stadium when DDC no longer in existence the staff now inclusive of Imagineering. With stadium construction failing, Ken Wong requested I sit in the construction meetings, a consultant role, directing necessary changes to turn the attitude around. Ken was hopeful I would provide positive insight during construction.

In addition, I led the effort to create minority and women owned business practices as well as developing a training program for the Disney Imagineering theme park construction teams.

I also created protocol requirements twenty-eight individual volumes, a guideline for our California Adventure construction teams, for example protocol to handle a strike, earthquake protocol, security etc.

Earthquake protocol fascinates me. I did not have an answer; I did not have a solution that I believed to be foolproof. I was watching TV on a Saturday following the Malibu fires. The news showed firefighting stations from all over California, Nevada and Arizona assisting in the effort. I wondered how they were organized; I assumed lots of fighting, disagreements. However, they appeared to be well organized. I scheduled a meeting with the Anaheim Fire

Department. They explained the firefighters' protocol (simple highest commanding position responsible for that areas control). Very basic and yes very simple … I met with them two additional times. I lifted the fire department's protocols for the manual. I also was assigned to some other items much less significant tasks. I did not enjoy my new role.

I got blindsided. Disney tried to convince me to go on permanent disability. I rejected the notion. I wonder if I had accepted could I still get a paycheck today. They moved me to be a staff member on the theme park transportation team. That was the last straw. Fortunately, IVIG treatments gave me my life back, after six weeks in this new role I was hired by Trizec-Hahn to turn around the Hollywood & Highland/ Kodak theater development.

You know yourself

What happened next was interesting and something that Dr. Klashman advise that I know my body better than anyone and I will learn how to manage same. I must exercise to get healthy again and rebuild muscle. That said if I begin to have a relapse exercising will accelerate my disease. Stay out of the sun; you must wear sunscreen, all this plays in concert to keep cutting my daily dose of prednisone. Weening off prednisone would be a long and slow process and he advised most likely I might never be free of prednisone completely.

I got to a daily dose of 4 ml prednisone. I was able to maintain this for several years. Twice I tried to go to 3 mg unfortunately this didn't work, each time I had to up the dose back to 4 mg.

While working in Texas for Thor Equities leading the development for Kirby Collection project I tried once again to drop to 3mg. this time it worked. I was so pleased and I was certain I could push this further, so after another six months I dropped to 2 mg, six months later to 1 mg. After about eight months I would take only 1 mg of prednisone on Monday, Wednesday, and Fridays. When I returned to California, I schedule another appointment with Dr. Klashman. I wasn't sick however I wanted to see my old friend/doctor and to show him how well I was doing and I guess I also wanted to thank him.

Oops I forgot to tell you that about two to three years previous on a trip back to California for the Christmas holidays I scheduled and appointment with Dr. Klashman so he could see I was down to 3mg. he was pleased and advised that maybe I could someday actually get off the prednisone. When asked how I was doing well I always said fine…I was always lying. I stayed positive; fortunately, I did get better…. I have been on prednisone now for over twenty-five years and this was causing other minor issues.

Dr. Klashman was very pleased; he shook his head and began to smile. Jack the prednisone isn't doing anything for you anymore. I believe you are now able to be prednisone free. Then to my surprised he advised if you are taking prednisone three times a week and only receiving 3 mg total for the week you can stop taking it.

Now, Jack, as we have discussed previously, if you feel a relapse coming, call me we will return to the prednisone and start over again. It was great to see him again. I gave him a hug. I also advised that my tongue cancer most likely has returned that I am waiting on results from the biopsy. We talked about cancer for a while as many dermatomyositis patients also contract different forms of cancer. It was great to see him, I assume I will be back again in twelve months just to check in. That night after I arrived home, I wrote Dr. Klashman a letter thanking him for getting me through a most difficult sickness.

No cure, dermatomyositis is a chronic disease. Per Dr. Klashman's direction, he never scheduled another IVIG treatment; fortunately, I have not experienced a relapse to date. When I feel off or see a rash appearing, that butterfly shape on my face, well I take some prednisone for a couple of days. No am not a doctor I just believe what Dr. Klashman told me, Jack, as you are in Texas now you know your body, if you feel it coming take some prednisone or a couple of days, stay out of the sun and do not over exercise you know the drill. If you need me, I will be here for you.

I do look in the mirror often usually after my morning shave as the rash always starts there first. Fortunately, so far prednisone always does the trick, I pray I never have a relapse unable to walk again and that itching it's absolutely debilitating.

Homeless guy

I began smoking cigarettes when was eighteen while I traveled around America and parts of Mexico with my high school friends Paul Galuska and James Bougie. I smoked at least two packs a day for about twenty-five years. I tried to quit several times unfortunately I would always continue. When I was diagnosed with dermatomyositis, I was told that I have to quit smoking. I tried and failed many times. That said I did almost get there. I know you are wondering what does that mean.

So, I knew smoking was very bad for me. I got there. Yep, I told myself I quit, but I also did something very stupid each and every Friday. You must understand my foolish logic; I believed I deserved two cigarettes each and every Friday. I also knew if I kept the remaining cigarette package, I would most certainly smoke all the cigarettes.

While leading the Kodak Theatre/ Hollywood and Highland development during 1999–2002 on Fridays as I was driving home, I would stop at a little store on Hollywood Blvd. and purchase a pack of Marlboro lights. I drove a little Porsche Boxter. Most Fridays in Hollywood the weather was nice, so I would put the rag top down and light up a cigarette to enjoy my ride home. I circled around my project driving down Hollywood Blvd. to Orange Street make another left to get to Highland, and then as I approached the traffic signal at Highland, I would pull another cigarette from the package. You see a homeless guy always took position at this location in the median between traffic and I would toss him the remaining cigarettes and matches, wave to him, and say see you next Friday.

Unfortunately, the only time we talked was one year a day or two before Christmas. I pulled my car over to the edge and asked him to come to me. When he crossed the two lanes and approached, I opened my trunk and in addition to the cigarettes I gave him two gift baskets. Merry Christmas, I said. These baskets of goodies are for you. There is cheese, crackers, some sausage, and other things here for you. He told me he looked forward to Fridays as during the rest of the week he smokes left-over cigarette butts discarded on the ground. I wasn't sure how to respond to that. We stood there in awkward silence for a minute or so. He smiled we shook hands and we each said Merry Christmas. These baskets were Christmas gifts I received from our consultants. I had a third basket, which I kept and brought home.

Just as I was getting back in my car, I got a call from one of the contractors Greg Wade with Matt Construction and he said there was an issue we needed to discuss, so I advised that I would be there shortly. When we finished our meeting and I got back in my car to head home I circled around my project again. To my surprise, when I arrived at the median where the homeless guy stood, he wasn't there and I was shocked to see the two baskets in the road crushed by all the cars that had driven over the contents. Then I saw two broken tops of two wine bottles also in the road next to the curb with red wine stained on the curb side. Cheese, crackers, sausage, and the baskets crushed to the asphalt by the weight of several passing cars.

I shook my head and said out loud Jack you are a dumb ass, you gave him gift baskets and each basket held a bottle of wine. The poor guy obviously did not have a wine bottle opener nor a wine glass in his pocket, so he busted the bottle tops of by hitting the bottles on the curb and left the cheese, crackers, sausage, and other stuff behind. It was a nice gesture, but yep, I most certainly should have removed the wine bottles. Driving home, I was thinking how desperate he was and hoped he didn't cut himself or swallow glass.

When I was diagnosed with tongue cancer the first time in the winter of 2007, yep that did it, which was when I stopped smoking completely.

Chapter 12
Driver's license [2002]

Can I drive? I found I could however I now had impatient issues so I needed to stay calm and alert at red lights. You see the light would take so long to change that I started thinking maybe the traffic signal isn't working properly. Should I go, be careful Jack, hell what are you thinking you can't go, there is no problem with the light just is patient and stop with all the thinking something is wrong the light ... it is not malfunctioning stupid. See, I told you. Now, it is green. Of course, the traffic light always worked; this was an implacable and most stupid thought of mine.

I had no problems driving Linda's Tahoe. That said my car was a different story. I owned a Porsche Boxster manual shift sports car. When I would remove my right hand to shift only my left hand was holding the steering wheel and of course I could not feel it. So, I kept looking to make sure my hand was still there. I did not like this situation at all, it was odd and awkward. Also most often driving in Los Angeles traffic I never got past third gear, second, third, second third driving like this for miles. So, I traded in my Porsche for a Toyota 4 Runner gave that car to Linda and I began driving her Tahoe. No excuses for Jack now.

Taking the driving test wasn't a requirement as my license was never taken away. However, Dr. Dhanda thought it wise for me to take a test through a group in Northridge that specialized with people recovering from a stroke. This way he believed I could be more confident and risk adverse in the event I had an accident.

So, I studied the California Drivers' Manual and on the day of my appointment Linda drove me to my driver's test. The test was not at all what I had prepared for. Yes, there was a small section concerning actual driving questions; however, that was very simple and easy. The main written questioner was based on symbols, diagrams, and bizarre images. For example, they would show four symbols in a sequence and ask what symbol would be next. Or what symbol does not belong here? I was told I could only have two mistakes. On the very first question I made the wrong choice. Not a great start, as soon as she said that is incorrect, you only have one more wrong answer and you will fail the test. I immediately saw what I did wrong.

So, I talked about my poor choice and I asked a couple of theoretical questions. This proved to be extremely helpful, one has to learn from one's mistakes or what is the point. I went slow and made certain I did not make another foolish mistake. I was pleased to find I got the remaining questions answered correctly.

Next, she advised was the actual driving test. So, picture this if you will, I find myself in the front seat with the lady who administered the written test with another gentleman sitting in the back. They both held clip boards and talked to each other constantly about my driving. Most often their words were muffled and I could not hear the conversation. They did make me nervous; they never ever provided encouragement or positive word. We drove for about thirty minutes mostly on side streets where the speed limit was only 35mph.

They would say something like when you approached that stop sign why didn't you turn your head and look around in each and every direction? I replied I did not need to turn my head as my peripheral vision allowed me to see. Or when you drive, we do not see you looking to the sides you always look straight ahead? So, as you can imagine, I was fearful that I may fail their test. When we arrive back at the parking lot, they said you passed. Not certain the test was worth all the cost, trouble, and anxiety; I am certain Linda felt better about me driving now. The cost was over $450 so I believed it to be a senseless waste of my time and most definitely money.

We, I drove and Linda sat next to me as I took a practice run one day into Hollywood just to make sure I did not have any issues. All was fine. This also probably was a bit of overkill? My driving is fine; however, what I do not understand why or how at times if I have been driving for a long distance, I get an odd panic, not an attack, just for moment things do not appear as they should. When this occurs, I will have Linda take over driving and if alone, I pull off to the side of the road and get out for a couple of minutes. Then get back behind the wheel and all is fine. It is an odd feeling, which once happened often and after a while thankfully never returned to haunt me again.

CHAPTER 13
TIME TO MOVE ON [2003]

Back to work for a month or so after my stroke, I believe I'm doing fine. We have the Kor Group projects also a fascinating development for NEW (New Economics for Women) a Hispanic women's organization on their behalf we created the development of an elementary school with adjacent community Center. I enjoyed this work as I believed the cause was noble and it was rewarding to give something back to the community.

Beatrice Strotzer was a strong leader and most impressive. I admired what she could accomplish and provide for the women in her community. We met her through a couple of attorneys Joe Avila and Will Putnam who I also admired and enjoyed working with. They were do-gooders who were well connected in their community.

Joe and Will were smart and they became our attorney but most important they had high standards, integrity, and I liked them. Sometimes it is just a pleasure to know and work with good people. We first met Joe and Will when a group called ABC, not the television company another Hispanic organization located here in Los Angeles who was trying to develop a new high school for their neighborhood. The school was abandoned in mid construction and beginning to show the wear and tear from being exposed to the weather, and lack of attention.

ABC wanted to help their community they needed the forlorn project back under construction and open for the children. The project faced several obstacles. The solutions were pragmatic and basic; however, a significant insurance and remediation concern with methane gases trapped below the surface put a dark cloud over the project. Unfortunately, the Belmont High School project ended for ABC which meant we lost the contract and LAUSD took over when to all's surprise due to a newly discovered earthquake fault that was too close to one of the structures, a relatively small structure. The solution for the new found fault was simple, demolish the building in close proximity to the fault and reconstruct in a more appropriate location. LAUSD took over the project replacing ABC. They also abandoned the insurance/remediation requirement; fortunately, the school was finalized and opened for the community.

One day around six weeks later, I got a call from the Art Center College of Design, this was a nice surprise. They said Frank Gehry is the architect and Frank recommended that the college retain me to act as owner's representative for their new master planned development. A fascinating master plan that included a library two additional class room buildings and a parking garage. I love working with Frank and find his design fascinating.

To be recommended by Frank and have the opportunity to work with him again was a dream come true. Our little consulting firm I believed off to a good start. The master plan was artful and his design beyond amazing. You see I was shocked to see Frank step well outside his comfort zone he was designing a glass library with all the curves and obstruction typical in his concepts. This would be a challenge beyond challenges. I worked and lead the team for about 6 to 7 months. The experience was absolutely rewarding.

I tried to convince the president of the school to raise funds for construction in pieces and phases put Frank at the center show him off to raise funds, I advised Frank was a rock star get him involved and certainly the funds would grow. He wanted to raise all the money for the total project in lieu of development by phases on his own this was beyond a heroic notion. As I had presumed, he fell short, funds were not available the project would never leave the concept phase and remain on the drawing board

Oops, yep, that's not good

One night while working late I went to the copy machine to make a copy of something I needed for meeting the following morning. When I lifted the door on top of the copy machine, I found a document that was inadvertently left behind. So, I removed the document and placed what I needed to make a copy on the scan board and made myself the additional copy I needed.

Walking back to my office, I began to read the document that was let behind. I planned to leave same on whoever's desk that was responsible for the document. I was surprised, shocked, and saddened to find that the document was a business plan created by my partner and friend Kevin with help from our employee John. My trust vanished.

Kevin and John were developing the notion for a new business they planned to stay as long as possible to keep the current health insurance in place during the transition. I was stunned, not certain what to do next. I wrote a note on the document to Kevin and placed it on his desk. The next morning, I was certain we would have a discussion; however, that never occurred. And when I got to the office, I noticed the document was no longer on his desk. I should have brought it up; I waited for Kevin to talk to me. I have never shied from controversy.

Over the years I have thought about this often maybe I was not confident with myself at the time due to the stroke, maybe I wasn't thinking or perhaps I was just acting like a little girl? I no longer have bad feelings. However, our relationship will never be as it once was. That said, all relationships adapt and change over time, or do they?

A couple of days passed. I was hurt. I guess I may have been acting like a little girl. I became disillusioned with the business. I had a discussion with my partners Kevin and Laura and our employee John. I advised that I plan to move on actually leave my company and that I will be taking the Art Center College of Design development with me, they can have the other projects. John advised that he would sue. I was surprised and advised Frank gave us this project because of me he doesn't even know the rest of you. The talks turned dark and awkward. For me to stay John had to leave. An exit agreement was put together for John.

A month or so later I was invited on a trip to Houston with our client Brad; he wanted me to meet his father and a couple of friends who invest in each other's developments. On the flight back from Houston Brad tried to convenience me to join his firm. About a month later, I drove to his office and we discussed the notion.

These adaptive re-use developments are difficult challenges as one does not know what one does not know about hidden issues and risk associated with the reconstruction. I was thinking about a problem we had with a schedule issue when I just couldn't stop thinking about my conversation with Brad on the plane. Actually, that was not the first time he approached me to join his team; it was the third.

Not certain why I changed my mind, maybe it was due to Kevin and John or maybe what I told myself is that I need to push myself to see if I can be successful as I had been prior to my stroke.

Brad was demanding one always had to be available for his call and the Kor Group had huge potential. I knew this opportunity would definitely test my resolve. I believed if I can satisfy any and all financial issues with our consulting firm Bousquet, Dennis, and Doerges and give projects to Kevin and Laura ... well I believed I could then accept the position and test myself.

Instead of driving home for the evening I drove to Brad's office. I was actually a bit surprised to find him available. I walked in and advised that I was curious and had a few questions concerning his offer for me to join his team, most important what would my role be? He advised you would be in charge of design and construction for all projects, adaptive re-use construction, the hospitality side and I want to grow outside of Los Angeles so you would be responsible for that as well. I began talking and said with that role I have to reconsider his offer; however, I can't just leave my partners. If he was willing to give a project to Kevin another to Laura and most important assume any and all of our cost for rent, insurance etc. so they would have no financial burdens that I will join him and we could use my office space in Pasadena in addition to Kevin and Laura working there as a satellite Kor location for design and construction staff. We talked about my salary; Brad's offer was fifty thousand less than what I asked for. I accepted the position, to my surprise less than three months later Brad said I like what you are doing here and advised, my salary would be increased another fifty thousand dollars.

The next morning after accepting Brad's offer the night before to join his team was interesting, awkward actually rather bizarre I met with Laura and Kevin and I resigned from my company. I told them all expenses and any burdens were no longer an issue in addition to the New Economics for Women project that they each had a Kor project, and if they desire, they could join me. Can you imagine resigning from your own company only to return the following day to the same office with Laura and Kevin sitting in the offices on either side to yours? Laura was saddened, and when we would pass in the hallway, I got the look from her like she was my 5th-grade girlfriend and we just broke up. Kevin on the other hand was calm and cool. Kevin, the only one to stop by for a visit after my stroke, maybe at the conclusion he assumed I was done, no longer capable?

So, I became SR VP Design and Construction, soon after Laura elected to join me, Kevin elected not, he wanted to remain a consultant. At the time the development company had less than twenty employees. A year later I was managing over twenty-five projects in three countries the Kor Group now had over 150 employees. Within weeks after I joined The Kor Group Lubert-Adler a real estate fund located in Philadelphia became Kor Group's financial partner. This changed everything; The Kor Group shinned.

Kevin /Jack previous lifetime

Kevin was my best friend we had worked together for over seventeen years. I met him in 1984 while I was working for Cadillac Fairview in Falls Church, Virginia. He was hired by one of our contractors H. C. Beck right out of College, Texas Tech. I was doing my best to find someone for my staff. After three or four months with little luck locating a quality recipient, my boss in Dallas, TX. Mike Dickens was touring projects and traveled to Virginia.

Mike toured my projects with me and was very pleased with our progress. When we returned to my office, he closed the door and took a seat; this was odd that he closed the door. I wasn't certain what would come next. Mike asked do you need help Jack finding additional staff? Mike advised he usually looks for someone with three to four years' experience so Jack what are you looking for, what qualifications do you require and how many years of experience do you believe necessary for a Construction Manager position? I replied years do not matter I can teach and coach anyone if they have what I believe most important ... character, integrity and are hungry and have a strong work ethic. Mike said you talk highly about Kevin in the past although he only has about six months experience. I was a bit surprised Mike even knew who Kevin was and I tried my best to remember our previous conversation. I did remember talking about how I was impressed with H. C. Beck I believed they had a great culture and strong leaders, most important Bruce

Roberts estimating and Paul Green operations manager. I did not remember talking about Kevin.

If I hire him, it might hurt our contractor, I responded. Mike smiled and said you are thinking small, I think not Jack as H. C. Beck has many candidates with several years of experience to replace him and said, if you don't you might be hurting us. If you really believe you can coach, just do it.

So, I did. Mike Dickens had confidence in me and I guess he helped me to believe in myself. I met with Kevin the next day and we talked for a while, I told him I was entertaining an offer for him to join my team. Not certain why I asked the next question as it is an odd question to ask, definitely an odd question for me to ask. So, I asked, Kevin what do you think a construction manager does for a developer?

I was shocked by his response. He said, well, they come to work late and pick out a color at ten only to change the decision later in the afternoon at, say, two. He sat there with this stupid grin on his face. It was a bit of a smartass response; hell, it was a huge smartass response; however, I believe he could be valuable to my team and I also liked that he stepped out of the box with a comment like that. He took a chance. I think he was trying to be funny show he had a sense of humor. I definitely knew he would not be a yes man. I hate yes men. I want people to talk openly to me, I like people with opinions I may not like or agree with their thought however I want to hear it. The response was so smart assed I thought about continuing my search, but then I also thought Kevin could be great so I offered him the position at our Virginia office. Needless to say, H. C. Beck wasn't too happy and now this very junior manager would be directing his previous boss at H. C. Beck. The beck team would now take direction from their previous new hire right out of college.

Mike Dickens was a smart man and a great manager. Our headquarters was in Dallas and I was located in the Virginia and the Washington, DC offices. I had two separate teams at each office; I went to the Virginia office Monday, Wednesday and Friday arriving at the DC office every Tuesday and Thursday. Mike trusted me and we seldom talked. In the beginning, I would send Mike a report. That said, he never responded so after a short time I stopped with that type of communication and began calling him every couple of months to see if he wanted an update on any of my projects. I learned from our conversations that Mike already knew the status of all of my projects. So, I learned to keep going and believed if Mike wants to talk, he will call me. I am certain as Mike was very busy as he was responsible for the construction of all projects nationwide; I also knew some of the problems that he had very difficult issues at other locations. I was lucky and I was on a roll every one of my projects was on schedule and under budget, I had an awesome team. Kevin made the team even better. He grew quickly surprisingly fast and became the best of our team, both offices. I trusted and most important I liked working with Kevin.

Years later April 1st, 1990 when I joined Disney Development Company (DDC) Kevin was my first hire. The next two about a year later joined me at the same time. Second was Doug Curtis who was an integral part of the H. C. Beck Virginia team and third Lynn Beckmeyer a very smart and capable architect who worked on one of my Washington, DC developments and another at Fairview Park in Virginia. I like putting the smartest and sharpest people around me. People I trust and know how to get the job done, to push a project not just keep track of what is happening.

I hired Kevin again when I took over the Hollywood & Highland /Kodak Theater development while working for Trizec-Hahn. Laura and Doug Curtis were on that team prior to me being hired, Carla Romero I added after Kevin. One of my best they were one hell of a team.

Many of my staff has worked with me for well over a decade and often with several different real estate development firms. I know what they can do as well as what they can't and I give them room to make mistakes, most important we all become a team. Maybe that is why; well, I believe that is why I have a history of delivering developments on time and on budget.

Laura makes an impression

I distinctly remember the day I met Laura. We were meeting about some logistical issues concerned with The Team Disneyland office building, a Frank Gehry design at the Disneyland complex. Norm Doerges Laura's future father-in-law was my client for Disneyland new office building, Team Disneyland. She would meet his son Norm about a year and a half later.

Norm called me previously to discuss what I believed to be a silly idea and he was hopeful we would alter the building's design to accommodate his idea. He scheduled a meeting in hopes to persuade me to reconsider his notion.

Laura accompanied her future father-in-law Norm Doerges to the meeting; Laura Becker was her name at the time. Norm was my client the one who my DDC team was developing the office building for. Norm had a foolish issue, a significant item he wanted me to consider, he knew I was not likely to consider his request, he asked Laura to join him and gave her the task to present his notion. Like I said above, earlier in a quick conversation we discussed his notion with me by phone; at the time I did my best to avoid conflict; however, Norm wanted to pursue his request further. So, Laura gave the presentation and articulated Norm's request.

Another DDC team member Bruce kept interrupting Laura and he became belligerent, curt, and most rude. I was impressed in the calm manor and resolve by Laura. She kept her focus and represented her boss well. My decision to keep the design as is was not altered.

A couple of months later I received authorization to add staff to my team; I called human resources and requested they reach out to Laura Becker from the Disneyland team be scheduled for an interview. Upon receipt of the list for potential candidates I was surprised to find Laura was not included. I called Paul in HR and asked what happened to Laura, did she turn down the interview? Paul said he believed Laura was not qualified for the position that he never called her however Laura became aware of the position and sent him her resume. So, imagine this if you will, Laura has a letter from Paul advising that she is not qualified and a subsequent letter from me offering her the position. We worked together for the next eighteen years, at DDC, Trizec-Hahn, and the Kor Group and finally partners at our own consulting firm Bousquet Dennis and Associates … changing our name a year later to Bousquet Dennis & Doerges.

CHAPTER 14
BEYOND THE HOSPITAL ... FINDING MY WAY AFTER THE STROKE [2004]

Seventeen years after my stroke was the first time I told this story. I was asked to speak to a group of nurses all who specialize in the field and medicine concerning stroke patients. Pamela explained to me that nurses see us stroke patients at our worst; they do not have the opportunity to see us recover to see how the nurse's assistance gave us a part or more of our life back. Pamela believed I am extremely fortunate as no one would see me as a recovering stroke patient a man who returned to the working world and found a way to make his world spin again. I enjoyed the day speaking to the nurses.

I am very lucky I do not get nervous speaking to large groups. I actually look forward to the event. In high school I was fortunate in my senior year 1971 to have the lead in my high school play Carousel. This prepared me, this gave me a great tool and confidence to stand before a group and speak. I have to thank Ed Byrne and Bill Gagnon as they prepared me for the demands of the business world.

Like I said I do not get nervous that is as long as I can say what is on my mind what I want to say, how I want to say it. While at Disney they always want one to speak from a controlled script. So only at Disney would I get nervous. I would have to memorize the speech, words to remember so as you can imaging the speech sounded stale, definitely rehearsed. I spoke to Disney groups four or five times. I had to read from notes to get it right. However, this moment near the end of my Disney days when I spoke about the New Amsterdam development accompanied by Laura... Well, this time I spoke from my heart and the presentation was great and well received. I know what you are thinking; the play has a controlled dialog. For the on stage plays I had more than enough time to learn my lines. In business I work ten to fourteen hours each day it would be imposable to practice. I found I can address a large group, speak without notes while controlling the audience.

Talking to the nurses that afternoon I spoke without notes, I recalled stories from the heart and I believe the audience saw value in my presentation as many nurses took the moment to thank and talk with me after the event. Several asked me to join them to speak at their hospitals.

I began talking about the day I suffered my stroke; next I discussed several challenges I was forced to overcome. I ended with this story like I said above the first time to tell my crazy story ...

Oh my God that hit me hard

One summer afternoon in 2004 I returned to the Cuisinart hotel in Anguilla, my home away from home. Our design team and I actually met in my hotel room on several occasions previously; this is the place where we cast the concept and direction for our new resort development.

On one very important strategic trip to Anguilla we scheduled a team dinner with a cocktail hour before including, our design team, Frank from my staff and Pierre. My boss Brad would be arriving late he planned to meet us for breakfast in the morning.

I thought it a bit odd that he would attend our meeting with the government the next day as this was the first and actually the only time Brad attended one of my development meetings. That said, this was a big deal and it gave him the opportunity to meet the team, most important spend some time with Frank.

I usually arrive to meetings early as I believe it rude and disrespectful to be late. This is a challenge for me with meetings in Los Angeles, so to navigate through LA traffic I usually arrive very early or just in time.

It was an extremely hot and humid Anguilla day. I drove from the job site to my hotel less than a fifteen-minute drive. Anguilla is a British island I found driving on the other side of the road exhilarating; however left hand turns on to another street made me always second guess my surroundings. I never had an issue driving on the wrong side of the road in Anguilla, However, after spending three weeks on the island working, I returned home to California. The very next morning while driving to my office, I took a left from my street when all of a sudden there was a car in my lane coming towards me fortunately about 500 feet away he was honking his horn, I quickly pulled my car to the proper lane and began to laugh. Jeez, Jack, what in the hell are you doing? Stay on the right side of the road, stupid.

When I arrived at the Cuisinart hotel, I decided to take a quick shower before cocktail hour and find a change of clothes. I was dressed and ready in about fifteen minutes before our scheduled cocktail hour. I thought I would go downstairs to the bar early and enjoy a beer. I have stayed here so often I knew a good number of the employees, so I was curious to see who I might find working this evening.

On most every hotel door you will find a security device that will allow the door to be partially open and remain secure while one sees who is on the opposite side. You remember that little metal thing? You will find a metal post with a ball at the end secured to the door; this post fits into a rectangular metal device with an opened slot in the center secured to the door frame. The device allows one to open the door slightly to see who is on the other side while keeping access secure.

I was eager to go to the bar to meet the team, I reach for the security device with my left hand and lifted the post from the slot, and next I turn the door knob and pull the door open with my left hand. The door doesn't open. What the hell, I am very impatient. I foolishly thought … it is always humid on this island the door must have swelled due to weather, with that stupid thought I pull on the door handle again with my left hand hard, it sticks so now I pull it with all my might, this time I have success and the door flies open. To my surprise the post with the small ball knob at the end …please be mindful, this post protrudes from the door about an inch and a half maybe two inches at most. I am able to stop the door from hitting my face however that nasty post smacks into my face about a half inch below my left eye. The impact is so severe that blood starts to squirt from my face.

I cannot stop the bleeding; foolishly I try to use toilet paper like when you cut yourself shaving. Obviously, the paper does not work. I look in the mirror and see a bulging bump with a slit in the center below my left eye. I try holding a face cloth drenched in cold water to stop the bleeding, as you can imagine this also does not work. I open the door again and look at the security device and realize I did not completely remove the post from the slot earlier. I step into the hallway and walk to the ice machine. I filled my ice bucket to the brim and return to my room. I find holding ice on my face helps to slow down the bleeding. After a while the bleeding stops. My shirt and pants are stained with the blood. I take another quick shower this time only cold water holding ice on my face all the while. I find different clothes and get ready to meet my team again. I look at my watch and I realize I not only missed the cocktail hour, I assume they are all in the restaurant now for dinner. I look back in the mirror and I find my face is a mess. I cannot go to dinner like this. What if they ask questions, maybe they will realize I suffered from a stroke what do I do? I am always afraid someone will find out I had a stroke.

I looked out the window it wasn't dark yet, knowing we would have sunlight for at least another hour I put on my sunglasses and joined the team for dinner. I walked down the stairs passed around the corner of the hotel lobby and spotted my team at a large table in the dining room by the window with a specular view to the sea.

As I approached the table, I found the team was in the process of ordering. I knew the menu by heart. As I reached for my chair, I apologized to the team for being late. I made up an excuse that I was on the phone due to a problem at another one of our developments. I am always on my phone talking to my staff, so they bought my story. I called out to the waiter and asked for my usual and took my seat.

No one seemed to notice my face. We were discussing strategy for our meeting in the morning with the government. We need the government to approve off island labor. This would be a first for Anguilla. I was certain the islanders could not build our resort. Maybe a hundred or so workers were available unfortunately only a handful held skills the remaining I believed were made up of gardeners.

Previously we constructed our Marketing Center hiring local island workers; this effort taught me a lot. I knew it would be absolutely impossible for the islanders to construct our resort.

For example, all structures are built from masonry block. Frank taught the locals how to plumb a block wall as the first wall they constructed was crocked and it was leaning off to one side. Frank was patient going step by step to teach them.

The tile setters were not up to par they were terrible, so we got contact information from Pierre for a tile setter named Walter from Georgia. We made travel arrangements for Walter and his team to the island; we asked that he also have the locals here, islanders, participate and that he teach the locals his trade. Walter's tile work was immaculate unfortunately the locals were slow to pick up the knowhow.

There was only one glass cutter on the island. Kelly's design called for lights on either side to be mounted to the face of the mirror at the master bath room. A very difficult circular cut was necessary to mount and attach the lights on the mirror. The glass cutter was a young man in his early thirties. Frank showed him how to measure for the cut as he could not figure out the process. We had our first guests arriving to our marketing center in the morning; unfortunately, he only installed lights in one of the three bathrooms.

I was at a restaurant with Frank and Daddy enjoying dinner that night when I told the story of how the glass cutter left early in the afternoon without finishing the job. Daddy stood and walked out of the restaurant for a couple of minutes. When he returned Daddy advised the remaining glass mirrors will be cut in the next hour, he also advised, you and Frank can attach the lights when you return to the site after dinner. Daddy seemed to be very pleased with himself. So, as you can imagine I was curious, so I said Daddy who did you call? Did you talk to the glass cutter? Daddy replied no, I called his mother and told her your son is lazy and he was messing up an opportunity for his future with Mr. Jack.

As it turned out Daddy was a close friend with the glass cutter's family. Remember everyone knows everyone on the island. Can you imagine this poor guy being yelled at from his mother, forcing him to return to work and finish the job?

The evening went well; no one asked what happened to my face. I believed I dodged a bullet. I had a drink at the bar with Pierre and Frank after dinner. Then I walked back up the stairs to my room.

I woke up early, went to the bath room to shave, brush my teeth and shower. That said, when I saw my face in the mirror, I took a couple of steps back. Holy shit … Jesus Christ … I said out loud. You see, my face looked like someone hit me several times with a baseball bat. I was a mess of black and blue. My left eye was partially closed. What do I do now; I can't wear sun glasses to meet with the government. This was my introduction to the government. Oh my gosh, I am going to make one hell of an introduction and impression. What kind of a guy walks into an important meeting looking like he was in a bar fight the night before? This is going to be embarrassing Jack, you look stupid. Jack, I bet they find out you had a stroke, you stupid idiot. You are a dumbass, Jack. Why did you use your left hand to free the post from the slot? You know you can't trust that hand, stupid you stupid idiot.

Okay… what are you going to do Jack? I could not come up with any ideas. I had nothing, absolutely nothing. I cannot just stand here hoping for a miracle.

I put on my reading glasses to look at my blackberry; Pierre sent an email saying he is at the restaurant putting a couple of tables together for our team. As I stood in front of the mirror I began to laugh. You have no choice stupid. I looked closer and found the glasses helped ever so slightly. Nope … Not really however it was important for me to believe. Although I really didn't believe my reading glasses helped at all. Come on, Jack. You can do it just take one step at a time. Wear the glasses and have confidence to be strong, to be in charge.

We all met at the same restaurant again for breakfast. I walked in only a couple of our team has arrived, the others including Brad showed up within minutes. We sat at the tables Pierre had assembled, discussing strategy again. That said, mostly we were talking about how awesome our resort will be.

I have no idea why we did not take two cars. We jammed into one vehicle and drove to the valley to meet with the government. Anguilla calls the commercial city center where all the island offices are located, the valley.

I actually get mail in Anguilla the address merely notes … Jack Bousquet at meads bay. We were so tight in the vehicle that Brad who is the smallest of the group had to sit on someone's lap.

Anguilla's government is small but efficient and most effective. A prime Minister leads the group comprised by a Minister of Finance, Minister of Tourism, Minister of Education and Minister of Infrastructure.

It was my role to lead the meeting, I was elated that absolutely no one said a word or asked me what happened to my face. So, I put it out of my mind. I had to run a discussion concerning labor from off island, and most important control and lead the meeting. As far as I was concerned, my face was fine. I did not even think about it. We needed to secure work permits, about 425 permits for the off-island construction labor as well as my team. We needed to sell the notion to the government to allow off-island labor.

I hired Dick Construction from Pittsburg to construct the first phase, which included rough grading, underground utilities, and foundations. Their labor would be sourced from Mexico.

I hired Carillion a United Kingdom contractor from London to construct the structures and interior finishes. Their labor was sourced from India.

The government voiced all the typical concerns, will they hurt our economy, will they be interested in our women, how do we protect our women, what if they do not leave when construction is finalized and most important to the government will they affect our economy over run our social services?

I laid out a plan an overall strategy and advised that their passports will be held by the construction company, they will live and work on our controlled property, the contractor will provide housing, food, and medical services. The initial discussion went well very well; we decided to meet again the following month.

I returned to the island the next month. While touring our site to review progress with my team I noticed a young staff member from the island's building department Ferro Bradley standing near the beach with a couple of others from the island. He was a participant in our first discussion concerning off island labor, he sat in the back and never said a word at our previous meeting.

I excused myself from the tour and walked over to say hello to Ferro, he saw me walking towards him, he turned took a step forward shook my hand, he responded good to see you again Mr. Jack. We talked for a while mainly about the beautiful island and great restaurants here. He advised he was looking forward to the next day's follow up off island labor discussion.

Then he asked what happened to you, I saw you the day before and your face was fine. I was surprised when you walked into the meeting it looked like you were in a fight. I thought to myself WHOA …this kid is brave; he is the only one to ask what happened. I smiled and said you know when someone has a black eye, they always say they slipped and hit the bathroom door? He laughed and responds I have done that myself. I smiled and said I feel very stupid and foolish, after a shower I slipped on the marble floor at my hotel and my head hit the door knob. Then he and I as well as the other two standing with him all began to laugh. I must be more careful, if I slip and fall again people will start talking about me. We all began to laugh. I told Ferro I was looking forward to meeting tomorrow, said my good-bye and walked back to join my team on our site tour.

Our follow up meting went well I knew eventually we would prevail, this time my face was clear. After a few more meetings with the Anguillan government, as expected they gave us the approvals and all work permits we were seeking.

Lessons learned; well Jack you must remember not to trust your left hand. That hand will most certainly be a problem. I also must remember not to hand something to another with that left hand as sometimes my fingers will not let the object in my left hand go, that hand holds things tight.; so tight one can't take it. This is awkward and embarrassing. I look silly, so I will make a joke and pull my fingers away with my right hand. Or often my left hand will crush what I am holding, not to trust the left hand for sure Jack. You must remember to always use your right hand stupid. That left hand doesn't like you. Like I said earlier the first time I told this story was to a large group of nurses. They laughed and laughed.

I meet my brother

Around this same time maybe a month before I met my brother Gary. I found he has the kindness of our Uncle Richard and the wit of our father Henry Norman (Hank).

You have to understand I did not know my brother as I left home at eighteen at the time Gary was only three. Anguilla brought two brothers together, my best; yes, my most fond memory concerning the Anguilla project is meeting my brother Gary. We are close today due to this story of how two brothers met on the island.

My team was in the final stages of constructing our Marketing Center. We had an issue with door hardware for the three guest villas. The hardware was at the manufactures factory in Brooklyn, NY. It should have arrived weeks ago. If we now ship the hardware it would have to pass through customs. This requirement would render the shipment to arrive late. Our first guests will be staying at our temporary three key hotel and marketing center in four days. We need a plan a solid strategy to ensure we do not fail.

So, I called my brother Gary. He is the owner of Grove Gardens a landscape company in our home town of Clinton, CT. It was late February I knew this was his off season he should be available however he also has a snow plowing business in the winter, I was hopeful no snow was in the forecast. Gary answers my call. Great as I did not want to leave a message, time is of the essence I must exercise any and all efforts available to solve this problem.

I asked Gary how would he and his lovely wife Lisa like to come to Anguilla for a week, travel tomorrow morning with all expenses paid. I went on to say, if you guys eat with Frank or me I have you covered for meals as well. I also told Gary I will provide an apartment; he will have access to a company car for his use on the island. He had no idea where Anguilla was, I advised just a short twenty-minute boat ride from St, Marten. He said let me talk with Lisa. I will call you back. Gary called back in less than ten minutes.

Gary said, that sounds great Jack it is very cold here in Connecticut we would love to come to Anguilla, what do I need to do? Well, I said go and buy a large suitcase and a small suitcase. Ok he replied … what for? I said put your bathing suits in the small suitcase, a truck is on its way to your home as we speak with delivery of hardware. I want you to put the hardware in the big suitcase. I explained to Gary the hardware can't go through customs it needs to travel as your vacation luggage. Gary asked what do you mean hardware? I replied fancy expensive custom-made hinges, doorknobs all the hardware to install the doors for three hotel suites. When will the delivery arrive? I responded should come to your home less than an hour. Gary laughed; oh my, you are confident, Jack. I guess you knew I would help you.

The next afternoon around four Gary arrived at our construction office with the hardware. He walked in the door with a huge smile on his face and said I feel like I am in a movie. I am a smuggler this is exciting… I made it guys. Immediately Frank called the workers who were responsible for installing the doors; they took the suitcase worked until they were finished that night. I introduced Gary to Frank and Sandra.

Gary told us a story how at the Hartford airport he advised the airport security, if you try to x-ray my luggage it will look like I am transporting gold bars, its door hardware do you want me to open the bag so you can see it? They replied no, however after he and Lisa boarded the plane about five minutes after they were seated Gary was asked to step out as the airport had an issue with one of his bags. So, my bother met the airport staff opened the bag he told them the story of how he was bringing the hardware to his brother developing a huge resort in the Caribbean. The rest of their trip was uneventful. Two snow birds on vacation to a lovely little island in the sun.

I introduced Gary and Lisa to our team, Frank, Sandra, Bill, Pedro, Aaron, and Michelle. I gave them a quick tour and showed them to their room actually, Carla's apartment at the old hide away apartment building where my staff as well as the IMI sales team lived. The apartment was next to a Swim with the Dolphins experience. That night Gary and Lisa had dinner with me and my team. The next morning, they investigated the island, Gary and Lisa found a couple of places I was not aware of. One place called Junks Whole on the windward side of the island where about ten months later we purchased the property for another resort development.

Now on Gary's third morning on the island I looked out the window and I was surprised to see my brother directing the landscape workers. I walked over to him and said what are you doing, your job is done. Gary, you and Lisa should relax on the beach and have fun. Gary said your landscape workers have poor direction look you have ten guys standing here, eight over there, no one is really working, well maybe two or three; you will never make your schedule with them working like this. To make a long story short Gary took over leading the landscape and hardscape construction. He hired staff, organized teams, and came up with a novel design notion for the long walkway to the Marketing Center.

My brother is an accomplished heavy equipment operator he is the owner of several pieces of heavy equipment back in Connecticut. At the end of the day Gary was coaching a group of landscape workers I watched him get on a small excavator. With the workers in a circle around him Gary started the equipment. In less than five seconds the workers began to step back away from Gary as the equipment he was operating started acting radically bouncing and jerking about. He could not control the excavator. Gary hit the off switch and advised he would continue his discussion with the workers in the morning. They walked away some laughing.

After Frank and I had dinner that night with Gary and Lisa we returned to our rooms. Or at least I thought we all went to our rooms. By the time I walked to my apartment on the second level I heard the excavator start up in the dark. Remember on the island there are no street lights the night here is black, so black one can see thousands of stars and the Milky Way. It is an awesome sight to behold.

For the next fifteen minutes or so, I watched my brother practice. You see the equipment's control mechanism was the exact opposite from his. What he assumed worked from his left arm and left foot worked the right and assumption from right well it worked to the left.

So, I had to watch in the morning as I was so curious to see how the workers would react. I stood in our construction office looking out the window. Gary walked to where the workers were waiting for him; He walked up to the group stepped up on the equipment. They all looked at each other making faces that Gary was crazy and stepped back a step or two to be safe. They watched Gary work the equipment to precise perfection. After that moment they followed his direction to the detail.

At lunchtime, Gary walked into the office and said, hey guys, what is the plan for lunch? I advised we don't eat lunch, it takes too long to go anywhere on the island and it takes forever to be served here, things are slow on Anguilla however we have some snacks here in the office. Gary, I continued, we usually have a big breakfast and dinner. Gary said no lunch … are you crazy.

Day workers would show up each morning in hopes to be hired. Some came to the site with rakes others with a shovel, and a few without any tool. Gary advised no one would be hired who did not show up wearing shoes.

The next morning all displayed foot attire and pointed to same as Gary greeted them. He placed the workers in groups of three and gave focused direction to each and every group. That said, most important he worked with them constantly moving from one group to the next.

Every day Gary joined his workers for lunch as they all would walk to a home where the woman of the house served chicken, rice, and beans; they enjoyed lunch on her front porch.

His leadership made the difference we made our schedule we were ready for our guests and most important the makeshift three key hotel and marketing center looked absolutely awesome.

There was one woman however who Gary refused to hire and each day she would return ... he would see her working in the distance he would walk to her and escort her safety off the property each and every day. To understand his concern, she this particular woman was eight months pregnant if a day; Gary was concerned for her safety.

We all pitched in to finalize our three key hotel for our first guest's arrival. Pedro and I painted; Carla and Michelle worked with one of the landscape crews placing plants. Frank helped the stucco guys render a block wall. Bill was providing assistance with the installation of the entry doors. To my surprise we even watched our boss the owner Brad providing clean-up of construction trash. His wife Kelly was directing the photographer for marketing photos. All pitched in we did whatever was necessary to make our marketing center / three key Hotel a temporary paradise for our soon to arrive guests.

Our first group of guests arrived the following morning. The night before, Brad requested for me to join he and Kelly for dinner to celebrate.

A month later Brad met me on the island, while touring the site I talked about constructing a plant propagation center. Growing plans from cuttings. The climate is ripe absolutely perfect for same I advised we could grow the plants quickly for our new resort while under construction saving hundreds of thousand dollars. I talked about how I saw it done by others on my travels. I discussed the process, the first satiation all the plant cuttings receive a mist of water every ten seconds as plants grow and mature the plants are moved on to a new procedure.

He asked, what happened to that Gary guy directing the hardscape/landscape could he be in charge of this? 'I replied Gary is my brother he has his own business back in Connecticut. Well, we need him Brad said look at what he did with the Marketing Center's landscape in less than a week. He asked if Gary would be willing to help as a consultant.

So, with that, Frank and Gary worked out a strategy, scope of service they finalized a consultant agreement. For the next year Gary traveled to the island several times, Gary came up with plans for the propagation center. He and his crew constructed structures; simple roofs to protect the plants from direct sun. Including concept of tables and trays to hold the plants before they could be boxed and available for planting. He developed the concept and constructed the watering and nutrient fertilization process for the stations. The propagation center was located on a half-acre portion of the backend of our resort property.

Unfortunately, I was not able to join my brother on a couple of his trips to the island. That said we were able to coordinate a few. I learned who he was, so very fortunate for Gary's help. Without Anguilla maybe we would have never had the opportunity to meet and become brothers.

Jack's cove partners.

The night before our first sales event In Anguilla we held a dinner for all the potential buyers at Mango Dave's beach side restaurant. I asked our designers and engineers to join us. I sat at a table that held three couples (big dogs) who were interested buyers for the villas. The sales price for one of the villas ranged from $4.5 to $5.5M.

The evening started with a cocktail party where all could enjoy watching the sunset on the sea. Our guest buyers had the opportunity to meet our designers and engineers to discuss details as well as find answers for any questions they had concerning the resort. The evening was picture perfect a lovely night indeed. Mango Dave provided an awesome dining experience. I was please as all three couples at my table purchased a villa the next morning. Actually, I was totally impressed with the IMI sales team. They exceeded our expectations the event was a huge success, totaling sales of $172.5M.

Later that evening my team and our consultants joined me for drinks at the Marketing Center. I said I wish we could all own one of the units. These investors are going to do very well with their investment here. We should do the same.

Well now the conversation focused on my comment many were in agreement, the conversation continued with … we design and build great resorts we should enjoy the good tasting good life as well. Someone asked me what unit I believe we should purchase. At this point I still thought the conversation was just talk. However, with a drink in one hand and a lite Cuban Cohiba in the other I said we can't afford a villa and we need something extraordinary. I believe we purchase a two-bed room lock off at building B. The corner unit farthest from building A the main dining structure on the point. We select the first or third level unit. Building B is the only structure other than Villas that are located at the water, well about fifteen feet above the beach a small cliff above Jack's cove below. If one of those two units is available at sales end who is with me for purchase?

The unit cost $1.75M. I advised we should create a corporation to hold ownership and purchase. I can get a 10% employee discount. I also advised that I believe I can convince IMI to forfeit their 6.5% sales fee. We need a down payment. So, what about creating a share for $20K each we hold $2k in reserve for future legal and accountant fees. We would need to secure eighteen shares to make the purchase. What do you think and who wants in? They were very excited and loved my strategy.

So, on the sales day all were excited as we exceeded our expectations $172.5M sold. The ground level B101 unit was still available. Several came to where I was sitting and began discussing the notion to purchase a unit from our conversation the previous night. Fifteen partners we were, that included my brother Gary and good fiend and attorney Jon Yudin so I call state side to see if he wanted in. To make the eighteen shares total work Frank, Vince and I held two shares each. I asked what should we call our corporation, they all replied at once… Jack's Cove.

The following year IMI held another sales day. We were all pleased as the other units similar to ours sold for an additional one hundred and fifty thousand dollars more. Be mindful only building B our unit was located at the water, well about fifteen feet above the cove the other structures are not located at the water. Our partnership planned to sell the investment in two to three years.

Frank, Gary, and I would enter into new partnership with Daddy; he owned a great property on the hillside just above the beach at Shoals Bay. We planned to construct two vacations homes with Daddy. Unfortunately, our good fortune would change in the very near future.

CHAPTER 15
FIND WAYS TO COMPENSATE [2003]

My stroke changed me; each and every day I would fight using all efforts available at doing my best to be normal. (What is normal …a setting on clothes dryer?) Some solutions were effective however others not. Fortunately, I found the resolve to never give up, however many issues I continue to deal with today. Well now I would voice to myself, Jack if you find yourself in a new situation something you have never done before and you are uncertain what to do, just pretend you have been here before … just do it, Jack, and proceed with confidence.

Emotional
I am far more emotional today than Jack. For example, I can become teary eyed just watching a TV commercial.

Distracted
Noise, any background sounds it could be something as common as tapping, something rattling or a dog barking can trigger my issue. However, when multiple sounds work in concert I lose control of my brain, it is impossible to focus impossible to concentrate I cannot think my brain just ceases to work…I get a dull pain in the back of my head. I have to remove myself from the noise or try not to think. This debilitating occurrence oddly can occur when I try to concentrate with a loud TV or music playing in the background.

Privacy ... yes privacy or maybe I should say secrecy,

You see I was so concerned that someone would find out I had a severe stroke. Actually, I was fearful my job would be in jeopardy. Unfortunately, this fear became constant my concern never left my thoughts. I was managing complicated difficult projects, balancing budgets worth well over hundreds of million dollars. The risk for others finding my secret at work always occupied my thoughts.

Please be mindful, outside of my family only a select few, my previous partners Laura, Kevin and a limited number of close friends were aware of my stroke. I had to protect myself. You see I was afraid for my stroke became common knowledge. I was fearful that the people I worked for might remove me from my position, if I lose my job, my world would stop spinning. That would have certainly have been the end for me.

Looking back now, I believe this fear actually helped me succeed. I was driven, focused, and worked at working hard. I double checked everything and I worked constantly. I was always good at my job, however now I was on top of everything aware of the smallest of details.

Interesting when I look back at my carrier to the beginning—well, before my stroke, I had a fear of failure. This fear helped me to become a success as I had to show myself actually prove to myself that I was worth it, worth the confidence placed to manage these risky, complex developments. I guess my new fear of someone learning I had a stroke became exponential.

Maybe I have an ego, you see I enjoyed being important. Looking back at my career now that I am retired, I do miss my job. I definitely loved the risk you see I made hundreds of decisions any one might be a wrong choice and maybe the poor decision could place the development in peril. Each and every day was different never the same routine, I found each day came with new and at times horrific challenges. The risk and fear of making a mistake drove me; it was like a drug for me. So, yes, I miss my job; I miss the risk. That said, I miss being important. I am no longer important ... I am just their grandfather now.

Looking back, I hold fond memories. I know how fortunate my life has been for me to lead so many important developments. I do have stories that I enjoy sharing. I defined myself by my job. Today I guess I define myself as a grandfather. I enjoy being with my grandchildren, just picking a grandchild up from school gives me pleasure I look forward to the moment and I enjoy spending some time with them after. I so look forward to their future I look forward to watching these little guys become men and women; each grandchild different and unique. I am no longer important, now I am Hayden (9), Taylor (7), Knox (8), Scarlett (7) and Savannah's (5) grandfather. My world revolves around them; today I am just their grandfather. They do not know who I was, they do not know I was sick or about my stroke. I am just that old guy who likes to be with them.

Some of the obstacles I faced caused by my stroke were easy to find a solution while others took more time, and often I was forced to experiment to find a suitable answer. Some of the obstacles were issues that could occur at home however I may have to explain something when at work.

For example, I have already told you that I have no feeling in the left side of my face as well as no feeling in my left hand. Sometimes I would forget this, I know that may sound silly to you, but it happens. So, I have to remind myself when I am in a situation that could cause me harm. I have to remind myself to focus, to be careful most important I have to remind myself to pay attention to what I am doing.

No feeling in my left hand.

One day at work while sitting in a design meeting for a new resort hotel a consultant siting across the conference room table from me. He saw the burns on my left hand, he said geez Jack, oh my God, you have severe burns on your left hand again what in the hell happened? Jack, what is wrong with you? I remember you having bad burns a month ago. I made a silly excuse actually made him as well as the others in the meeting laugh; yes, I made a joke of it.

That said I knew I had to find a way to compensate for the lack of feeling in my left hand. My burns were severe sometimes on face of my hand sometimes on the back side. I knew I was making a huge mistake causing me harm and I could not continue to allow the attention the burns were causing. Always on my mind what if someone finds out I had a stroke. No one would allow a guy with half a brain to manage several difficult real estate developments some worth as much as three hundred and fifty million dollars.

So, imagine while I am at home in our kitchen, I find myself unable to do such a simple task without hurting myself; very many times I burned my left hand taking something out of the oven. It could be cookies or nachos hell it was just about everything. I would always use a pot holder however a fingertip or a thumb might slide and expose my hand to the extraordinary hot metal. You would pull your hand away immediately so you would not be burned… unfortunately for me it may take several seconds before my left hand tells me something is wrong, several seconds to feel the pain. My exposed hand got severely burned many times.

I know I have to be accustomed to being mindful and pay close attention ensuring that my left hand is always protected. I have to remember to focus. I usually overcompensate with my right hand. Every once in a while, I have one of those forgetful moments when I fail to focus, and as a result I burn my hand; fortunately, this is no longer a common occurrence. With practice, focus and determination I am able to protect my hand. Funny as it may sound to you, when I take something out of the oven, I constantly remind myself to focus and be careful. That voice in my head keeps saying watch out Jack, are your hands safe, are you sure, you better look once more Jack. I most often applaud myself for a job well done when I do not get burned.

Fortunately, I was also able to overcome this next issue as well, today it may happen only on rare occasions; I had to work on this one as in the beginning it was a baffling problem and a constant concern.

Unable to acknowledge items to my left

I know what I explain next may sound strange, I imagine you may not understand, you may even smile or laugh…. You see I would ignore things just about everything or anything that was located to my left. It could be something simple like a water faucet or maybe a light switch. So, if and when an object is located on my left side, for example I would leave lights on and or allow the water to run constantly not realizing I never turned it off. I may find the water running hours later and say to myself what hell Jack you did it again, or Linda would ask why I didn't turn the water off, hey Jack why did you leave the light on in the bathroom?

Oh, crap I would think, you must remember Jack to turn the water off … you must remember to always take the time to create a moment and look to your left and consciously confirm all appears correct in that direction. Jack, make sure you didn't miss something. I had no issue turning the item on; I guess I would see the light switch head on. Only a problem when the item as directly to my left. That said this object ignorance left side issue was my smaller concern.

The larger concern was people. If, for example, someone was standing to my left or sitting to my left at a restaurant table or in a meeting at the conference room table, well, I would ignore them; yes, absolutely ignore anyone located to my left. Sometimes that person may talk or ask me a direct question; yep, I would continue to completely ignore the question. I would ignore anyone to my left. Can you imagine having to figure a response to compensate for ignoring someone to my left? I found myself in too many awkward and embarrassing situations. I knew I couldn't solve this problem by myself and I desperately needed guidance, so I decided to share my problem Dr. Dhanda.

My doctor explained to me, Jack your brain does not know someone is there; it is as if the person to your left is invisible to your brain. Your brain no longer senses someone to your left. Really? Oh my God I thought, really are you kidding me. I must fix this problem this is serious I can't work like this. Jack you must turn your head search to the left you must see the person and make a mental note that someone is there. Jack you must keep reminding yourself occasionally to turn your head to the left to retain the memory. Yep, they are still there I will check again in a couple of minutes. I always find I can control an issue by talking to myself.

At first, I overcompensated I went too far in other direction I became a chatty Cathy. No one wants an annoying person that cannot stop talking to sit next to them. So, I also found that I need to understand and practice balance. I keep talking to myself is this working, I think so yep you are doing fine. I guess I find myself in the best of company listening to my voice talking to myself in my head. If anyone who was paying attention watching me, I imagine they would think it odd that guy keeps turning his head to the left. Does he have a tick? Nope his issue is much bigger than that. His brain does not acknowledge anyone to his left. So, by talking to myself and looking to my left making the mental note actually worked.

With practice and determination to appear normal I was able to overcome this obstacle. If on an occasion I falter, well I would just make a quick joke and carry on. I found humor will diffuse most awkward situations. Today I find the issue to be nonexistent this concern seldom returns, only on that rare occasion when I am extremely tired or when I am very sick.

Can't trust my left hand.

I believe it doesn't like me. I have to constantly remind myself not to trust my left hand. There are many instances where my left hand has let me down however this one comes to mind as a perfect example, one day I went mountain biking with my son Geoff. I broke my elbow not the left elbow I went flying over my handle bars I broke my right elbow.

Perhaps … I guess I should stop the story at this point as I believe my broken elbow story mountain biking to be exciting however the story is lame not very exciting at all. You see I never made it to the mountain. Geoff and I were peddling to the mountain about half mile from my home. On a hot August Sunday in 2006 while riding to the mountain I was drinking a bottle of water. In the short distance I saw a garbage can on the side of the road. As I was nearly finished drinking the water, I decided to toss the plastic bottle in the trash can. Approaching the trash can with the plastic bottle in my right hand I wanted to slow down to ensure I would hit the target so I squeezed the brake with my left hand the one who doesn't care for me. Unfortunately, I could not control my hand the bike's rear tire went up and passed over my head I went flying to the asphalt road. I hit my head I scraped my face and right side of my body. My elbow twisted behind me now fractured.

Geoff heard the crash he was riding in front of me. What are you doing dad what happened we are not even there yet how could you crash? Geoff helped me to the grass I sat under a tree nursing my wounds while Geoff rode back to my home to get his truck as it was impossible for me to continue with our mountain bike adventure.

So, picture me sitting on the lawn of a nice home in a quiet neighborhood under a shady tree with blood running down my face, scraped-up arm and knees when a family…the dad, mom, and a young daughter…stepped out of their front door walking towards their car. The daughter, maybe seven or so, screamed, Daddy, there's a scary man sitting under our tree! Her parents became alarmed running in my direction asking if I was okay. Of course, I was not okay. That said I stood up immediately saying I fell riding my bike pointing at the bike laying at the roads edge. I am fine I said my son is on his way in his truck to drive me home. I began walking to my bike as I stepped back in the street the family got in their car and drove away. Once I saw the car turn the corner believing me now out of site I returned to that shady spot under their tree.

Unfortunately, I have several stories where that left hand let me down.

Short term memory issue

You see the stroke also left me with a severe short term memory problem, by far this issue was my most my most difficult problem.

For example, say I ordered something and now I have to put it together. It is impossible for me to read directions and follow them. I will forget what I read within seconds. Just about any situation where I needed to recall the information I just read escaped me. For example, looking at directions on a map, I would forget what I read in seconds. Now think about work ... what can I do how can I function with this brain when my memory disappears so quickly?

What was fascinating to me and I found very interesting is once I solved this problem, I found my long-term memory actually increased. I became more knowledgeable. I took a new interest to learning, the internet opened new thoughts and ideas. I have become an information junkie.

Before my stroke, I had a better memory than most of the people at work this was definitely an asset for me. I may not have been the smartest one in the meeting that said my memory was better than the rest. In business I could read and recall the information for example say a multi-page contract or report even knowing what section and where my recalled thought was located and on the particular page to prove my point. In a business discussion, if I needed to remember numbers and facts to prove my point, I was very fortunate with this great memory. It was easy for me to pull information I needed and find it clearly at hand.

So, getting back to my short memory problem. Small talk as you can imagine became a huge challenge for me. Business trips were a new and most difficult situation; as you image think of yourself on the plane with me and I say so how is your family, what did you guys do this past weekend? Only to hear me say ten minutes later say so how is your family, what did you guys do this past weekend?

People traveling with me, for example, my architect or consultant, would look at me like I was crazy, Jack you just asked me that a couple of minutes ago, have you been drinking? I would make a joke of it say I am tired or oh my, it appears I am having a senior moment, sorry. The person would smile or laugh. Now I would be worried most often I would keep telling myself be careful, Jack. It appears you are slipping again. Stop talking or they will find out you had a stroke.

In meetings I solved the problem with ease I could rectify my issue of short-term memory loss by making notes in the margin on my note pad of questions I had already asked. I could easily look down at the notes to keep me from embarrassing myself.

On an airplane I was without a note pad and I believe it would appear odd for me to write down everything I say with a traveling companion sitting so close to me, so most often in this and other similar situations I decided to re-main quiet. Business was easier to recall for whatever small talk memory es-caped me. This was difficult for me as I am definitely an extrovert. However, with time and practice and a temperance to add a dose of balance I was able to compensate for my memory short comings.

Due to the ever-continual conversations with myself, the practice and focus I overcame my short-term memory. At least the people in my meetings didn't notice my issue. Best of all I increased my long-term memory and I found a new thirst for learning and reading. I so enjoy the internet one can find anything and everything in a matter of seconds.

I found this short-term memory problem had a silver lining. It definitely was also a benefit when my wife Linda was talking to me. You see, if I found myself preoccupied when she was talking to me, I would just say sorry I have a short-term memory problem. What, can you say it again? Unfortunately, after a while Linda knew I was preoccupied and not paying attention to her. I believe all wives know, this is selective hearing, husbands at times just do not pay attention

Acute pain

In my left hand for no apparent reason hurts like hell as if a truck just rolled over it. Yep, the same hand I told you has no feeling. I know very odd isn't it and I think the pain is in my head, I do not believe it to be real. This occurs to this day randomly maybe two or three times a week, however far more frequency when I am sick say with the flu, for example the sharp pain would occur significantly more often, as much as four or five times each day. The first time I experienced this as one can imagine I believed something to be terrible wrong, however in just ten to fifteen seconds, the pain disappeared. What the hell was that? Jesus, holly crap that hurt.

I found myself holding my hand out in front of me staring at my hand whenever this would occur. As you can envision if the pain occurs while in public this practice causes immediate unwanted attention. I have also learned NOT to make a sound for the pain as that requires a response from me when people ask what's wrong are you ok Jack? Today while in public as well as alone I remain quiet, I do not hold my hand up for inspection staring. I merely massage and pull at one finger at a time beginning with my thumb until the pain disappears. I found this practice calms me and does not cause attention from anyone who may be in close proximity. I learned to accept this odd occurrence to live with my pain as my pain only lasts ten to fifteen seconds, that's not bad at all.

Boredom

Is another issue which is a huge problem for me, and unfortunately, this issue continues to be a problem today, I get bored easily. I am talking really bored, I got to get the hell out of here bored, oh my God this guy is beyond boring and he is driving me crazy. I have to keep telling myself don't do it Jack, I have to control Jack from saying would you just shut the fuck up.

So, when this happens, I most often get a dull pain in the back of my head, it becomes impossible to concentrate, I can't think. My heart beats faster I become tense and nervous. I start to lose the conversation and after a while I have no idea what is being said. I start thinking how to disengage from the conversation, I wish I could disappear.

Sometimes someone will be talking to me and my mind keeps yelling oh my God he or she is so boring, get to the fucking point. I do not want to be or appear rude or sound curt; unfortunately, I have no answer for this problem. I do my best to look engaged with the conversation; I try to stop listening to the guy or gal in my head saying this is boring would you just shut the fuck up. So, like I said, I have no answer that said I do my best to move on through the issue. This definitely is a constant issue with Linda. As you can imagine I cannot say what you are saying is boring. She believes I am preoccupied. So, she usually gets mad, thinks I do not pay attention to her.

However, if and when this occurs in a meeting sometimes I can't prevail over that voice in my head telling me this is boring what in the hell is he or her point. So on occasion in meetings I may cut the speaker off, say something like I believe I know where you are going with your thought, however I believe you are misguided I believe the answer is this ——- with that I could cut off the conversation and control that dull pain in the back of my head, my mind would clear and I would guide the participants in the meeting to the direction I believe best for the project. I have tied to solve my boredom problem many times and I fail so I just decided to move on and I deal with it, by ignoring and disregarding my problem.

Patience.

Before my stroke I knew I was not blessed with patience. Well now after my stroke my lack of patient's became a problem for me to deal with definitely an obstacle for me to overcome. I do my very best that said this is another issue that I have not found a simple solution or any solution.

You see I was always a quick thinker most often I would be able to get to a conclusion before the others in the meeting. Unfortunately, after my stroke I no longer had the patients to listen and wait. That said, several times I would see the hurt on the face of who I just interrupted and find the sad feelings I caused. I would apologize. However, I do not believe they believed me to be sincere. All I can do is keep saying over and over in my head be patient Jack, they will be done talking soon.

In business I always believed speed and quick decisive decisions is the key for success. Focus to get things done early get thing done in advance, push and pull the project. If for example I could see in advance an issue coming I would go out of my way to correct same well before it occurred. I believe if I could eliminate the issues there would be no, absolutely no excuse for the contractor to fall behind. Usually, this strategy moves ahead in the assumed project schedule, most certainly we would not fail and fall behind.

However, I am impatient with most everything, I want answers immediately. In business I could be a smart ass and say there is three full working days in every twenty-four-hour period, I am certain a good contractor can do this faster, or I am certain a good architect can get this done in the period I request.

I always had a problem with being patient. Unfortunately, my stroke took my lack of patient issue to an exponentially increased level. Everything must be done now; I need answers immediately. Stop what you are doing my need is more important.

On the positive side of the business coin, I always drove projects to success under budget and ahead of schedule. After my stroke I pushed even harder. I also relished in the project's success, my success.

Storms in my head.

I talked about this storm in my head issue earlier. My brain shuts down; I get a dull pain in the lower portion of back of my head. I can't think I feel like my brain is short securing. I call it a storm. I have learned to step away go to a quiet place outside or try to find a quiet room. Once I retreat to a quiet and calm place the storm disappears faster than it arrived. I am able to return to what I was previously doing.

When I am in a situation with distracting noise for example at a party where everyone is talking simultaneously or at a restaurant with hard surfaces with lots of talking and commotion in the background. I believed I had beaten the problem. Today the issue seldom occurs.

That said one day while working in Houston. I wanted to create a marketing event to show off my development during construction. I held similar events several times previously; I found setting a first-class dining experience in the middle of a construction site gave insight and purpose, a great way to preview a development. I make certain every detail is addressed from valet parking, an extraordinary arrival experience, to the dinning setting, catered by a prominent local restaurant including waters and bar tenders to see any and all needs a well as ensuring all expectations are exceeded. I have my key staff and consultants available to provide tours as well as aid in providing information for the development and responding to any questions our guests may have.

I was one of the speakers scheduled for the luncheon event, we invited over one hundred and fifty commercial real estate brokers they were sitting in the audience at fancy white table cloth settings at the fifth-floor lobby of the office building eyeing the impressive views of the city of Houston in one direction and the Galleria business district in the other.

I was the third and final speaker. I do not have an issue speaking to large groups; I usually enjoy the moment and look forward to the event. You see I love to show off my developments I could answer questions and engage the conversation forever.

However, on this occasion when the microphone was handed to me, I took a couple of steps forward to address my audience in a more intimate manor from the first two speakers. This was a big mistake as I stepped to close to the speaker system and created loud annoying feedback immediately. The piercing feedback noise filled the room bouncing intense irritating sounds off the walls. Several from the audience motioned waving hands and shaking their heads while a couple of others stood and called out to step away from the speaker's while holding their hands over their ears.

I had only said a couple of words, I want to thank you for accepting our invitation, and I believe you will find Kirby Collection....

The storm began immediately, distracting noise, people moving in slow motion, pain in the back of my head. Now when this occurred previously like I said I would go to a quiet place maybe another room from the cause or outside. In quiet the storm allays disappeared in minutes. I began talking to myself, come on Jack stay calm no need for you to panic. We need you stay smart Jack.

So, as you can imagine I could not step away to a quiet place I had to say something and I certainly could not continue. With that thought I moved away from the speaker. I found myself stepping to my left however even closer to the audience. The storm was strong.

I said I am Jack Bousquet I am the developer for Kirby Collection I am responsible for this exciting project. I believe you all want to enjoy your lunch; I do not believe it necessary for this impressive audience to listen to another speaker. They smiled and some clapped. I went on to say ... We hope you enjoy our hospitality. My team and I are available for tours of Kirby Collection after lunch. Our team is very talented and all knowledgeable. If you have any questions, we can help you with same. Please enjoy your stay with us today. Thank you.

As I turned off the microphone, I began walking to my table the storm became calm and my headache disappeared. I was however angry at myself that I missed an opportunity. I also had a fleeting concern that this could happen the next time I spoke to a group. That voice in my head returned, stop doubting yourself Jack, stay positive dammit. So again, I escaped an awkward moment. I have spoken several times since that day, fortunately without incident.

Can't find my way back. Disorientation.

I discussed this issue earlier as well when I told you the story about not being able to find my way back to the main lobby of the hospital after speech therapy concluded. I believe you may remember this unfortunate situation. I was a nimrod. Please be mindful, for over three months with speech therapy sessions twice every week I was never able to find my way to the lobby where I entered the hospital. So, I created a simple however ridicules and odd solution. My disorientation would always happen at the same place. Oh my, Jack how can we (me and that guy in my head) find our way and we would begin to panic. I would see the outside by looking through the side light of glass on an exit door that opened to courtyard. Once I stepped through that door, I merely walked around the building perimeter on a sidewalk path to the main arrival point. My wife, Linda, was waiting for me in her car at the porte-cochere.

Linda was always very confused and she could not comprehend my failure. We would talk about it and she could just shake her head with disbelief of my failure. On my last week of speech therapy when I got to my point of confusion on my journey to the mysterious lobby, I started to walk again through the exit door when she called out my name, Jack stop. Linda she said look at me and asked let's talk please explain your confusion. Well now can you imagine my surprise to see Linda standing behind me? What do you see and why are you going to the courtyard she questioned? I did the best to articulate my ill guided logic. Linda smiled and said Jack turn to your left and walk through this other door she was pointing to. I began telling Linda, I do not remember that door I do not know where that door or the hallway beyond will take me. I am afraid to get lost and have to ask someone to help me find the lobby. Jack, she said strongly, just steps to your left, open the door, and continue to walk. I was certain this is a mistake however she is here and I know she will not get lost. So, I stepped left opened the door walked about twenty feet and to my shock and happy surprise I could see the lobby I had been searching for the past three months about fifty feet ahead.

So, one night I attended a small business dinner with five or six consultants and colleagues at Morton's restaurant in Burbank. After dinner I went to the men's room. When I stepped from the men's room, I was uncertain. Do I turn left or will right turn get me back? Must be right, yep this looks like where I came from. As I began to return to my seat, I became disoriented and even more confused. I slowed my pace and started to turn my head looking in several directions hopeful to find a mental marker that would give me a clue on how to return to my table and join my colleagues. Panic gripped my body, where are they sitting, what in the hell do I do now? I kept telling myself to stay calm, think; yep, think Jack. There is always a simple solution. Has this happened before? Think, Jack. Well, my memory took me back to the hospital with my in trepidation trying to find my way back to the lobby. I began to smile; I actually started to laugh however quietly. Our table was located next to a window; I now see the main entrance in the distance. I thought to myself hmm, that would be stupid, Jack. You can't step out of the restaurant and walk around the perimeter looking through the glass hopeful to relocate my table, I would be a nimrod and all would know I have a problem, all would know I had a stroke. Maybe I just ask someone who works here if they know where I was sitting. Jack, that is stupid. Come on, Jack, get it together figures this out. Try the left, just do it, go left now, Jack. So, I turned left and began walking after a short distance I saw our table off in the remote corner.

Left hand fights me.

You know I cannot feel my left hand I struggle with buttons, plugging in a charger for my phone, I found this simple this task only works when I hold the phone in my left hand and the cord to the charger in my right hand, keys are also a big problem sometimes my right hand also lets me down. I have to tell myself to remain calm use your right hand and stay slow and steady. My left hand will crush what I am holding; putting a candy bar in that messed up hand is a huge mistake.

Fear of heights.

When I was a young boy, I believe I was four at the time, my mother and I were at Riverside Amusement Park in Massachusetts. On this unfortunate day and moment, we were riding an old-fashioned Ferris Wheel that ran on diesel fuel. When we were coming around again close to the top the fuel supply ran low and the wheel stopped turning in a manner of seconds we came to a stop. The operator below called out through a bull horn, sorry folks we need to add more fuel, this should only take ten or fifteen minutes. Please remain calm. Hey you up there stop shaking your chair. The ride operator was yelling at a couple of teenagers who were seated just below my mother and I. my mom has a fear of heights, she was so afraid, she kept talking and talking about how we would never ride a Ferris wheel again. My mom was holding me so tight so very tight. I grew up with a fear of heights

My fear of heights prior to my stroke was manageable. That said, after my stroke, my fear became intense and debilitating. I have difficulty driving over high bridges, I will drive miles out of my way to avoid high elevated freeway structures, most difficult for me is attempting to drive in the mountains this is impossible for me. So, you know I develop commercial real estate, yep, I have to force myself to go to a high elevation. At first the third or fourth floor during construction causes fear, just think about when I am at say the twenty-fifth or at a higher elevation? So what I have learned to get around my height issue, I visit my project on a weekend I force myself to go here I find my fear. See Jack that isn't too bad, you can do anything for ten or fifteen minutes. I found this practice works for me and as the structure grows higher the lower levels that once gripped me with fear are no longer an issue.

Can't sing.

I have completely lost the ability to sing. I can no longer carry a tune my issue is even more complex I also have a timing thing I find it impossible to sing impossible to sing the words in the correct place. Yes, I am way off usually a bar or two in advance. I cannot sing. Interesting before my stroke I could feel music now that feeling one gets for me is gone.

Playing guitar.

Without feeling in my left hand, I no long played my guitars. I kept working at this fortunately I took one of my guitars, the acoustic Yamaha with us when we relocated to Houston for five years. Linda split her time in Houston and back here in Newhall to visit our family staying close with the grandchildren. So, while Linda was away, I tried to play my guitar. It took a while before my stroke I always sang while playing guitar … however I did learn to play the guitar again. Today I play more blues than folk or rock. I enjoy the guitar so appreciative I did not give in. Interesting the songs I play are old from my previous lifetime when I was a kid, I do not know or care to learn any tunes from today's music.

Food preferences.

I hated sushi, I hated peppers. After my stroke, I found I enjoy these foods. However, I still dislike onions.

I am different, still Jack but not me.

This has been my greatest challenge, I gave up.

CHAPTER 16
KOR GROUP EARLY DAYS [2004]

Well now I did it, yes, I actually resigned from Bousquet Dennis & Associates and I became Senior Vice President Design and Construction responsible for all projects. Fortunately, after a couple of weeks Laura elected to join me; however Kevin wanted to remain a consultant. The real estate development company I joined, The Kor Group at the time had less than 20 employees. Ten months later I was managing over 25 projects in 3 countries and we now had over 150 employees.

Shortly after I joined, Lubert Adler Real Estate Funds became our financial partner. This changed everything. Brad immediately began thinking big we were no longer small, in attitude as well as development expectations.

I found it fascinating and exciting to be an integral part of the Kor group. Like I said earlier we had only fifteen or sixteen employees when I joined the Kor Group, less than a year later our ranks grew to be well over 150 and we definitely grew way too fast. The economy was booming each week it seemed we picked up another project. Brad was a deal junkie; he was always looking for another opportunity. It was difficult to establish our culture. Most often I found it a challenge to find qualified people to assist with managing the design and construction. Brad had a keen eye for development; he absolutely understood the market, with solid financial backing the sky was definitely our limit.

We were without a culture and the team was void of any management protocol systems. I found this bizarre and alarming. For example, there were no systems to track cost. As you can imagine I had to fix this issue. I set up meetings every Monday, I would preselect two or three projects for the meeting not to discuss design or construction the agenda was money status, did the project for discussion have funds available for the month, longer or are funds short, are we in trouble? I invited my staff working on the particular scheduled projects, accounting, and our CFO Afshin Kateb. Sometimes our CFO would attend and sometime not.

Some of the projects were fine; however; others were short and we needed to scramble to find a strategy to keep the project on course, where and how can we shore up dollars to keep going until we can create a protocol? After a while, say 3 or 4 meetings I had a handle concerning project cost status and knew which developments were in financial jeopardy as well as which projects were fine. That said we needed a system a cost control accounting system to manage all the projects.

I called Sheila Nelson a friend and former colleague from my Disney days. Sheila is by far the best at her position, Project Cost Controller. I met Sheila 1995 while working on the Angel's Stadium renovation. Sheila is a lovely lady large in stature who can manage dollars to the penny; she has the confidence and strength to force protocols and systems on those who need assistance and guidance.

Most important Sheila shines when dealing with the lenders as she always is on top of the financials and can articulate a positive response from the lenders' questions, the lenders like her and find confidence in her approach and accuracy concerning her Cost Control reports a valued asset. Adding Sheila to the team provided huge value from her first day. She took over the accounting department, built a cost control system on excel project by project and trained her staff. The Monday meetings to confirm available funds were no longer necessary. At the end of each and every month Sheila provided our team with an updated Project Control Cost Report for every project in the states as well as the overseas developments. Our CFO was threatened by Sheila however in due time Afshin understood she was not challenging his position he also realized Sheila's value to the team. Afshin however was definitely nervous of me and my relationship with Brad unfortunately his fear created a wall.

Our property's projects included the previous adaptive re-use condos, apartment developments, several hotel renovations and exciting, sexy ground up resort hotel/condominium developments in Mexico. However, the absolute prize was a resort hotel/condominium development in Anguilla, a little island in the Caribbean about a twenty-minute boat ride from St. Maarten.

Life was good actually great, I was back, the stroke definitely behind me. Yep, I was fortunate to find a challenging workload and a couple of exciting projects. I traveled constantly, three out of every four weeks I found myself traveling. At first, I believed the traveling to be an adventure. The only holidays I enjoyed with my family were Christmas and Thanksgiving. You see we had so much going on and to manage same was critical that on many holidays for example, the Fourth of July, Labor Day, and Memorial Day even Easter I found myself at one of our developments enjoying the holiday with my staff not my family. I found I could handle the workload, navigate through the pressure and stay on top of the issues. This was my therapy; I can still do my job and support my family. I did not give up; I did not let the stroke define me. We were living the sweet tasting good life. Jack is back.

I definitely had to make adjustments as travel expenses were crazy. One time I was shorted over $3k on my travel reimbursement. You see ... for example I would fly to Mexico believing I would return home at weeks end only to find I was needed in Miami, the next day say I was needed in Anguilla. In addition to development projects most often I was traveling with architects and or consultants looking at new opportunities as we wanted their opinion and proposals concerning a possible new hotel, resort or condo hotel prospect for an exploration trip. I would take care of their expenses as well as mine. Finding I had shorted myself over three thousand dollars caused me to be more focused concerning organization of the travel receipts.

What helped the greatest was to use one credit card for my personal expenses (not mixing my family expenses with business expenses) and two other cards for business expenses, one for projects in America the other for expenses in Mexico and Anguilla. This worked fine and I never found I was short funded again. Please be mindful, not often however on occasion Brad would travel with me. He never ever paid for any travel expenses. Traveling with Brad usually meant there were several others who had been invited on the trip.

So I know from my previous employment lifetime that it was important to delegate and keep smart people around you the smartest and best I could find. I promoted Laura, she became Vice President her responsibility to manage the Los Angeles based projects. Once or twice each month I would attend a project's design meeting at the architect's office or if a development was under construction I would attend the weekly construction progress meeting at the jobsite. We talked often and these projects were progressing on target.

The Mexico projects were moving slower than I would like, due to a ... well I guess he was a potential partner who specialized in Mexico developments that Brad was working with. An odder guy from Dallas who seemed difficult and I could never figure out his value or why he held Brad's ear.

He brought one project to us we named the Waddie Development; Mr. Waddie was the owner of the property. Carla Romero assisted me with all Mexico developments as well as Anguilla. From the documentation provided all in Spanish Carla was able to confirm that the land in question was much smaller than proposed. After a month or so of concept planning with the information at hand we dropped the idea to purchase the Wadie property showing the property less than told. The owner of the property and the older guy from Dallas was shady, not the kind of people to trust. However he from Dallas still held Brad's ear. The Dallas based consultant sent Carla a nasty letter written in Spanish.

Carla and I had worked together for more than twelve years. She is a valued colleague and dear friend she spoke Spanish. She grew up in Mexico and received her education there becoming a licensed civil engineer in Mexico and California. Carla was my interpreter, most notably with contracts. Often Carla would advise slow down Jack you are talking too quickly for me to remember and translate correctly. On occasion Carla would say that isn't nice are you certain you want to say that? I would respond YES exactly, please tell them what I said.

We met at Disney; Carla was a contract employee working in the infrastructure group for Disney Adventure, the new theme park. She is extremely smart I saw she had a strong work ethic and is by far the most detailed of our team. Subsequently I convinced her to join me when I took over the Hollywood and Highland development ... I was also fortunate that she followed me here. Years earlier she also followed as a junior partner joining Bousquet Dennis & Associates.as well as Fifield.

So to help with the work load and establish a more efficient communication protocol I had Randy manage the Mexico projects and I also included a hotel renovation project that was developing nicely in Miami (Tides South Beach) this worked much better for me and I believed our team would receive information and direction disseminated quicker. Laura was a good communicator she provides status updates and kept me in the loop to attend critical meetings when she believed an issue could get out of hand or required assistance. Unfortunately, Randy was not a good communicator, actually I seldom heard from him? This caused me to have to call or when we were both in the office schedule an appointment to catch up. The Mexico projects were encumbered by the Mexico specialist so most often I was getting an update only on the Miami hotel renovation.

What is that?

My first week at the Kor Group, about two or three days after I joined, I drove to Palm Springs late in the afternoon to our Avalon Hotel for a minor renovation meeting with the architect scheduled for the next morning. The hotel had recently gone through a major upgrade and renovation.

The drive from Los Angeles takes a couple of hours so I arrived in the early evening. I do not recall where I went for dinner most likely a Mexican restaurant as one of my favorite Mexican restaurant is in Palm Springs. I believe it must have been the Blue Coyote. My morning meeting the next day was scheduled at our hotel restaurant so I went elsewhere for dinner.

I was impressed with the Avalon Hotel, an old hotel with history. I checked in and introduced myself to the manager who I would be meeting with in the morning. They took me to my room; I found it to be a lovely suite with an eclectic design on the ground level. I walked through the suite and went back to the living room area and watched TV for a while. It was getting late and I was tired from the drive so I decided to go to bed. I left the living room area and went to the bedroom. It did not take long in a short time I fell asleep.

About 3 or 3:30 in the morning I woke as I thought I heard a noise in my room. I sat up and looked around; I did my best to listen for anything that would be out of the ordinary. I heard nothing as I sat on my bed in the darkness. Come on Jack you are being silly this noise you thought you head is in your head. There is nothing going on here, you have a busy day tomorrow go back to sleep. Well now, just having that conversation with myself I laid my head back down on the pillow. After maybe a minute or two I heard a noise again. I think I heard something but I am not sure. I sat up immediately and through the black darkness waited to see if the noise would continue.

Nothing all was silent, what is wrong with you Jack; you are going to be tired tomorrow. But then I heard a noise again, or did I, hell I don't know. I have to check this out make certain I am just hearing things and all is ok. So I got out of bed and began walking towards the bedroom door. Please be mindful, I can't see a thing I was blanketed in total darkness I held my arms out in front of me and slowly move them side to side to make certain I do not walk into something and hurt myself.

I know when I arrive at the doorway to the left is the living room and the door to the right is the bathroom. Just a couple more steps and I will find the light switch for the area where the rooms converge. I continued with my steps forward, and paused abruptly. My feet just stepped in something wet and slimy. What is that... dammit that feels cold and nasty? I have no idea what I just stepped in; I do know nothing was there before. Yep something is wrong. I begin to touch the wall and feel for the light switch. What the hell am I standing in? I finally find it and turn on the light. I am facing the bathroom and the door is open, hmm I thought the door was closed? This is an odd sight, I see mud on the top of the toilet tank running down the front, I also see mud in the shape of footprints on the toilet seat cover and the muddy steps are coming towards where I am standing. Then I notice the window above the toilet ... oh my half of the sliding window is no longer in place. I look down at my feet; yep, I am standing in mud.

My mind begins to race to every awful conclusion. Yep, I am thinking terrible things, awful things and mad at myself for questioning that the noises were a figment of my imagination. Would I have been smarter if not for my stroke? Well, isn't this special ...I know someone is in my hotel suite, I know they are most likely somewhere behind me. I know that to open and remove the window they must have a screw driver or maybe even God forbid a knife, that they used to slide and pop out the window from its frame to get it out of the track.

Doesn't matter a screwdriver will do the same damage as a knife? So I know I cannot keep this conversation going with myself and I know who ever is behind me can see me standing in the light. I have to do something, I must do something now, and I hope I can be bold?

The words just flew out of my mouth I even smiled as I listened to what I was saying... you fucking son of a bitch I am going to kick your ass and I turned around quickly to face my intruder. He was in the middle of the living room about ten to twelve feet from me and he a tall thin black man wearing jeans and a gray hoodie, was already running away from me towards the sliding glass door which I could see was now about half way open. He moved quickly through the door opening and I started to run after him. He ran out to the patio. There was a built-in bench at one side of the patio with a tall hedge behind it. I watched him run towards the bench, with an effortless motion he stepped up and landed on the bench seat then he stepped up to the back support of the bench with continued movement and jumped over the hedge. I was close behind and fortunately when I jumped to the bench I stopped my chase and grabbed on to the bench so I wouldn't crash into the hedge.

I don't think I was moving that fast as I still have difficulties running. You see, I had nothing on but my boxer underwear, If I went over the hedge how in the hell would I get back? I can't walk around dressed like that and Jack do you really want to confront this guy? Also I am not sure actually ... I believe I am certain, my post stroke body would crash into the hedge, I am not even sure I could jump to land on the bench seat?

I must have looked like a sight, very silly for sure. Well I sat on the bench for a moment I was feeling fortunate and a bit stupid, continuing in my head having a conversation with myself. After a minute or so I walked back inside and I found the phone, called the hotel front desk. As you can imagine at this time of night no one answered. I called again making certain I had the right number for the front desk, this time I left a message ... someone broke into my room, they are gone now, let's discuss in the morning. I have an idea to put clips on the windows from inside so this type of a break in can never happen again.

I walked back to towards the bedroom and of all stupid things I started to clean the mud on the floor with toilet paper. I definitely was not thinking clearly. I stopped what I was doing and paused. Should I call the police? Well that would take all night and do I believe the intruder will return? Nope I thought he will not come back tonight. I decided to go back to bed and try to sleep.

The next morning I got an early call from the front desk, they were concerned and wanted to make sure I was all right. I said I was fine and advised that I would be at the front desk shortly and could they be so kind to have someone from staff available so I could explain my clip idea to secure the windows from inside. I thought this is definitely an interesting way to start a new position. I believe I laughed out loud. I called Brad and advised him about the incident at his hotel and discussed my notion for security. Brad was concerned about the break in and glad I was all right.

The next day I also told Linda as well as Laura about the intruder break in story. Both women were shocked they each chastised me and thought I was crazy for going back to sleep. How could you do that JACK is what they each said, Linda several times. Lesson learned I never ever again accepted a ground floor room not on any return trips to the Avalon or any other hotel anywhere.

Never without my Blackberry at hand

Brad was a demanding boss, who would call at all hours of the night and several times on the weekend. I learned to keep my Blackberry (that was the phone of choice at the time for business, the first device to receive and send emails remotely) with me at all times. I believe the only time I was without my Blackberry was while I took a shower. Sometimes I would get a call from Brad on the weekend and I could not figure out why he called. I believe he just loved talking business, some guys love fishing others love golf, I believe fun for Brad was talking business and playing with his Blackberry.

Most often I would see an email from Brad as I was usually traveling I would read his email on my blackberry. I was leading the development of over twenty-five projects more than not I would have to read his email several times before I answered his question in an attempt to figure out which project his question was concerning. Sometime this was a challenge I actually felt like Sherlock Homes looking for clues, other emails the question was so focused I knew immediately what development he was talking about.

I knew from previous calls on Saturdays he and his wife (Kelly) would be with their two young sons for family time between 11:00 and 2:00. So imagine if you will when I called him back at this time I could always hear Kelly yelling at him in the background to get off his phone. So this was a good strategy on my part to call him back during this time, if he didn't answer I would leave a message. You see he saw that I did call back so I was free or awhile, sometimes he called later and sometimes he didn't. Brad was a driven man who enjoyed talking business. I think some of the calls he made on Sundays were out of boredom. Like I said on occasion I could not figure why he called, just seemed like he wanted to talk business. During this time Linda would get the kids together in another room or outside and keep them quiet while I was talking on the blackberry. Crazy as it must sound I actually enjoyed his calls, our work was exciting and we had some huge challenges.

The city of Los Angeles wanted to clean up the abandoned buildings and create an opportunity for residences to actually have people live in the city. For an incentive the city relaxed some of the building codes that said all life safety codes remained in place. This strategy opened a huge opportunity and the city became a hot bed of adaptive re-use residential development and construction, one could find construction cranes staged throughout the city and the city grew and with residences added to the real estate mix Los Angeles became a thriving live, work and play community. High rise ground up apartments as well as high-rise ground up condominiums quickly followed within the more affluent areas at the cities center.

At our first condo conversion attempt; a development called Molino we converted tired, shabby apartment into a for sale loft condominiums located in Los Angeles in the industrial area. We started five additional condo conversion projects while the first was under construction. However the others were much easier to develop as they were empty warehouse space that we converted to high end loft condos just blocks away in that same area.

We provided upgrades to, all public areas, the façade, added a swimming pool with lounge area at the roof. A few of the units, a rather small percentage of the apartment residences at Molino were still occupying their units during construction. The plan was once one of these leases terminated and the space became vacant, we would commence construction to convert and reconstruct the interiors of the previous occupied unit.

Fire Marshal Bob

One afternoon I received a call from the Fire Marshal, Bob was concerned said he was doing an inspection at my project earlier in the morning when to his surprise a pregnant woman passed him in the corridor on her way to the apartment laundry room carrying a basket of laundry. Bob was very nervous about the situation having tenants living in the building during a renovation. I had a great relationship with him from previous projects and believed he was correct, I told Bob I would talk with the owner and see if we could move the tenants to another apartment complex that he owned. My conversation with Brad was very positive, our team was advised, they made quick arrangements and the tenants were relocated to another address within the week.

Challenges

Life was good the real estate market was strong; we found purchases for residences as well as condo purchases for investors. We added additional condominium developments in Hollywood, Chinatown and located at the arts district near Los Angeles cities' center we converted a previous high-rise department store to condominiums. At this location our Eastern Columbia project we were very fortunate when Johnny Depp purchased a unit. He later purchased three or four adjacent units from original first buyers to create a huge residence.

Our Hollywood and Vine condo project provided a couple of huge challenges. One we took two additional buildings and tied them together, however one structure we added two additional levels to increase the structures height. The unsolvable problem was parking; we looked at several options including automated parking. Nothing appeared to work the slab to slab height of the basement levels would not allow for same. The location as well as the bones of the structure was amazing however without a viable parking solution the development would never be realized.

That is until a trip I made to Philadelphia. I went to meet with our financial partner. While walking towards their office I passed by a parking garage that housed automated parking. So yep I couldn't help myself I had to go inside the garage and check out the automated parking system. This didn't help me at all as I could not see how the automated parking system could fit in the tight space back in Hollywood. Then I was perplexed how the vehicle was delivered vertically, as there were no garage ramps to be found. Vertical transportation was made by industrial elevators. I returned back to our office the next day with a notion I hoped would be a parking solution. I drove to our parking consultant's office as I wanted to discuss their idea face to face. He ran some quick numbers and advised it would work with only one elevator is required that is providing a valet parking strategy would work logistically? In addition I needed to confirm as well as financially this idea did not impact the Proforma. I met with a couple of valet providers requested cost proposals. The solution worked well and did not compromise the Proforma. I did however add a second elevator as two elevators provided quicker logistics and if one elevator required down time for repairs the second elevator would prove the required service to move the cars vertically. Hollywood and Vine was a huge success. The units were sold far above assumed values.

Viceroy Resort on the island of Anguilla was definitely my favorite project, a lovely little island in the Caribbean about a twenty minute boat ride from nearby island St. Martin. This little thirty-two square mile island was very fortunate to have missed the earlier real estate development boom during the seventies and eighties, the private vacation club fractional ownership days. I was surprised to find a natural under developed paradise.

When we arrive we found a lovey paradise, beautiful white sugar sand beaches, phenomenal restaurants a virtually underdeveloped island. We were surprised to find only four existing resorts. Three operating, the fourth Brad purchased in Reno, Nevada at Bankruptcy court.

Sometimes one just gets lucky, Brad was very fortunate you see a previous staff member from the Cocoloba Resort in Anguilla contacted family working at a hotel in Los Angeles and told him the Cocoloba failed that the property was scheduled for an auction sale in Reno. As lady luck would have it, that Los Angeles relative was an employee at one of our Los Angeles hotels.

The island was amazing absolutely gorgeous, that said for me I also found the islanders to be kind and friendly. I was fortunate to discover several friends, fond relationships I still cherish today.

Brad wanted Kelly to be the designer for the new Viceroy five-star resort /condo hotel destination. Resorts are complicated and typically to create an extraordinary destination a historical knowledge and history designing hotels provides creative insight and huge value while planning any resort's concept. Just imagine how difficult and intimidating it would be to lead the resort design and not be aware or have a history concerning hotel demands and requirements for area uses and space relationships as well as space criteria.

So I had an idea, you see at Disney we often used in the primary concept role what we called an art director to lead and set the idea for the design notion. We also would have a design architect accompanied by an actual architectural team take the art director's thought through implementation further to allow the team to create the construction drawings

I called an old friend who I had the pleasure to work with previously Brad McNamee with WATG. He and his firm specialize in Hotels WATG has designed thousands of great destination resorts. I explained my notion to Brad fortunately my strategy was acceptable for his firm. I was also looking forward to working with Brad again, and I was confident he would take her notion and create something extraordinary.

My assistant Jeanne made arrangements for Brad to join me on a trip to Anguilla, it was important for Brad to see the site and I believed even more important to understand the island of Anguilla. We flew to St Martin arrived in the early afternoon. Next we took a cab from the Dutch side to the French side to board the ferry boat to Anguilla. He joked as in a matter of an hour we passed through three countries.

When we arrive at the site Brad McManee was extremely excited and he said you were not exaggerating, I believed the location will provide a fabulous resort. The island is flat with very slight changes to the typography. I found only one surveyor on the island and engaged Nigel to develop a site plan establishing boundaries and areas and most important close the dimensions. Unfortunately Nigel advised the requested document would not be available for several weeks and as he was the lone island surveyor I had no choice but to wait.

I believed it important to begin the concept phase immediately. I thought it imperative to find Kelly's thoughts and put them in Brad's hands. You see I knew this would not be a simple or easy process as Kelly doesn't draw or read drawings. She is an extremely talented interior decorator … but how does one articulate her thoughts and get them on paper?

I met with Kelly earlier one afternoon in West Hollywood. I drove to her office and we discussed her idea. She wanted a midcentury modern design with strong clean lines. Unfortunately she could not provide details and that did not give me much to go on; hell you could drive a truck through that statement. She did put together a couple of focus boards, a kind of collage of images she cut out of magazines; people, art, furniture, interior images a collection of ideas that helped me to begin to see her notion for the design concept. I shared her notion as well as focus boards with Brad we both could imagine the villa concept, however the only mid-century modern commercial structure that came to mind was the famous performing arts structure, the Lincoln Center in New York. However this famous building is not an attractive model to pull architectural lines from to design our resort.

I showed Brad the island and introduced him to my new friends there. Remember Jack is impatient; I will not have the Survey for weeks? The island is very flat I want to get started, so we had an idea. We spent the next day creating background data to allow Brad to set the basic concept footprints to the design. The island is relatively flat as crazy as this sounds we measured out a simple grid we marked the area with wooden stakes. Brad mapped this layout on paper and we took photos in each direction. This provided Brad and his team a basic and most simple roadmap back at their offices in California. It actually worked and we could begin the concept process while we were waiting on the site map from the island surveyor Nigel.

I took a trip to Cabo San Lucas to check out competition. I stayed at the One and Only Pamilla resort with the other Brad, the one I worked for. This resort was a huge success. The resort had recently been renovated .The architecture was not extraordinary it …well kind of just blended in. I decided to walk the property the next morning to see what I could find, why was it a success. I woke early and began my walk through the resort. I was confused and literally had nothing, no idea whatsoever why the resort was a hit.

So I started to walk through the property for a second time. That said this time I did something very different, you see I would stop at key or interesting locations outside or on the interior I would find a seat and take several minutes to take in my surroundings and most important to understand my view. I would just begin writing, making notes of what I believed was significant, what was compelling what was pleasing in my view. What are you looking at Jack and why do you I believed it great? I spent most of the day on this adventure and I filled several pages with cryptic notes. I still did not know what I did not know, why is this resort a hit? Well late that night after dinner I sat by the pool with my notes. I had an epiphany and began to smile. I am certain vacationers at the poolside which opened to the bar must have found me smiling a sight.

Two notions from my notes were repetitive and consistent. The interior design was one the design was awesome and the other was landscaping. The landscape design was spectacular; it enhanced the topography as well as the architecture. I took a leap I actually was surprised he knew the answer. You see the bar tender walked by my table, I said hello have you been here sense the reopening? He replied yes. Do you happen to know who designed the landscape? He said isn't it gorgeous, George Girvin did one hell of a job.

I called my office first thing the next morning, I asked Jeanne to research George Girvin confirm he was the landscape architect at the One and Only Pamilla. Jeanne put together an outline and summary of George's work and scheduled a meeting for me at his office in Santa Barbara for the following week.

Kelly Brad's wife couldn't draw or read drawings as you can imagine getting the ideas from her head would be a challenge. Kelly wanted a midcentury modern design with strong clean lines. In our business we communicate with drawings.

I had an idea and I was most hopeful it would work. I scheduled two consecutive Saturday meetings at Kelly's office and chose two renders (draw three dimensional perspectives drawings) I knew from my previous Disney days, artist who could produce great renderings. In addition to Kelly and myself I also invited Brad and George. I wanted to meet on a Saturday so no one would be distracted and I could control their attention for most of the day, I advised all to turn off their Blackberry and we held a closed discussion with our team, Kelly the project art director, Brad our architect and George our landscape designer.

My idea was simple imagine you have been robbed and the police bring in a sketch artist who from your description does his best to sketch and to place on paper the face of your assailant. In this case I was hopeful Kelly could provide information for our artist to put on paper what mid-century modern ideas she held in her head.

The first Saturday meeting was an absolute disaster. My artist wasn't confident and had difficulties putting anything of substance on paper. Brad and mostly George began to take over the meeting. George actually began sketching French Mansard roof concepts. I ended the discussion a couple of hours early. When I walked Brad and George to their cars after the meeting, I advised that next Saturday I implore that they remain quiet and merely listen as it is

Kelly's role as art director to set the concept notion. Once we find her thoughts then and only then they can assist to further her concept.

As you can imagine I was not as confident walking in to our next Saturday discussion. That said this time things began a bit smoother. Kelly would talk about her idea for the architectural concept and our second artist had confidence to draw as she spoke. This dialog between the two went on for a little over an hour with numerous sketches that quickly became trash. Then to my surprise our artist stopped sketching details and began to create actual building perspectives. Kelly would say no that is too Palm Springs, or to another sketch she said that is too Santa Monica or looks like Las Vegas residential from the fifties. I had no idea what she meant a mid-century modern residential architecture look the same to me. I also believe Brad and George did not have a clue either. Fortunately, on this day George and Brad remained quiet allowing the meeting's discussion to Kelly and the artist. The artist drew another image and Kelly said that is more like it and she began to smile. You see, I believe she thought my idea would not work. The artist saw that he was a getting somewhere with his latest sketch so he began to add detail and shading to accentuate his perspective. She said yes, that is my idea. With that the artist reached into his briefcase and pulled out a book. He opened the book and began turning pages. Kelly's eyes light up page after page. The book was, Architecture by Paul Rudolph, a mid-century modern architect and chair of Yale University's department of Architecture.

Now it was my turn to smile as we finally held the template for the design concept. From the photos and image in the book Brad began to sketch three and four story ideas for the hotel. The next couple of hours all contributed and we worked as team. I drove home that afternoon with a huge smile on my face.

Brad began to develop the concept and most important the resort buildings layout on the site. Our discussion added great ideas for example three swimming pools, several restaurants and bars as well as opportunities for weddings.

The resort was huge and within the next five weeks we purchase two adjoining sites. We brought in a residential architect from Beverly Hills, Ken Hilgendorf to design the villas and kept the hotel resort design with WATG

When I received the survey from Nigel I was shocked, it did not make sense and was easy to see that the survey was inaccurate as it did not close. For those of you who are not in the real estate or construction business that means the math did not add up. I met with Nigel on my next trip to Anguilla. The conversation was awkward he was adamant that his survey was correct. Some of the property lines boundaries fell on angles so this made the survey complicated. The issue was larger than a simple math area as four of the villas were impossible to find approval due to proximity to the beach and or adjourning property. As you can imagine this would kill our Proforma. After several discussions on phone as well as in person with no resolution to what I believed were an error, well I had to develop a solution to this problem.

I was confident from the grid Brad and I created that Nigel was incorrect. I also had a difficult emotional issue as any survey to seek approval for construction had to be submitted to the Anguillan government by Nigel and him alone as no other surveyor was registered in Anguilla. Nigel was the key and if I alienated or made him angry I could put the development in jeopardy. Nigel or members of his crew were usually on our site on a daily basis.

On a trip back home to Los Angeles I devised a plan. When I landed in Miami with a short lay over for my next flight I called a Los Angeles surveyor who I had worked with in my previous work lifetime, Mollenhauer Group. The next afternoon we met at their office. I brought Nigel's survey as well as our cryptic grid and explained the issue and my concern. I retained Mollenhauer group they planned a trip to the island for the following week. We also discussed the importance of keeping a positive relationship with Nigel.

Mollenhauer Group worked quickly within a couple of days they finalized their survey and to my delight all the structures worked even the four villas that were an issue with Nigel's earlier survey. So our next step was to meet with Nigel and give him the Mollenhauer Group survey so he could submit to the government through Anguillan protocols. We had included Nigel and his team of our progress during the actual site survey, he was on board and all including the relationship was working well, in fact better than I could have expected.

Nigel called me about a week later and told me that the survey was not working. As you can imagine I was very confused after a long discussion I realized that he took the raw data from the Mollenhauer Group and ran it through his computer. So what do I do? How can we move forward? What in the hell?

I drove over to the Mollenhauer Group. After a very long discussion that also included Nigel by phone no one could understand why Nigel's computer was finding a different conclusion concerning geometry. The best we could think of was to fly Mollenhauer Group back to the island and we could continue our meeting with Nigel in person.

Well that ended up being a great idea. You see what we learned was Nigel had a virus in his program, that altered information when the property boundaries were not at right angles. I made a decision to purchase a new survey program for Nigel at the cost of ten thousand dollars. He ran the data again on the new program and this time all was fine. Nigel submitted the documents to the government, we were able to keep our concept as designed, our relationship with Nigel remained positive. The Mollenhauer Group provided huge value and they enjoyed their time on that little island. Traveling back to California, I smiled, pleased that with half a brain, I could still solve difficult problems.

CHAPTER 17

FRANK FARANDA ...HOW HE CAME TO LEAD MY ANGUILLAN CONSTRUCTION TEAM [1995]

In 2004 I put together our team for the Viceroy Anguilla Resort and they relocated to the island. I desperately needed to find a project leader a strong construction manager who would relocate to Anguilla to lead the team. Most importantly, I believed this candidate must possess great people skills not only for our team and the consultant team of architects, engineers, and specialty consultants. Most importantly, I needed to find a leader to be an ambassador on our behalf to the island's government as well as the island residents.

I could think of no other than Frank Faranda my dear friend and colleague from my previous lifetime we worked together at Disney Development Company. I called Frank and fortunately after two or three telephone discussions we came to an agreement. Two weeks later I met Frank at the island, introduced him to the team and gave him the key to his island apartment. Frank was a big man I never knew his weight four hundred maybe five hundred pounds maybe more?

When I met him on the island, I was surprised that the weight had taken his toll unfortunately now Frank had difficulty walking. I said Frank looks like you are in pain you are having trouble walking. With that he replied I need to lose some weight get back to his fighting position. Frank shook my hand looked me in the eye and asked if his difficulty walking was a problem, if so he would return home. I told him I wish he would have confided in me and advised it, will be a challenge. I went on to say, if he can meet the challenge, I can help him.

With assistance from Pierre Rousseau my Caribbean logistics consultant we obtained a vehicle that Frank could get in and out of with relative ease. We tried four or five trucks and we were all surprised that the only truck that he could get in and out of with ease was a little Toyota RAV4, the smallest of all the options however the step up into the car was best for Frank. The RAV4 truck was bright red. I believe it worked well as it was a little higher raised from the ground with a huge door.

This will sound odd and maybe you can't understand… When Frank walked, I as well as others enabled him; you see Frank would place his hand on my shoulder to steady himself while we walked. This practice occurred at the site, meetings in New York or Los Angeles and at airports. Frank would not allow anyone to get him a wheelchair.

A week later Brad came to the island Frank was scheduled to meet my boss, the owner. I knew it would be impossible for Frank to walk the site with us as we toured the development. So I devised a plan orchestrated a route in advance. Frank would step away while we were talking and drive to the next location. This worked fine and Brad was never the wiser. Brad did however voice concerns about Frank's weight. He said this guy Frank is huge; I assured him that Frank was the right choice and best man for the development.

Previously about nine years earlier during my Disney Development Company days when I worked for the mouse, I was searching for a Construction Manager for the New Amsterdam Theater; the home of the Ziegfeld Follies on 42nd St. my absolute favorite of all projects while at DDC as well as all the other firms I have worked for.

My first trip to the New Amsterdam Theater was more than a bit shocking to find Times Square not the friendly of places and 42nd St. actually closed, even the street's topless and gay bars had moved on. One of the New York City redevelopment agencies had placed what they hoped to be inspirational messages on the closed and abandoned theater marques. It was like being in a made for TV movie walking on an abandoned 42nd St.

The evening prior to my meeting I decided to walk through Times Square and was approached by a big black man who stepped in my way and demanded my wallet. In a situation like this one can either be bold and say something like fuck off or disappear asshole or one could take a safer well a crazy route and start talking about God saying as loud as possible Jesus Christ praise the Lord and waving one's arms in the air and definitely keep walking never make eye contact. It works, I can vouch for that.

That night I told the guy, disappear asshole and I was surprised and pleased when he stepped aside and let me pass without any confrontation. I was with another Disney staff member and he said are you nuts? I replied my only other option would have been to start talking about Jesus and act mentally ill however I was fearful you would trip me up. So I elected to go with the bold route and fortunately it worked aren't you happy he didn't take your wallet? He smiled and said oh my gosh yes, I was afraid he would stab us.

I arrived at the theater early in the next morning found 42nd St. to look like a ghost town. 42nd St. was actually closed, like I said, even the topless and gay bars had already moved on. I began to read out loud the inspirational messages on the closed and abandoned theater marques.

I met someone from the city redevelopment agency who gave me a tour of the New Amsterdam Theater. I ruined my suite trousers as the orchestra level floor; yep, the complete floor was covered in one to two inches high of mushrooms. It was eerie to step on the mushrooms. The juices from the crushed mushrooms absorbed in the bottom of my pants and caused them to be stained. Can you imagine that I could poke my fingers through exposed steel columns and beams?

This once gorgeous historical theater was now in decay and terrible ruin. You see about a decade earlier the Netherlander's wanted to bring the theater back to life. They created a team who drilled probes (holes) in the roof and exterior skin walls to get their arms around the risk and cost for redevelopment. They elected to pass as they thought the effort to reconstruct the theater was a heroic challenge and could not be done. So after a decade or so of rain, snow and severe weather the unfortunate theater was exposed to the elements, she took a beating. The theater was also hacked up they removed the box seats just cut the structures from the walls. They painted her brown from floor to ceiling when she was modified to a moving picture theater to dampen lighting. I believed the brown paint was a humiliation for a once glorious theater. It was painful to see her. The final movie show before closing the theater was Conan the Barbarian.

We, who included me, Laura, and a couple of other Disney staff, cannot recall why they the other staff was in attendance and a human resources employee interviewed several candidates. After the interviews the HR lead said I have a form here for all to fill out it is based on points and from same I will tally the answers and we can find who is the one to receive an offer. With that I stood up and said I do not believe this to be a difficult decision we do not need your forms as Frank is head and shoulders the right choice for the position, I said I am certain everyone agrees. Frank was added to my team we also worked together on the Angel's stadium renovation and ABC Studios Times Square. Pound to call Frank friend, Francis is the kindest man I ever met.

Angels Stadium

Frank relocated to Anaheim in late 1996 for a couple of years. The stadium development was a labor of love, such an amazing project to be a part of. My son Drew's pony baseball team World Series Champions, his team and coaches was honored by walking on to the field before a game, definitely a proud moment for me and my family.

I lead the design effort traveling to Kansas City every two weeks for design progress meetings with HOK and our consultants. I also negotiated the contract with Turner Construction, during this period DDC cease to exist and became part actually absorbed by Imagineering. My role at the stadium came to an end. That said, during the early construction efforts things were not smooth the construction team was fighting the outlook was grim, lots of drama.

Ken Wong asked me to step in get the team issues resolved and be somewhat of a consultant to make things happen and move to a successful and timely completion. I was also very sick the dermatomyositis had taken its toll; I was worn down from this disease.

It was easy to fix this drama problem as in most cases where one finds drama at least two people are fighting they are doing their best to not get along and the remaining team members choosing sides. After investigating and watching the Disney team interaction I knew one of the two most senior managers must move on the same two who were at the center of all the drama. It was a hard decision as neither manager was a leader or particular adept at solving problems and I believed it would be more disruptive to replace both. I chose who I thought was the better of the two and gave my recommendation to Ken. However, I also recommended that we relocate Frank from New York to Anaheim. You see I knew, I was actually certain, Frank would ease the drama crisis and be a calming voice to the team.

We looked at sharing Dodger Stadium during the three year renovation or possibly enter into an agreement with the City of Los Angeles to host games at the Coliseum. At the time Angels had a small fan base and Michael was fearful that by relocating the team for three years we would hurt the limited fan base. In a meeting he asked me to find a way to keep the Angels games in Anaheim and to my surprise he said you must complete the construction in two years in lieu of three. I smiled and I told him it might be easier to solve poverty and prostitution worldwide. He did not smile back without hesitation he said two years and keep the team in Anaheim. There is no other choice that can work for Disney. I do not believe he thought my comment humorous. That said I believed it important to advise Michael to make him aware that he had requested the impossible.

I met with the Turner Construction team the next day and told them we need to keep the team here in Anaheim and construct the renovation in two years not three as had been proposed. As you can imagine they did not take my notion well, they laughed and told me I was crazy, impossible this can't happen. After about twenty minutes of complaining and saying this is an absurd request, I said so you want me to go back to Michael and tell him we failed, we can't honor his directive and we just gave his request less than a half of an hour of thought? I love YODA, "do or do not, there is no try," I said. I stood and advised that I have to find a solution I am not returning to Michael to tell him I failed and I do not want to waste any more of my time listening to why this can't be done. That said I will give you four more minutes and no longer to try and convince me that you are correct.

Dave...the projector director with Turner...began speaking, I took my seat again that said after thirty seconds I looked at my watch and said be advised only three and a half minutes remain, After one minute I again looked at my watch and advised only three minutes remain, At a minute and a half I started to follow with the count down when Dave stopped in mid-sentence and said, You ae going to do this with or without us. I replied I have no choice we got to do this. Dave said I am dying to see what do you have in mind, and shook his head; they under estimated me, I do not believe he imagined that I had already thought about a strategy or solution? I began speaking and I was a bit sarcastic truly very sarcastic. Well now I had to convince them to try, to think, give it the old college effort, didn't I, certainly we are not going to fail, I can't fail?

I slowly pulled my chair back from the conference room table and stood with copies of the Angel's upcoming baseball schedule in my left hand and began to walk as I spoke circling the conference room table moving towards the white board hanging on the opposite wall and said as I walked, well I believe there are three full working days in every twenty-four-hour period. A few in the room laughed the others smirked and shook their heads smiling at each other. I was certain they were not expecting much from me. I reached the white board and turned to face them. I spoke again with a huge smile on my face saying- I can't believe you guys give up so quickly, you do not even make an effort ... That said three shifts would be impossible to manage so let's propose two ten-hour shifts. This will work fine during the off season as well as when the Angels are playing road games once the baseball season begins. However, when the Angels have a home game, if the game is during the day we work at night or of the game is at night we work during the day with a ten-hour single shift. Next I gave three or four Turner team members who were seating close to me copies of the upcoming Angels Baseball schedule and asked that they pass the schedule out to the remaining team members.

Now I had their attention, I said let's break down a couple of disciplines and make certain we have the necessary infrastructure even if that means part of the infrastructure might be temporary ... to allow guest in the stands and a perfect field for baseball games, for example demolition, press area, food and beverage concessions stands, parking, security, locker rooms, what has to be constructed first and what can we put off or delay for the off season when only we occupy the stadium not the baseball teams ...I think you have the idea, do you get it? Next steps in the discussion were amazing as they began breaking down the criteria to schedule major components with all working as a team. It was amazing to watch them strategize to formulate a game plan that could be understood on paper in a comprehensive schedule. I left late that night about five or six hours later with a straw man schedule. The schedule was rough however very little changed after a week or two of the Turner Construction team providing more detail and substance. It worked. I was very impressed with the Turner Construction team. They did the impossible. We opened to a sold-out house against the Yankees. Linda joined me for opening day including the design and construction team to watch the game in Michael's suite.

I was very sick during this time; I had a severe Dermatomyositis flair up. I could only walk about fifty feet before I need to rest. Sheila Nelson our Disney cost controller was part of the Angels construction team. She exercised all efforts to take good care of me. For example, she knew my schedule and made certain a charged golf cart was always available for my use parked adjacent to the construction trailer entrance.

Perfect seats

One night I happened to be watching a Cleveland Indians baseball division game on TV. The announcers were talking about the corporate club box seats at ground level and how terrific and amazing this was for the fan to a see a game with the same perspective as the ball player. Four corporate boxes between the dugouts behind home plate. The box seats linked by a stairway and elevator to the corporate suite above. I knew HOK was the architect for the Indians stadium; I had a design meeting with them the next day. I flew to Kansas City and asked the designers to explain to me how they accomplished the box seat at grade design. I learned we would have to change the elevation of the bowl behind home plate. By weeks end Turner Construction provided cost estimates and figured out a way that did not impact our schedule. The solution included precast concrete structural members stepping up through the bowl to make this work.

I have been invited several times by Mike Long a colleague who previously my attorney and friend to enjoy a game there. It is amazing and I just smile during the games recalling the challenges, discussions and obstacles to make this notion work as well as the challenges for the stadium. Sometimes lady luck is on your side.

We opened April 1st. 1998 against the Yankees; yep, you are correct April Fool's Day. We opened big the stadium looked awesome, another project on time and under budget, one hell of a team.

Frank was a calming factor our team needed him. As soon as Frank arrived the drama began to disappear, direction to our contractor and consultants was clear and most important they became a team.

Baseball hats

I like hiring the little guy someone hungry for work, a company that will go the distance to make things happen. I have based my career giving a small company a chance. Sometimes things just do not work. To understand what I am talking about watch an angel's game on TV or better go to a game you will see the huge Angel's baseball hats framing the arrival point the entry to the stadium?

We got a great bid from a guy in his mid-30 and new company and asked for a mock-up of one of the hats, the mock-up was about the size of a VW bug Looked great much better than all of the other mock-ups.

I was a bit concerned as the guy was working out of his garage; he advised he had rented a production space near by assuming he won the contract for the hats. We scheduled a morning to meet him.

Well … all was in his favor when his mother stepped into the garage and began to scold her son, telling him she was sick and tired of his mess and clean her garage up.

Little did the mother know he was meeting with Disney, HELL she killed his contract; we decided to select another to construct the hats. Can you imagine the day when IBM came to meet Bill Gates? Fortunately for Bill, his mother did not run off the IBM team. I imagine the home computer industry would have been very different for sure.

ABC

With a successful development behind us, well then Frank returned to New York to be the construction manager for ABC Studios development in Times Square.

We worked with a glass manufacturer to develop a window where the ABC studio camera could film unobstructed by shadows or reflections it was placed on a 32-degree angle. A couple years later I was leading the development team for the Kodak Theater and we believed a studio would be perfect location on Highland Ave. to be able to view from inside the famous HOLLYWOOD hills sign in the distance. I called the manufacturer to secure two more glass sections; the second was put in storage to be ready and available in the event the first glass ever got damaged. The space never became a TV studio as imagined however the space became the home for Ryan Seacrest's radio show. Unfortunately, I do not believe the window glass was ever put to use to see the Hollywood sign on TV.

New Amsterdam Theater

On the New Amsterdam Theater, we worked with the UDC and EDC a state and city redevelopment agency; the third government agency the Port Authority funded the development. The New Amsterdam Theater was delivered on schedule and under budget, a first for the city of New York. It was a pleasure to work with Hugh Hardy and Michael Jones from Hugh Hardy Architects for the renovation they kept the project design at a delicate balance to preserve and enhance the original design intent.

My challenge, and it took almost a year, was to obtain approval from the NYC Building Department for another 200 seats. At the time seats were selling for $65 each, so a couple of shows per day six days a week was imperative ... we needed the additional 200 seats to make our Proforma pencil. I wanted to locate the seats at the back of the mezzanine. This was the most logical area and it would not disrupt the architecture. Initially the city did not understand. All I got was red tape and double talk.

So, I directed our design team to do something radical. At first Hugh refused, he said this would destroy the theater. I smiled and advised my notion is only a mere tool to wake them up and give me what I want, what I already asked for and what they refused. It took a little over two weeks to develop the drawings and finalize the plan. Hugh's drawings blew out the side walls of the mezzanine area; with a push and a shove we located 200 additional seats. When we presented this notion to the city, well now the planning department was in shock they called me crazy. Absolutely not this cannot be done we would prefer for the theater to remain vacant. That said this conversation provided me with another opportunity to reinforce why Disney required additional 200 seats. I guess you know what happened next; yep, the city approved our original request to add 200 seats in the back area of the mezzanine. While I was fighting this problem with the city, we were simultaneously developing our design process when we got approval for 200 additional seats our construction drawings were in the final stages. So immediately we were able to submit our design for the building permit. I now knew the New Amsterdam Theater would soon be under construction.

Rebecca Robertson with EDC actually came to tears when we gave her a tour of the theater at completion. She was so happy to find the theater back to her glory.

The development was a huge success; in addition we brought 42nd St. back to life. Disney would not enter into an agreement unless two conditions were finalized; first we required two additional venues would also move forward. Fortunately Madame Tussauds and MTV agreements were settled quickly. The second condition was equally as important. Disney needed to ensure that the topless and gay bars would not be able to return. We worked with the mayor's office Giuliani to create restrictions that were imposed to not allow topless and gay bars within a certain distance unfortunately I cannot recall the footage I believe it was somewhere around 650 Ft. We found a beauty school that had a dozen or so students to make this work.

Big day

The final step to move the theater forward was predicated on our negations with the city. Disney was looking for a long term lease and required the city to provide the necessary funds for reconstruction. We needed to ensure funds adequate and timely. I had my team working in the city for a little over two weeks. I believe this the greatest effort for one of my teams; we developed the strategy to ensure Disney would receive the required funds necessary, devised a schedule requiring three months funds available in our account, tied to a sliding protocol for example after using first months funds for expenses the city must deposit fourth month funds in our account and so on. My team doing our best working crazy hour's arriving at 10:00 in the morning working round the clock leaving for our hotel in the middle of the night at 1:00 or 2:00 the next morning, seven days a week for two weeks. However on the second Saturday I thought we needed a rest a little team building, we took the day off enjoyed a night of fun at Atlantic City casinos.

Frank Ioppolo Disney's chief attorney from the Orlando office chosen to lead the negotiations with New York's EDC/UDC state and city's redevelopment agencies.... Frank on a couple occasions would meet us around midnight arranging sandwiches delivery from the deli, he asking questions probing our strategy. To ensure Frank's success we developed a game plan, first we imagined any questions or issues. Second, we found the perfect answer for Frank's response; arranging same in the proper order, a war battle strategy. We went out of our way to prepare to guarantee Frank Ioppolo would shine. Our team created a daily report that we emailed to Frank at the close of each day.

Our reports long, I did not believe Frank actually read our reports I think this notion came from Norm? One night, placed precariously hidden in plain sight located in the middle of our report we ran a scenario, does a left-hand pitcher have a greater chance of making MLB than a right-hand pitcher?

The next day, after an extraordinary long night, as me and my team were leaving the building to return to our hotel, by chance we happened to pass Frank coming to work in the office lobby accompanied by his wife and another Disney attorney. I said good morning, Frank. He joked: wow you guys do work late. As I approached the revolving door, Frank said, Hey, Jack, I believe you are correct a left hander does have a better chance of making MLB however I believe your team analysis is mistaken I believe a left hand pitcher has even a greater chance than what you guys assumed. Well, now I guess that settles it; Frank does read our reports.

The morning for the negations to start Frank met me and my team for a final overview. At the conclusion he gave his goodbyes to all he stepped through the door on his way to the elevator. Minutes later Frank returned he said Jack I want you to come with me; the lemo is waiting hurry....

So, I assumed Frank wanted an advisor someone who could whisper a technical response in his ear in the event he was uncertain. I was dead wrong. Picture us sitting in the limousine driving to the meeting at the Times Square Marriott. Frank said I'm not going Jack I want you to lead the negotiations. I replied hell I'm not an attorney. Frank saying you know the game plan better than anyone, you will be fine. Frank what authority do I have? He replied Jack you have absolutely NO authority, none, nada… your role is to piss them off, I will close the deal when I believe the time is right most likely this afternoon in the hallway.

Our car pulled over I stepped out of the lemo Frank said break a leg. I entered the Marriott Marque finding the conference room with about 20 plus people waiting. I introduced myself, hello I am Jack Bousquet Director of Development and Design for DDC, New Amsterdam Theater will be my responsibility. I must apologize on Frank's behalf unfortunately an issue taking precedence requires his attention. The room sounded with groans and moans. I took a seat opened my briefcase retrieving our game plan…. I started the discussion. During our first break I found the pay phones calling my assistant Rachel back in Burbank, I asked her to place a call to find me in twenty minutes.

Back in the conference room things were progressing splendidly our game plan working as hoped, I seldom needed to look at or refer to my notes you see I had worked on this so long I knew the format by heart. A young woman stepped into the conference room asking if a Jack Bousquet was present, the city team of lawyers pointed to me. She approached my chair handing me a note while whispering in my ear saying you need to call your sectary you have an emergency on another project. I opened the note after a couple of slow precious seconds reading same. I placed the note on the table, I stood, and said I apologize it appears there is a problem I must attend to, I will return a quickly as I can.

With that I am back at the wall of pay phones in the lobby talking with Rachel. What happened next scared the crap out of me actually caused me to jump; I had to look down to check my shoes making certain they remained on my feet.

Frank Ioppolo tapped my shoulder and said what in the hell are you doing out here? I Thought Frank drove away after he dropped me off. I smiled I said Frank there is a lot of people in that room concerned that you are not here most believing I am a nobody. I had my secretary call there is a huge problem that needs my attention, I imagine by now they all read Rachel's the note left behind. Frank, laughing, said, Well, Jack, don't leave Rachel hanging on the phone. I replied, Frank, she hung up about ten minutes ago; I just wanted the room to wait a while longer for my return. Frank smile shook my hand and said you got it kid. That afternoon just after our mid-afternoon break Frank closed the deal in the hallway; every condition in accordance with our game plan. Frank Ioppolo is one hell of an attorney.

That evening July 18, 1995 I stepped out to the street to hail a cab, I found a young boy standing on a box holding a handful of newspapers The Village Voice yelling the days headline Sleazy does it come savor Time Square's TOPPLES BARS before, Disney takes over. Well, I had to purchase six; I gave five as gifts keeping one for myself the first page framed hanging on the wall at my home in my pool table /music room. The Empire State Development Corporation leaked the story to the press earlier in the day.

Hidden treasures

We were extremely fortunate and it was absolutely amazing for Frank Faranda to meet with a couple of Ziegfeld Girls. As you can imagine the lovely ladies were elderly. Two could still walk ever so slowly the third now in a wheel chair. One does not ask a lady her age, I imagine all were in their nineties. They were happy and excited to find we were bringing their old theater back to life.

Our team found the meeting fascinating you see the ladies told outrageous and riveting stories of the theater's great historical past. They talked about how they met their husbands you see there was a club for men at the lowest level the room with the oval bar, the girls had to walk through this room to get to their dressing room this gave the ladies an opportunity to spend a moment and talk with someone who they thought might be interesting. It provided the men an opportunity to meet the Ziegfeld Girls. The ladies told stories about a couple of shooting at the roof top theater (a mini theater club, this is where Ziegfeld would preview his show before it hit the main stage below). Most important and wonderful becoming most valuable surprise giving us design direction you see, the ladies brought old photos and theater posters to share with Frank which provided huge significance to our team. That said the photos and posters showed the girls as young, beautiful with dreams for their boundless future. The discussion that day and their enthusiasm brought back a sparkle in their eyes and the girls remained beautiful however no longer youthful. The Ziegfeld Follies Ladies were fascinating a most lovely time indeed.

New Amsterdam Theater was the most ambitious and difficult development for me, I was so proud of our team, Laura project manager, Frank construction manager and Norm assistant construction manager who also became the future husband to Laura several years later.

You see there are areas in the theater where we had no clue as to the original design. The Ziegfeld Ladies photos and posters provided huge clues, for example in some of the photos at the entry once inside the main doors we discovered were an ornate and delicate glass ceiling with leather bound doors framing the entry.

We did some minor demolition in the ceiling of that area the next week and discovered remnants of the frame that held the once gorgeous glass ceiling. What we assumed for that ceiling was not even close. With some additional exploratory demolition, we found an important treasure. You see hidden in the cavity of a wall was a box that held many small and telling pieces of the theaters past Art Nouveau design. We found several pieces of the plaster ornamentation for example a ladies head with ornate carving, light fixtures and so much more. Someone from years past took the effort to hide and place in waiting these design features for us. Hugh Hardy was elated; this find gave him a road map to bring her back to be a glorious theater once again.

Frank called me one day and advised he knew a guy who was now retired a great craftsman who had worked with plaster. This man had planned to travel the world with his wife to see all the sites and visit exotic places that they had dreamed about, unfortunately before the couple had a chance to begin their journey she was diagnose with cancer and shortly thereafter his wife left his world.

Frank and I met him for dinner; we discussed Disney's plans to refurbish the theater. I wish I could remember his name, unfortunately his name escapes me, I can't ask Frank as my dear friend passed from a heart attack while working in Anguilla October 13, 2008.

He asked Frank and me what I can do for you. Frank replied we want you to come out of retirement; we have retained a firm from Canada to recast the large major plaster pieces. That said we are struggling with a strategy of how we recast the hundreds of smaller pieces. At dinners end an agreement was finalized, his major concern, he wanted to pass his knowledge onto a younger generation, so eight apprentices were added to comprise his team.

He set up shop in the back of the mezzanine level the area where we added 200 additional seats. He was a master indeed it was fascinating to watch him.

He would make molds from small ornamental specimens found throughout the theater for example hand rails detailing at a cornice or plaster framing build into the walls. One day we reviewed his work with Hugh and Stewart this provided Hugh with an epiphany that changed the direction and approach of our construction. You see Hugh thought this work was too perfect, he believed we should bring the theater back to what she may have looked like say after two or three years of life. So we talked about random imperfections he should add. This strategy was next set globally for all finish disciplines. I believe this decision from Hugh is the contributing factor in her rebirth to a great theater again and why the public was enchanted with her reconstruction.

I found a young woman, Janet Hanchie, she became our artist to create the damaged and destroyed paintings. I met Janet at one of Vince DeSimone's Christmas parties. She at the time was dating Vince's accountant. She invited me to her studio. I will never forget that day the building elevator was out of order. Her studio was located on the 5th or 6th levels and with my dermatomyositis caused my legs hurt like hell. I could only walk two stairs at a time before I need to rest. I returned twice to check on Janet's progress, and both times the elevator was still not working. Yep, I struggled, you can do it, just put it out of your mind, Jack.

Janet did an awesome job recreating the lost paintings. Most of which ceiling murals located in the New Amsterdam room that area just outside the Ziegfeld Girls' dressing room. One of the photos given by the Ziegfeld ladies became Janet's template. One never knows what you can find at a party.

Disney likes to have a smaller what we call soft opening to get all the bugs worked out prior to the grand opening to allow the public to see our best face. So, we opened the theatre with the music from King David. Along the entry from the outside doors to the theater doors along the long wall to the right we placed several framed photos and articulated descriptions of the before and after reconstruction per Laura and Norm's direction.

The quests were mesmerized by the theater and the theater's transformation. During intermission the people would stand long after the call to return to the theater to see and appreciate the reconstruction story. This became a problem so the operation team removed the framed pieces. We opened about a month later in the grandest way with The Lion King. Now that is the way to open a great theater with the greatest of all Broadway shows.

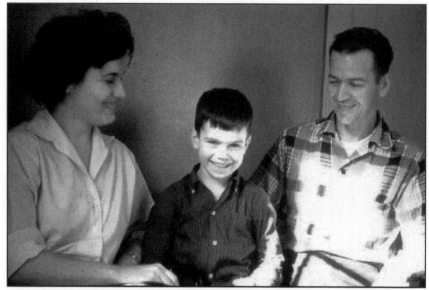

Mom, me, and Dad - beginning I have a dad.

Just 17 Me, Dad, and Paul Galuska [1971]

Linda and I – age 15 [1968]

Anguilla Marketing Center [2005]

Frank Faranda and me at Mango Dave's [2004]

Gary and me at Little Bay in Anguilla [2003]

Me, Frank Faranda, and Daddy [2004]

Vince DeSimone and Me [2013]

Jack and Linda [2007]

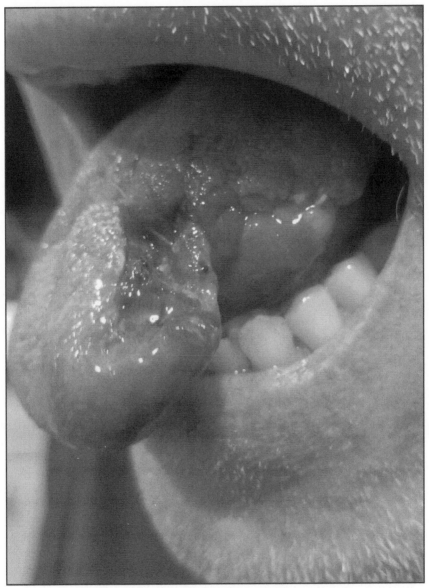

Tongue cancer the second time [November 12, 2018]

Linda and me – Thor Equities Groundbreaking [2015]

Kirby Collection … my last development [2018]

CHAPTER 18
ITS LINDA'S BIRTHDAY;
I'M HAVING A SEIZURE [2004]

About eighteen months after my stroke.

On May 11th, 2004, that lovely lady I live with, Linda was celebrating a special birthday a big one... her 50th.

As this is a significant event and most definitely a noteworthy milestone and with all that she has done to help me get back well, I want her birthday to be over the top a special and extraordinary weekend.

This year has been interesting at best, the stroke eighteen months ago is now a distant memory and most definitely in our past. Without a doubt we have put our lives back together, things are back to normal, whatever normal is ... I joke normal is only a setting on a clothes dryer. That said, we are back, I am back and life is good.

Well now, I have recovered I also have a new job that is challenging, exciting, sexy and I am on top of all the projects budgets and schedules are being met without compromising quality. Most important I enjoy what I am doing.

With the exception of Laura no one at the Kor Group is aware that I suffered a stroke. We have over 25 projects including hotel renovations, apartments, adaptive reuse condos and 2 ground up resorts in Mexico and another in Anguilla. I am back...living the good tasting sweet life.

So ... I begin planning Linda's birthday party with assistance from our daughter Ashley, we planned a party for about fifty people that will take place at our home, inside as well as outside got to love southern California weather. We create a list of friends, figure out what we need from the Party Rental

Company for tables and chairs to be placed in our yard. We decide to select the same caterer Margaritas a lovely Mexican restaurant we enjoy, who also catered our oldest son Geoff's wedding. Linda does not like surprises, so we bring her up to speed on the party and I decided to fly two of Linda's dear friends, Sandy and Lynne to California from her previously lifetime, high school days in Richmond, Indiana.

As Linda's birthday would fall on a Tuesday this year we decided to celebrate Linda's birthday on Saturday May 8th

We woke up to a beautiful sunny California day the skies were clear and blue, the temperature was significantly higher than normal.

Linda was excited for her friends to see her store named Impressions, a jewelry and lady accessories boutique. After a tour and visit I drove Sandy and Lynne back to our home, on this hot sunny day they were looking forward to swim in the pool. I left to get some last-minute items for the party. When I returned our oldest son Geoff accompanied by his girlfriend Melissa and her mother Beverly were enjoying the pool with Sandy and Lynne.

Tables and chairs were delivered to our home early that morning. Upon arrival home from my errands I started to set up the tables, chairs and get everything ready for the party. I was moving quickly after an hour or so I had most everything done. Sandy and Lynne tried talking me into joining them in the pool. As I was close to being finished, I only needed to hose off the patio I said, I would jump in shortly. I looked around and I thought all looked ready. Yep, I am done, its hot, I was looking forward to a cold beer and a dip in the pool.

So ... with the garden hose in hand I walked over to the hose bib located under an enclosure at the back of our home that supports the kitchen patio above to put the garden hose back and to turn off the water. Unfortunately, the view of this area from the pool is partially blocked by 3 large columns.

Everything suddenly changed, the back of my head got a sharp pain ... I smell burnt popcorn again.... Oh crap, that smell is awful ... slow motion ... what the hell ... a violent storm in my head, I could see myself that said this time different from my stroke, as I did not see the others in the pool. Everything started to go small, this is hard to explain. It was like looking through the wrong end of a telescope, I began to fall my legs could not support me they felt like jelly. As hard as I tried, I could not move fast enough to protect myself oh crap I thought as my legs give way and I watched me scrape my head as I slid down the side of my stucco house and fell to the ground. I began shaking watching convulsions take control of my body. Oh my, I am bouncing on the concrete pool patio floor. Another birthday and I wake up in the same hospital.

I recovered quickly leaving the hospital after three days. It is odd though you see the seizure had a different effect then my stroke as there are four days that are completely blacked out for me. Nothing to remember, I absolutely have no memories what so ever. Four lost days. It is strange; I have tried so many times to remember. They just do not exist for me. Four ... that's right. I also cannot recall anything from the actual day I left the hospital. I know I wonder too, maybe I should have stayed longer? I only missed two days at work and I believe because I was always traveling that no one noticed I was absent or realized I was in the hospital.

Dr. Shultz and Dr. Dhanda were surprised and the seizure caused them concern. I was placed on medication and advised to refrain from drinking alcohol. After three or four months, Dr. Shultz ran some tests and believed that I was doing fine again. It was scary to smell the burnt popcorn again, to black out and lose consciousness, to again similar to my stroke watch me doing this from afar and to have no memory what so ever over a four-day period.

When I returned to work the next day, I found a huge issue concerning one of our ground-up apartment developments, the General Contractor was failing badly, I made a quick decision terminating the preconstruction agreement and placing a call to Gary Hopkins a contractor who I had always received excellent results to take over the development.

So, I remember smelling burnt popcorn, falling against my home and then four days later my next memory is walking into a meeting and receiving bad news concerning cost and schedule that required a decision to change the construction team.

I was later told that Geoffrey was the first to see me shaking on the ground, Melissa called for an ambulance.

Email from Lynne: *They (the ambulance guys) were trying to get Jack on the stretcher and by then he had come to so wasn't being too cooperative but he hadn't realized, I don't think, what had happened. And then he was taken to the hospital.*

He was busy, busy getting things set up for your party and it was a hot, hot day. We (Sandy, Geoff—is that how you spell his name?—and a girlfriend of his, and myself) were in the pool. We tried talking Jack into getting in and he said he would as soon as he got whatever he was doing finished. The next thing we knew he was down on the ground, Geoff was the first I think to see him and was calling out "dad" and then was out of the pool running towards him. The rest is so much of a blur to me. Things seemed to happen so fast. The ambulance came (I think maybe Geoff's friend had called them). They (the ambulance guys) were trying to get Jack on the stretcher, and by then he had come to so wasn't being too cooperative, but he hadn't realized, I don't think, what had happened. And then he was taken to the hospital.

So now that I have written you all of this, what is it Jack is wanting? Is he wanting more details?

Yeah, I'm available both Friday and Saturday. I do have to work Saturday morning but it's just for three hours. No big deal. And, Linda, if you need a place to stay a night or more than a night you know you are welcome here. Our rooming (Tom's sister, Carol) has moved out. So, we actually have two beds available.

I'd like to have you and Mel over for dinner one night if it can be worked in.

See you soon
Lynne

Email from Geoff: *I remember it being fairly hot, I was in the backyard talking to mom's friends, Melissa, and her mom. You were doing tidying up stuff. I think I had just gotten out of the pool. I can't recall who saw you first lying down by the hose. It was Beverly, Melissa, Sandy, or me. Don't recall who approached you first either. You were lying on the ground moving, and at first, I thought you were just lying down to adjust something. When I realized you were shaking for bad reasons I turned you over, Bev called 911, and then you stopped. It's really fuzzy after that. I think maybe we just told you to lay down and got you some water. Then the ambulance came and you didn't want to go. So, they strapped you to a backboard and left. After that its blank. I think I remembered that much because*

I read Lynne's. Whatever else thoughts come to me I will send.

I have a bad memory; I don't remember what I had for breakfast two days ago.

Geoffrey Bousquet

CHAPTER 19
THAT LOVELY LADY I LIVE WITH
[1968]

We were only fifteen, merely babies, we met by chance, or did we?

On a sunny summer late afternoon in my hometown of Clinton Connect-icut, my childhood friend Jim Therault and I were walking on the sidewalk along Glenwood Road to meet up with friends for a pick-up game of basket-ball. We never made it to the game.

We noticed in the short distance two girls approaching in our direction. As we advanced one and other becoming ever closer, I could see both girls were pretty. However, one to be beautiful, the prettiest girl I had ever seen. Immediately I spoke to my friend Jim saying I have the little one. (Now: Linda hates when I tell this story. That said, I made my intentions clear to claim to choose her immediately).

It was all so innocent we began talking; I learned Linda a summer girl on vacation is from Richmond Indiana visiting her friend Cheryl Fox whose family just recently moved to Clinton. Most important I learned Linda and Cheryl had plans to go to Hammonasset Beach the next day.

The summer of 1968 was a romantic stage for Jack as this was my final summer to be a kid, a young boy of fifteen who found each and every day an adventure to appreciate life without accountability or responsibility.

Clinton is a small town along the New England shoreline whose economy appreciates the summer vacation people who come to enjoy our beaches and small-town, quaint lifestyle. During the summer months each week new fam-ilies would come to the beaches for a vacation, older girls from the cities would

187

plan a beach day so with each summer day arrived a young boy found the opportunity to meet girls. Most often the girls were older than my friend Paul and me.

Wonderful days indeed, my dear friend Paul Galuska and I partook in a summer mission to meet 100 girls before the new school year put an end our indolent life style. We spend the days at Hammonasset Beach in Madison our evenings most often together however sometimes alone along the beach road in Clinton and Westbrook Connecticut. Our notion was to meet new girls being so bold and confident to initiate the first words to reach out to strangers to conquer our young boy's fears. This practice gave me tools for my future for example I can attend a business function or enjoying an evening at an art gallery being confident to approach and talk to men and women while controlling the conversation.

That summer Linda was number 36 her friend Cheryl 37 I fell short meeting only 98 girls. I cannot recall Paul's total however I believe somewhere in the mid-eighties. Many of the girls were older already possessing a driver's license.

So, the next day with very little effort Paul and I found Linda and Cheryl at the beach just where they said they would be by the big pavilion. Linda was sweet, a bit shy, kind and of course smoking hot. Linda was that girl a boy fell in love with before they ever even met.

I cannot recall a single day that summer where Paul and I did not find a ride by hitchhiking to the beach. As we were just kids, we did not carry money so with only change in our pockets most often for lunch I ordered a coke and French fries, sometimes we might share the fries that said on occasion we found days without lunch. For a week or more Paul and I look forward and enjoyed spending our days with Linda and Cheryl. The following summer I engaged the ranks of the working world, his day being a boy behind me never to be seen again....

Linda's final day of vacation was winding down; it appeared the magical days would certainly disappear. At days end when Cheryl's mom arrived to pick up the girls to drive them home. I can't remember how it happened, that said on this day Paul and I joined them for a ride, we got out of the car in Clinton in front of Friendly's restaurant. The car stopped at the roads edge, we said our goodbyes Paul stepped out first next I began to depart the car when Linda touched my arm, as I turned back to look at Linda she asked, Jack can I have your address? So, it appears Linda is actually the bold, yep the daring one.

That summer… well I wanted to kiss Linda I thought about it, hell I thought about a kiss constantly, unfortunately I never ever tried. Linda was shy; she was sweet and I fearful to be brave. Not for a single moment did we find ourselves alone, you must understand Paul and Cheryl always with us. So the summer kiss avoided these kids, Linda and Jack would have to wait.

Gibson Hummingbird

I was just fifteen, hitchhiking to Hammonasset Beach on a summer day. A huge Cadillac pulled over, I got in and started to talk with who I believed were a couple of rednecks. The conversation turned to music; the fellows were saddened that I did not know who I was in the company of. To my surprise the car stopped and pulled to the roads edge. I was asked to follow the gentlemen to the rear of the caddy. They opened the trunk pulled out a guitar and banjo. They played just one tune. I knew the song and sang along, hell everybody knows that song. That said I did not know it was Lester Flat and Earl Scruggs. They performed at Bill Hahn's resort in Westbrook, Connecticut the previous weekend. Oh my, if I could go back to the moment. Yep, they let me play the Hummingbird. Maybe one day I will get one. They were two great gentlemen trying to impress a little kid and a most intriguing day. Isn't it ironic? I didn't have a clue concerning Lester and Earl. The TV theme song by roadside was cool. I thought the hummingbird was the most beautiful thing ever. I played house of the rising sun, I bet they laughed and laughed after they dropped me off. What a stupid kid.

Friends

Paul and I continued as friends, hell Paul and Jim (remember Jim, he was with me that day I met Linda) both were in our wedding party we remain good friends to this day, however over time our high school relationships with others compromised the bond we enjoyed that fateful summer of '68.

Paul and Cheryl became a couple, high school sweethearts a relationship that lasted until Paul graduated from high school. Cheryl a year behind us as well as Linda back in Richmond. Indiana. I dated many until the summer of my junior year when Barbara Bullock and I became a couple, a short relationship that lasted until the fall of '71 after our graduation.

With Linda returning to her home in Richmond, Paul and I continued our quest for that summer's mission. Linda became a memory; understand I did not think I would ever see her again. Linda did write to me the first letter arriving soon after her departure; from then on actually I received mail from Linda most every day. She included cut outs from magazine imagines like eyes that she thought looked like her eyes and pieces of candy or gum to enjoy while reading her mail. I began tacking items she sent often with a letter or two on my bedroom wall. I regrettably not as diligent of a writer, I however would find the effort to mail Linda a note each week. Our relationship grew through these letters, an innocent remembrance of how we began.

The following spring Cheryl was excited to tell me Linda was returning to Clinton, she would be here for a week, Linda's spring break and our spring break did not coincide so Linda accompanied Cheryl to classes.

I turned sixteen the previous September blessed to receive my driver's license on my birthday. I asked to use our family car and drove to Cheryl's home excited to see Linda again. So, imagine a sixteen-year-old boy who relates to every movie running images of grandeur through his head dreaming of the moment he and Linda see each other again. Well I imagined Linda would run to me, I to her, she jumping in my arms and we would have that first kiss. Not a kid's kiss, no not at all, I imagined a passionate lustful kiss.

I parked the car in front of Cheryl's home; I could see Paul was here as his mom's car also parked on the street. Cheryl's family home is a split level so when I knocked on the door and heard come in once I stepped inside I saw Linda, Cheryl, Paul and all of Cheryl's family standing at the upper level along the railing smiling down at me. I am not certain what Linda was expecting or how she imagined this moment to be? It all proved to be far too much for that young girl.

It went like this ... I stepped inside our eyes met. With that Linda ran down the stairs passing me running through the open door and outside to the front lawn. A moment later her friend Cheryl followed after her. I gave her a moment then followed myself. Yep, not at all what I imagined.

That spring I saw Linda at school, we went to a friend's party, interesting Linda recalls I ignored her that evening she remembers being stuck with Paul's older brother Stefan all evening. I recall a different experience. Actually I do not remember the details of that night so as you can imagine I must take her word.

I do however as well as she remembers in great detail another night, the night I took Linda parking at our Clinton town beach. Our first kiss was nothing like I had imagined and Linda well she recalls me to be a terrible Lech. With no other cars in the parking lot on a clear early evening night we watched the sun disappear along the shoreline into the water beyond. We were sitting in the car talking; I slid closer placing my arms around her holding Linda's face in my hands we began to kiss. We kissed for a while when I tried to unbutton her blouse. Please be mindful, there were only three tiny little buttons these gallant guards were located within mere inches to her neck, even if all could have unbuttoned each and all three I believe it would be impossible to realize the prize I was seeking.

So picture if you will I release a single button move on ever so patiently to the next button only to find Linda quickly securing her button to its fasten place. All the while she continued kissing me and when I released the steadfast button a second time well she moves her hand to refasten keeping all secure once again. We were two young kids making out enjoying a night of kissing in a parked car at the beach. Foolishly I planted a hickey on Linda's neck.

Linda flew home to Richmond the very next day. Prior to her trip I received several letters each week from Linda. Unfortunately I would not find another letter from Linda; well that is, I would have to wait for 3.5 years. On rare occasions I think only three or four times we talked on the phone. At the time only land lines available the cost for long-distance call was expensive, Linda most always placing the call. One night I called Linda, her mom answered, I asked to speak with Linda when her mother said, and she was not in at the moment that Linda was out on a date.

From that point forward we lost touch, never talking by phone and the letters well like I said above they just stopped. Her Indiana boyfriend at the time was none too pleased to find the mark I left on Linda's neck

John...Can I find him?

I was curious I hoped to find John Malinowski I thought maybe during the upcoming summer I could meet him? John left us he abandoned me and my mother I wanted to meet him. Who is this guy, why didn't we matter, why didn't I matter? Did John remarry, did he have more children, and do I have another brother or sister out there?

I talked with my parents explaining my curiosity. My mother was very adamant she became extremely emotional, I made my mom cry. Our conversation took on a turn I was not prepared for. My mother was fearful John and his family would hurt me, they are not nice people she wanted me to promise her that I would abandon my search to find John.

Prior to this conversation my mom never talked badly about John, actually we never talked about him. Her grandmother and mother advised her, it best to protect me as John is my biological father. So on that night I learned my mother's story all her pain and anguish and why we moved in with her parents my grandparents. My dad (Hank) was not emotional he helped my mom through her memories and got my mother back to calm.

He did advise due to the Vietnam War that it is important for me to understand it is in my best interest to remain registered in school, however if I still want to meet John he would help. Now understand my mom was terrified I would develop a relationship with the Malinowski family. I decided I would find John this upcoming summer, as I was so very curious. I just did not talk about him or future plans again with my mom.

One night during the spring of '71 my senior year of high school while I was at my girlfriend's Barbara's home my mother called her house. This had never happened before, when I got on the phone my mother said please come home right now. There was no hello... just please come home right now Jackie. I questioned her asking what is wrong. Again she said I need to see you Jackie, please come home right now. As you can imagine she startled me. NEED yep that is an interesting word I kept running need through my head, need what in the hell is going on, something is definitely wrong?

Well now I came home immediately only to find my parents waiting for me with my mom standing at our front door. I entered our home seeing my dad sitting at the kitchen table he wave to me and holds out a chair, my mother and I taking a seat to join him. It was all so mysterious my mother reached over and took my hand in hers, she being the first to speak, Jackie I have something to tell you, bad news. I am not certain how you may respond. My mother continued to tell me, Jackie I received a phone call from John's sister. John suffered a heart attack it was very bad he did not make it. Jackie John is dead.

So I finally meet John, at his funeral with my girlfriend Barbara joining me. When we arrived I was surprised, although pleased, to find my aunt Gail (my mother's sister) sitting in the small funeral home lobby waiting for me. My aunt Gail stood as we entered giving me a hug whispering in my ear saying I am here to make sure you are ok. My aunt Gail was always there for me. Gail pointed out my Malinowski grandparents as well as John's sister on the far side of the room sitting at a sofa and chairs organized in a corner just to the right of John's casket.

I stepped to the casket with Barbara at my side. I could hear the room buzzing saying with banter all at once … that's Jackie, look at him, he is all grown up, with yes that must be Jackie.

So in peaceful repose lying in a casket, well I saw John for the first time. He looked so very young. I thought I will never know him, or why he left us. We knelt before the casket with the buzz continuing in the background. My mind continued to wander. I took Barbara's hand we stood. I guided Barbara to the corner now just a few feet away, when I approached the Malinowski's I said you must be my grandparents? We all talked for a while, I learned John never remarried, he was a heavy equipment operator living in Maryland, and most important to me he did not father additional children. I found the conversation to be pleasant however not warm our discussion was just strangers conversing. Like people talking about the weather or maybe getting directions to a restaurant … just meaningless words. I felt a hole, no emotion, no concern … well nothing from them. My aunt his sister did smile when she spoke at one point she touched my arm. I did however ask for my grandparents for their address.

About two months later we were attending a wedding for my cousin in Massachusetts. My grandparents' home was just a half hour drive. I told my mom I was going to visit them, she desperately tried to hold me back saying, that is not a good idea Jackie. I do not want you to be around them they will hurt you.

Barbara and I drove to their home they lived in a poor unkempt neighborhood. We walked to the front step and I knocked on the door. My grandmother opened the door. I said hello, I hope this isn't a bad time I apologize we were attending my cousins wedding nearby, I wanted to stop by to see you guys as I would like to get to know you . I hope this isn't an imposition. My grandmother shook her head vehemently saying, you are not getting anything from me, go away. The door slammed shut. I never saw her or any of the Malinowski's again. My curiosity disappeared with the close of a door.

Bike crash 1971

Sometimes you get lucky. One summer afternoon I was riding with my friend Jim Therault. Jim was in front and we were enjoying the day riding fast, crazy fast. So … to set up the story: Jim was on a Honda dirt bike, me on a Yamaha street bike … (you see my bike was about an inch plus lower to the ground (or maybe Jim was just a better rider?) on a right sharp hairpin curve my foot peg hit the asphalt the foot peg was ripped off my bike my bike went up in the air, spun 180 and I landed with my right arm and leg trapped under my bike. I used my free hand holding the handlebar steady to keep my bike from flipping again. So I slid for what seemed forever. Fortunately on the side of the road was a small pile of sand about a foot and a half high a remnant of the previous winter's sanding of the road. That allowed an eased stop. Jim saw all in his rear view mirror. He was surprised and came running to find I was fine just lots of road rash my right pants leg ripped to shreds and hurt pride. Be mindful Jim and I were NOT wearing helmets. I was lucky, my bike more damaged than I, however that was an easy fix.

After a couple of days my arm and leg became badly infected. Late one night I knocked on my parent's door. Come on in, I walked into my parents room they already in bed. Hey dad I have something wrong with my arm, look at this. With that my dad flew out of bed what a seemed to be a single bound landing inches before me, He started yelling are you crazy, I am going to cut that bike in half. He cleaned up the scrapes taking small pieces of asphalt out, applying a liquid bandages to seal the wounds. The next morning I was fearful he destroyed my bike. To my surprise she was untouched. The road rash finally healed a couple months later, actually while on my trip around America.

The draft, instead I take an adventure

August of '72 a year after high school graduation I was working at G&H precast for my dad's friend Don Gustafson. During the year I also attended night classes at Middlesex Community College. While at work in the late morning with the radio playing in the shop, the concrete had been place in the forms for about an hour and now I was finalizing last steps to allow the concrete to cure. I was listening to the military draft. Remember the Vietnam War? The radio program was calling the draft, the second to the last draft for that War. Now on that morning events fell in place that changed my impending future, my life was about to embark on an adventure that would set the course for my destiny.

The military draft worked like this ... by random a date would be selected in my case September 27. Next a number selected ranging from options of 1–365. So when I heard September 27 called out in the distance on the radio. Well now I walked closer to the radio which was on a shelf at the opposite side of the precast concrete shop. About fifteen feet before I approached the radio the man speaking on the radio said September 27th /336.

Holly crap, did I hear that right? The man on the radio repeated September 27th /336. With that I took off my apron folded it and placed it on the shelf, I reached for my tools and cleaned them up for the last time. Next I jumped in the air yelling yahoo while clicking my heels in flight. Charlie Chapman a coworker in in his early forty's asked what in the hell was wrong with me. Charlie was the hardest working man I ever worked with he worked harder than anyone that I ever met.

You see I was elated joy was running through my body like a race car. The draft board would first call all 1s to be drafted and so on running up the numerical order. I, however, knew from the previous year's draft they did not reach 300 I believe that year's draft ended somewhere around 280? With that I was most certain I was free from being drafted.

The overhead garage door to the shop was kept open allowing air to move on hot summer days as the shop humid and the air thick a strong smell of concrete curing in the forms. I could see Gus the owner pulling up in his truck, as he began walking into the shop I approached Gus and advised I will be quitting, I want to travel around America. I told Gus about the radio program, I went on to say I know my draft number position and I am certain I will not be

195

considered for this year's draft. I am free from the military; I want to see what is beyond our little town. Gus a crusty old guy who seldom smiles a guy who is far taller man than me placed his hand on my shoulder looking down at me he said, I will miss you, your family will miss you Jack, have you spoken to your dad about this? I replied, I just found out my draft number minutes ago so no, not yet. Gus told me, I was fortunate. You can't quit. What he went on to say next stunned me, you have been a good employee you are a hard worker Jack, I will lay you off, if you quit you would not be eligible for unemployment.

That night Paul and I began making plans for our trip, we could go in Paul's 62 Plymouth we discussed mounting a rack off the back bumper to carry my motor cycle a 72 Yamaha 350, however Paul's old Plymouth not the best in shape we knew it better for my bike to remain behind. At first it appeared we were merely being excited kids however by night's end I was certain our adventure could be realized.

The next night Paul talked about James Bougie our high school friend joining us. Jim who had just returned home from Norway where he was a foreign exchange student wanted to come along.

I approached my parents telling them what we are planning, I found the conversation to be easier than I imagined, my mom did not want me to go, and my dad thought the trip to be a fabulous a great learning experience. My dad joking that he wished he could join us.

Over the next week plans finalized, maps purchased we each had one small bag and sleeping bag. We carried extra gas and water in the trunk. My mother purchase 100 pre-stamped blank post cards, ones which I could place a note and drop in the mail so she could know me to be fine. I would write her a letter on 5 or 6 cards however I would mail only one at a time in random order so she would require receipt of all to know where I was when the letter was written. Paul's mother gave him a dozen rolls of film for his camera. Paul would mail the film home; his mom developed same this was an awesome treat for us to see the photos when we returned home.

Our trip around America and parts of Mexico was an absolutely awesome experience. Jack grew up he saw the world beyond his backyard.

Each day we smoked pot (kept our stash hidden in a huge flash light) when the car radio was compromised the three of us would listen to a cassette player Paul brought along for our trip. There are a couple of songs which always take me back to our adventure. Today when I hear these songs, Long Cool Woman in a Black Dress by the Hollies well that song as well as the next two Rod Stewart's Maggie Mae and the Eagles take it easy will fill my thoughts with fond memories of our trip, We drove through Winslow, AZ unfortunately we never saw that girl my lord in a flatbed ford slowing down to take a look at me. We did however play that song as we drove through Winslow, Arizona.

We traveled most often on secondary roads transferring to highways at night as highways often have rest stations; we slept at the rest stations. Me, well I slept on the rest station roofs or on the hood of Paul's Plymouth, the windshield wiper at the passenger's side fell off one day the during a rain storm the wiper post well that thing just rotted away while we were driving, so this provided an acceptable flat surface with a nice incline for me to sleep. Jim always slept in the back seat Paul in the front seat. I however did not care to sleep in a stuffy car.

Once we paid to take a shower at a YMCA in Salt Lake City as we had camped in the Teton Mountains the prior week we smelt awful like mountain men. At restaurants we only drank water, a coke being far too expensive. I only ordered a hamburger or pancakes. Eating on the road we each held odd preferences. Jim enjoyed canned sardines I thought they smelled disgusting, Being on the road Paul and I learned to purchase day old donuts at the time fresh donuts went for ten cents each, usually we offered a quarter to purchase a 24 donut bag of day old donuts. We both like glazed donuts so glazed it is. Can you imagine hiking through the mountains for a couple of days eating only stale old glazed donuts from a bag that got squished just an hour into our hike?

Sleep on the ground…never

Once upon a time while we were traveling in New Mexico we met other kids who also were on a road trip. Actually we met many while on the road doing the same as us. However this night was one of those moments I will never forget. That evening we shared a couple of joints with our new found friends. When it began to be late with sleep in our eyes we decided to turn in for the night. One of the guys we met slipped into his sleeping bag he had left the bag on the ground from the previous night. About a minute or two after he in the bag this guy began to scream. Loud piercing terrifying screams, he was thrashing around the ground doing his best to exit his sleeping bag. We all could not understand nor could we figure why he was acting so crazy. I thought it may be due to bad drugs… oh my gosh was I wrong.

When at last he found his way out of his sleeping bag, the boy stood taking huge strides while he continued screaming and began jumping and lurching from one place to another like a mad man who had lost his mind. We all stood there flabbergasted totally dumbfounded without a clue as to why and what was wrong with him. That is until…imagine this…the boy now to be a good ten plus feet away from his sleeping bag when … his sleeping bag began to move, and it kept moving that is until a rattlesnake came slithering out of his sleeping bag disappearing in the night. Now it was clear now we understood. The boy never calmed down. His head kept jerking back and forth. He was in a bad place. One of his friends ran to a payphone near the rest station bathrooms he called 911 for an ambulance.

We … Paul, Jim, and I moved on with our traveling adventure at daybreak. I never knew if the boy recovered. Of course, we never saw them again. I did however file lessons learned from that boy and that evening; Jack you must always rollup your sleeping bag, Jack never ever leave it on the ground. I took the lesson a step further I never slept on the ground, that night was my first time to sleep on a secure and safe height like a rest station roof.

My future remaining nights on that trip I imagine I looked rather silly to others who camped near us. You see before I entered my sleeping bag I would always open it unzipping the bag completely turning the bag over to shake it around over my head to next close the bag just to be certain rolling it up tight while feeling for anything inside. Finally … well now I am ready to unzip my bag again and make my way inside.

Twice we slept at motels once in Idaho the other while traveling through Las Vegas. Things changed at Yellowstone. Due to the bears we were required to sleep in a cabin for a week at Yellowstone State Park. Jim became very sick with a high fever he remained in bed most days Jim was not getting better; our logic well we decided to travel to Mexico where it is warm certainly we believed Jim could recover away from the cold damp snow. It worked Jim got better so our adventures continued on. That is when he began drinking apricot brandy. For the remainder of our trip Jim kept a small bottle in his back pocket.

Early in our trip we stayed at Jim's sister Jane's college we learned how magical and accommodating Colleges and Universities could be. We also stayed at Jim's girlfriend Carry Powel's college.

I thought it amazing how absolutely easy it was to meet people; if we were attending one of these schools, I imagine it may be more difficult to make friends and meet new people? Girls are far more compassionate than guys they also would become totally enamored with these three guys without a care in the world being free and adventurous to travel around America. I bet if we had been students the girls would not even give us the time of day.

So we look for girls in a group, make our introduction next begin to talk about our adventures traveling America. With an introduction behind us well first things are first we want a place to take a hot shower and most girls were on a food plan so a hot cafeteria meal was enjoyed, party with the girls and their friends that night and last find a bed to sleep.

Should we stay or should we go? As there are three of us a simple vote cemented our next move. If two wanted to stay we stayed if however two preferred to travel on we packed up and got ready for our next day's adventure checking a map for the next place to catch our interest. Life was so easy and simple it would not matter if we slept all day although we always jumped up and made the most of our escapade. I have so many stories we met many fascinating and interesting people, found ourselves in a couple of jams, saw many amazing places we met people from all walks of life. I could write about our adventures for days. I believe it best to hold those stories for another book.

We meet again

September 14, 1972 we drove into Richmond early in the afternoon and found Linda's home on the other side of town. The three of us knocked on the front door, her mother Geraldine (Jerry) greeted us she asked if Paul was Jack? I stepped up closer to the door and replied I am Jack; so nice to meet you is Linda home?

Jerry invited us in she advised Linda was at work however she will be home soon. We visited with Jerry for a short time when Linda's car pulled in to the driveway. I was very excited to see her again; I saw her getting out of her car from the kitchen window. Linda was even more stunning then I remembered an absolute beauty. I started to walk to the front door to go outside and greet her when another car pulled up, the guy in the car called over to Linda. Jerry said oh my gosh what is he doing here, that is a guy she dated, I do not believe Linda will be happy to see him? After a minute or two the guy drove away. I later found he wanted to take Linda to a Peter Paul and Mary concert or maybe it was a Cher concert I guess it really does not even matter.

Linda's parents were exceptionally nice, Harold and Jerry invite us to stay at their home, Jerry made dinner that night we slept in our sleeping bags on their living room floor. After dinner Linda took us for a drive to show us her Richmond hometown. We were walking downtown somehow I cannot remember how Paul and Jim ended up a block or so away from Linda and me. I stopped took Linda in my arms and kissed her, just a single kiss. A kiss I had dreamed for, a kiss like no other a moment forged in time, one I will never forget. Linda melted in my arms. We walked through the streets we talked all night we discovered each other. In those moments we began what had escaped us in the earlier day when we first met tonight to be so very different. Linda was no longer a little girl I guess I grew up as well.

A couple of hours later with Linda's sister Cheryl her parents, Paul and Jim already turned in for the night we found ourselves alone standing in her kitchen. I kissed Linda once again. I wanted to do more, I fought myself, one long passionate kiss…this kiss cemented our future.

Trip continues, I want to see her again

A couple of times I sat at a picnic table at a rest station or camp site where I wrote Linda a note. Our trip beyond fascinating the adventure at times a challenge. One day we found ourselves in California the next week Mexico, the circle poised a return back home to Connecticut with travels this leg though the southwest. I wanted to see Linda I hoped to spend some time and actually get to know each other. When we were a week or so from Indiana I mailed Linda a note advising I plan to stay In Richmond for a while.

Jim and Paul thought me to be crazy. When we drove in to Richmond I left the trip gave my goodbyes to my pals at Linda's home. I stayed with Linda at her home for two weeks. I fell in love. I who was looking for something most anything that I believed could give me balance, strength reason well something to forge a foundation for my future. Maybe a lovely place- possibly a job? Nope… I found destiny, mine with that lovely lady I came to live with.

Time to go home; I flew back to Clinton on Allegany Airlines with transfer in Pittsburgh. While my second leg was on the tarmac rolling to depart for takeoff merely feet from the runway, the pilot asked if a Jack Bousquet was on board to please press the attendant call button overhead. Well me not being a worldly traveler only my second time on a plane the first when I just 4, the stewardess advised I was on the wrong plane I should have departed to change planes.

Remember 1972 was a far simpler time. Our plane navigated to the edge of the tarmac a moment later two trucks each with stairways attached approached my plane. Minutes later another jet airplane came to a stop near my parked jet. I depart the jet walking down the stairs only to cross over to the second stairway boarding the correct plane for my trip back home to Connecticut. I smiled as I turned to depart down the stairway thanking the flight attendant waving goodbye when the pilot made an announcement he said, well folks we will continue momentarily we just needed to get this senator's son on the right plane, all in the cabin began clapping.

Christmas night 1972 I said goodbye to my Connecticut home with my family standing on the front step waving goodbye, while my mother cried as I drove away. I drove through the night in a snow blizzard following a snowplow through most of Pennsylvania visibility so dismal I got off track following the snowplow north to Eire, well out of my way however making a correction arriving at Linda's home December 26th the next day just after noon.

Nut dream

Days prior to my Christmas journey talking with Linda by phone telling her about my silly dream, a nightmare about nuts. You see in this dreadful dream one that at the time appeared so true, I was never with a girl only a nut. Barbara for example walnuts in ice cream I do not care for nuts in ice cream. DJ peanuts, Dawn pistachios, the girl from the Sage Allen store unfortunately I no longer able to recall her name almonds and Linda well she was cashews.

So, imagine if you will, during my nightmare I would find myself at a department store purchasing a bag of nuts, next taking a seat eating the nuts cast me in motion with a particular girl dependent on my nut of choice. Realizing at dream's end, I had never been with a girl only nuts. The realization apparent topped my dream off you understand my dream a terrifying realization as this nightmare ended with me running to Linda's kitchen only to find cashews no Linda at her house. .Cashews is my favorite nut.

So, the day after Christmas as I pulled up to Linda's home with Linda standing at her front door. I ran form my car we hugged we kissed to my surprise when we walked into her kitchen I laughed when I saw a huge bag of cashews sitting on her mom's kitchen table. I know just a silly dream however my dream made certain Linda to be cashew.

Harold and Jerry ... let their daughter go

I searched every day for a job; times were hard a recession gripped America. Richmond fell hard as five of the seven large factories closed with even smaller facilities closed jobs moving to the southern states. Hard times hit Richmond. After a couple of weeks searching for a job, I decided it best to travel back to Sarasota, Florida as I was certain I could get rehired at my old job with Paver Construction building retirement homes. Without a source of income, I could not continue to stay in Richmond, her parents so nice and accommodating that said I did not feel comfortable being jobless while having food and shelter provided, I felt weak, I saw myself to be small.

All packed and ready the night before I departed back to Sarasota, Linda was sad tears filled her eyes. Her parents are conservative folk very conservative. That said, what happened next will always reinforce my belief for their love and adoration for their daughter.

Linda's mother Jerry requested for her daughter to step in another room they went to Linda's bedroom. The two women sat on Linda's bed and began talking. Unfortunately Linda has a very poor memory she recalls her conversation with her mother to be short nonetheless rather simple, Linda does however recall a story her mother told her when Jerry was young a time when her mom felt stifled a missed opportunity. When I asked Linda about the actual story details well she has no memory other than her mom telling her she was not allowed and held back unluckily her mother now years later wonders what if?

I know what you must be thinking; wouldn't it be nice for Linda to be able to recall the details regarding this pivotal mother/daughter moment? Yes I agree, however the emotion and the careful poise from her mom remains locked in holding Linda's memory which is what I believe most important. I for one will never know what Jerry missed I do however give great applause with thanks to Jerry as this mother did not want for her daughter to look back to feel the same. Unfortunately Linda's memory does not allow her to recall the details. I questioned was your mom talking about another man Linda's response, hell no she was merely reciting a lost opportunity which at the time her mother believed held her back.

Linda does remember clearly her mother being overly concerned with what people my say If Linda joins Jack with the two off to Florida. Linda replied, mom I only care what you and daddy think. Now this is crystal clear for Linda's memory. Please understand, Linda was not planning to leave with me. Her mother closed their conversation by saying, Linda you will do what you want.

A short while later with tears falling from her face Linda return back to the living room she sat on my lap with a hug and kisses advising she will make the trip with me in the morning. Jerry returned to the living room standing behind her daughter.

Linda's dad Harold who was away from the home that night at a meeting Harold a leading member of the Optimist Club, the Conservation Society, and the Odd Fellows lodge was at one of those events. Please be mindful, I applaud her mother's courage her compassion you see Jerry took the initiative earlier in the evening to call her husband, the two talking by phone, her parents confirming their decision prior to Jerry's parent's approval she blessed on Linda. The next morning Linda's parents did however ask their daughter to find a motel in Sarasota. Linda and Jack began our journey together January 10th, 1973.

When we arrived at the one-bedroom apartment that I shared with Jim, Linda and I reorganized the furniture. We moved one of the twin beds into the walk-in closet. Yes, Linda and I started off living in a closet sleeping on a twin bed. Today I believe Linda would rather stick needles in her eyes than sleep on a twin bed with me. She called her parents and told them there were no vacancies at the motels.

The ring story ...

January 26th, 1973 Siesta Key Beach access #9 Sarasota Florida. Call to mind, Jack is young, just nineteen at the time a mere eight months older than Linda. We were babies. His plan to ask for Linda's hand although he believed it to be romantic, his plan was actually silly.

I asked the sales lady at the jewelry store to wrap a small box of jewelry cleaner placing a perfect ribbon and bow on top. We drove out to the beach that evening parking at access #9 walking the path to our favorite beach Siesta Key.

After a short walk we found the sun disappearing on the water, I stopped turned to face Linda placing my arms around her waist, I reached up to hold her face in my hands looking down into her eyes saying I love you sweet baby... we kissed on the beach in the moonlight.

Moments later I reached for that small box in my pocket. I placed the box in Linda's hand at sunset our favorite beach my perfect plan working to precision. After Linda tore away the paper, opened the box, and saw the small jar. Please understand, it was too dark for Linda to see the label. Linda said you are not painting me naked on the beach. I was surprised Linda did not immediately see the jewelry cleaner realizing an engagement ring would follow.

For those who do not recall the '70s, she thought I gave her body paint, knowing I was a letch. Well, now I was young and yes, a bit stupid. I said no ...look here. I took the ring from my other pocket, I asked her for her hand. Linda cried out YES, we hugged again on the beach kissing in the moon light. I never got on one knee. We were married in June.

January 29th Linda would be returning home back to Richmond our time together just a couple of weeks, I wanted her to go home wearing a ring. I did not have enough money to purchase her ring I was short $130... I had to become creative, very creative... so in addition to my savings I borrowed $50 from Linda; she thought the money was for construction tools. I also was in possession of $80 worth of American Express traveler's checks. You see a couple of months earlier I received $80 in replacement traveler checks only to find the misplaced checks I believed to be lost in my suitcase. I used the original checks to pay my portion of rent. The checks received from American Express were now worthless. I believe I could use the checks and when American

Express called I would say ... oops I am so sorry. I was paid once a month believing by this time I would receive another pay check, I would be able to reimburse American Express immediately.

My plan worked, on my next payday two days after Linda flew home I went directly to the bank advising the manager while reimbursing the $80 that I had used the traveler checks only to realize later my mistake. I apologized. All was forgiven. The manager thanked me for responding to remedy my error so quickly. Yes, a simpler time indeed, I do not believe in today's fast pace of electronic instant recordation my plan could work. No not likely. Was it wrong, do I have any regrets, well it was corrected, intended to be corrected, was it wrong, most likely. Regrets NO, none.

In late March I flew to I Indiana a quick weekend trip, we met with the Pastor of her Lutheran Church. We both were surprised as her pastor did everything possible to talk us out of marriage.

We were married June 23, 1973 in Richmond Indiana at the Rothermel family's Lutheran church. Six weeks prior, Linda purchased an airline ticket to return to Sarasota, ten days before our wedding we drove to Indiana. We celebrated our honeymoon in the Pocono Mountains at the Mount Airy resort. After our honeymoon we drove to my parents' home in Clinton, Connecticut. My parents held a wedding reception party in their backyard for my east coast family and friends well over 100 guests. As only my immediate family, Cousin Michael just six at the time, my grandparents and Aunt Gail being able to make the trip to Richmond. We arrived in Sarasota a week later moving in to our new apartment.

Linda added up the actual days we were together totaling just sixty days before our wedding day, please note, this included the time when we met that summer of 1968. As I sit here writing hard to believe we will celebrate our 48th anniversary in a couple of weeks.

Linda worked as a commercial teller at the Sarasota National Bank, me shortly after I returned; I got a promotion moved up from the retirement villas'... I worked for Paver construction a developer/general contractor creating an upscale single family housing development called Glen Oaks, a custom home development adjacent to Bobby Jones Country Club. At nineteen I was responsible for final construction meeting with the new owners at completion providing any punch work to close out construction.

Creative Financing

Six months later in an effort to provide a more favorable lifestyle for Linda, earning far more money I became a drywall finisher, Jim Therault my childhood friend taught me the drywall trade we became partners. To ensure we always had work, we worked for three drywall companies (piece work $1.65 per 4 ft. x 12 ft. Board to hang, the same amount to finish). We approached the three firms requesting they advise us of any small jobs that they would normally pass on. Within a years' time we found ourselves competing with the companies we previously worked for. We were just nineteen with no financial backing we found it difficult to compete. I tried to secure several ninety-day notes; the process took so long with business moving quickly the loans always failed. I found it impossible to compete with no financial backing. I even grew a mustache to appear older.

By pure magic one day I received in the mail a credit card, the first of its kind. Bank America Credit Card known today as Visa. The card fascinated me it provided an immediate $300 cash credit; billing took twenty-eight days with first payment due in another twenty-eight days. So virtually a two month cash grace period/ interest free funds.

We decided to collect several credit cards first visiting all the Sarasota local Banks also Saving and Loans. Next we began a journey south along the tamiami trail (Tampa to Miami Hwy) stopping at very bank/savings and loan. While checking in to our motel I noticed at the rack displaying vacation options for example pamphlet brochures for Florida Gardens or Ringling Brother Museum. However also occupying the vacation brochure racks we found several credit card applications from Nebraska, Ohio, Missouri and many more. Great fortune struck like lighting once again. No need to continue our journey I grabbed every application from all the out of state banks returning to my apartment.

That evening sitting at my kitchen table I applied for all the credit cards. Less than a month later approval received, I now was in possession of a small stack of credit cards with immediate credit available just under $5,000. I wanted to pursue work Jim was not as ambitious so we each elected to follow our own path. With one very important stipulation, in the event one of us secured a big job we would partner working together. With everything else we worked on our own.

My credit rating soared it was high, in addition my available instant cash request available was constantly increasing over $10,000 due to my quick and timely payment practices. Now I can definitely compete. I found I could use 75% of my cards to make payroll and or material purchases, while using the remaining 25% of credit availability to make my monthly payment due in two months, flipping the cards until receipt of payment from the General Contractors.

I would go to the bank at 1:30 as the banking day starts at 2:00, giving me a bonus day before interest commences. This was well before computers so I carried a note book keeping track of all cash advance as well as payments for each card. I decided not to use Linda as my teller for these cash transactions depositing the money to my checking account as I was nervous this practice may not be, quite kosher. One day while transferring another deposit the teller said you know Jack you can phone this all in and I can have it all ready for your signature when you arrive. Again Jack gets lucky.

I imagine many others took advantage of the bank's credit card protocol, twenty-eight days to be billed with additional twenty-eight-day requirement to make payment. As in short time a couple of years later the banks began charging interest immediately upon request for cash credit card purchase. I even bought a 1973 Yamaha 650cc motorcycle on a card flipping two cards every two months until I sold the bike; never using a cent of my money for the purchase. I had a friend who recently graduated from dental school. After telling him about my good fortune to start a drywall business with credit cards he learned how to purchase his dental equipment for his new office.

On Friday afternoons I drove to the work sites a to hand deliver checks always with cold beer in the trunk of my rag top 1970 Malibu. One day Jim and I stopped for a beer at the five o-clock bar. This bar always had telephones at each table (remember time did not invent cell phones for another decade) so now workers could meet me Fridays at the bar. Linda always worked late on Fridays not closing until 7. Most Friday nights I would pick up Linda after work we would enjoy dinner usually at the Ponderosa Steak house. Sometimes we went on to enjoy lots of drinks and dancing at the Shrimp Boat.

With only one car the 1970 Malibu rag top Linda would ride her bicycle to work each day with her dress in a back pack. Linda never complained she was a trooper. I worked long hours six days a week often setting up lights when dark fell to further my progress, sometimes adding a short day on Sunday's . I felt bad that I worked so much so we took off to Miami Beach for a lovely weekend at the Doral Hotel. We enjoyed the good tasting sweet life, we joked years to come that our dinner that Saturday night at the roof top restaurant… well the bill was $45. To put things in perspective our weekly groceries cost $20. We learned to work hard we played hard.

Chapter 20
Georgia Tech January 1975...
Graduation Jun 10, 1978

In an effort to gain information to broaden my horizon of the construction industry, strengthening my general background for my drywall business, I enrolled at night school attending Manatee Junior College in Bradenton, Florida.

I chose three classes, a Methods and Materials course to further my understanding of basic construction, a Specifications Writing class to learn technical aspects of the construction business and most valuable an Architectural Design course to learn how to read drawings. My logic... if I could learn how to draw and detail, most definitely I would learn how to read and understand Construction Documents.

I designed a single-family home where I created a complete set of construction working drawings. The fireplace with the supporting chimney was my challenge, lessons learned, my professor advised the smoke would linger as my math and detailing was flawed. The design articulated a large living room comprising a two-story elevated sloping ceiling with a grand stair leading to the second story including an open elevated walkway providing a majestic view below.

Interesting more than thirty years later, when I purchase my home in California the home holds this identical two-story design aspect with a majestic view below. However, the view of choice here also looks out to the valley below; we are located on the top of a small mountain.

Who is he?

Previously I never cared for school actually I not the best of students. I never did any homework, and I did not know how to study that may sound amusing. I had to learn how to study (what is important and why) I would be happy just getting C's; however I enjoyed these classes most important I gained valuable knowledge. So, working most often six days each week while attending night school two nights was draining. I came home from work one night late in the evening I sat on our living room floor watching Linda prepare diner. In merely a matter of minutes she found me a sleep lying on the floor.

That weekend an October Sunday Linda asked if maybe I would like to do something different, maybe find an easier way to make money. I talked about how I wish I could build great and important buildings. That afternoon we visited the local Sarasota library researching engineering schools.

I told Linda how at work the other day while taking break enjoying a cigarette standing on my stilts looking out the window of a high rise condo when I saw this guy walking around the site with roll of drawings under his arm usually with one or two other people who were dressed nicely definitely not construction workers. How he would stop every so often and call people over, I watched him unroll the drawings while pointing and talking with the workers standing around him.

The next day I saw him again, so his time I removed my stilts as quick as I could and ran down the stairway moving outside searching for this mystery man. I saw him in the parking lot; he was placing the drawings in the trunk of his car.

I had to talk with him I ran navigating through the exterior construction dodging pitfalls before he leaves. I approached the man I said hello I am Jack Bousquet drywall finisher working here. I reached out and shook his hand. I told him I had been watching him how I was curious. I went on to ask who are you and what do you do are you the owner? The man in his early forties smiled and said; no I do not own the development. I am the owner's representative. I make all the decisions for the owner. He went on to talk about preconstruction how he managed the design effort providing decisions and direction to the architect and engineering team. He talked about the difficulties securing zoning rights and the building permit. The man continued with details about crazy risk and the pressure his position holds, that he can never actually be away from work. He must always make himself available. I was fascinated, I believed this man to have a dream job.

So now I became more curious. I asked how one does, hell I actually said how can I get a job like this? He asked if I was good at math, he went on to say I would need a college education engineering or architecture. He also advised I suggest you take a couple of basic business courses as electives this will provide a well-rounded education it will make you smarter than your competition. You will see and understand the bigger picture. It's about real estate development not construction son. I am so grateful for his time his guidance at that moment he provided the key that changed my life. Most important I am glad I made the introduction, my awkward questions made to a complete stranger. As I watched the man drive away, yep I began to dream to dream big.

Miracles can happen

That afternoon at the library Linda and I talked about me going to school full time, how she could work to put me through. We would have to change our lifestyle we would have to scrimp. Linda helped me select five options to further my education. Finalizing the application and writing a compelling attachment letter advising why Jack should be accepted. A week later all applications deposited in the mail, so ... will I be accepted, will I get a response? Maybe I'm foolish, maybe just a dreamer, maybe a fool?

We chose five options for the main reason they all did not require an application fee ... the University of Connecticut as this school was close to my parents' home, Perdue as this school being close to Linda's parents' home, George Washington University, Georgia Institute of Technology and Kansas. They all possessed good programs that said Perdue and Georgia Tech great programs. However, I chose Kansas as I believed Kansas would be the only school to accept me. To my surprise I received a response from all schools I was accepted to all with the only exception denied by Kansas. Isn't that special?

George Washington was far too expensive, the others looking for me to attend the following September. However, Georgia Tech advised I could start midyear that January 1975. I was fearful to wait for September what if I change my mind? I am impatient so Georgia Tech it is. I knew the song, I so excited for such a prominent school with traditions and a rich history to accept me, I could not wait to begin my studies.

The Pen

I being so very excited called my parents to tell them our good news; I got accepted to Georgia Tech we are moving to Atlanta. My dad said, no you didn't, Georgia Tech is a difficult school you cannot be accepted there, JP you are pulling my leg. I replied yes I know what you are thinking Dad we were also surprised, actually I was also accepted to a couple other schools. Georgia Tech sounds amazing and I can start in a couple of months, this coming January. Jack he said I am certain you must be mistaken read me the letter. So, I motioned for Linda to give me the Georgia Tech letter, I told Linda he does not believe me. Linda handed me the acceptance letter with the two of us smiling as I read the letter to my dad. He said, oh my gosh the world has gone crazy JP that is wonderful, what an opportunity; I don't understand it, but wow. I told him I composed a touching letter about how I never excelled at school until enrolling at a Junior College receiving all A's taking courses to help me further my knowledge for my business. I am fascinated with the classes I hope to become an engineer or possibly an architect. I want to provide a better life for my wife and our future children. My dad laughed and a said, JP you have always been a good bullshiter. You never studied or cared about homework, you are in for a rude awakening, you are going to have to work like you never did before, you will have to work you butt off,

Hmm ... about a week later a package arrived by mail a gift from my dad. I opened the box to find a case holding a Cross mechanical pencil, the mate to a mechanical pencil where a Cross pen should be was missing. I found a small rolled up note in its place, Curious I opened the note reading... if you graduate you will receive the pen. The pen and pencil set are kept in the original case and box as a reminder to the challenge and accomplishment. After my dad's funeral while we were all sitting at my parents' home with friends and family reminiscing, the Cross pen/pencil story was my last story to share.

The argument

My freshman year we paid out of state tuition. I knew it would be absolutely impossible for us to continue this way; the cost was far beyond our means. I did a lot of research, seeking strategies and supporting protocol to allow us to pay in state Georgia tuition; at the end of the 1976 fall quarter, I became eligible to petition the Board of Regents for in state tuition.

When I entered the small board room at the administration building to petition my case I found six other students also petitioning for in state tuition. I was scheduled last. I watched all six students before me fail, one after the other rejected, yes quickly turned down.

When it was my turn I took my place at the small podium standing where the others failed before me, I began by addressing the group of five sitting about fifteen feet in a perpendicular line in front of me at a long opposing table. I thanked them for the opportunity to speak and saying my name. I stepped away from the podium and approached the regent's table. The previous students argued that they were Georgia residents I decided to take a very different path.

As I approached the regents' table holding a small folder containing various documents, I addressed the group advising about a year ago my wife and I relocated from Sarasota Florida. I expressed my excitement and gratitude advising I believe it a privilege to be a future Georgia Tech graduate.

I placed on the table in front of the farthest regent to my right while continuing to his left a Xerox copy of the regents in state definition articulating while the page highlighted in yellow also circled in red ... a student may if approved pay in state Georgia tuition after one year being Georgia resident. Continuing to address the group without pause next I placed a copy of our electric bill saying my wife and I live at the Royal Coach Apartments off campus as evidence here is our electric bill. Next here is our rent bill with accompanying lease agreement documenting our residence over the past thirteen months see right here as I pointed we occupied our apartment in December, I continued to place documents of evidence along the table in order saying here I provide my wife's paystub she is employed by Trust Company Bank where Linda works as a teller, next placing our income tax return advising we paid Georgia state income taxes and expect a slight return… yep see right here on this page, I place canceled checks proving we, Linda and I, not our parents paid for my Georgia Tech tuition last year, we paid for Georgia Tech required books placing several checks, I placed our vehicle registration from the state of Georgia while next putting mine as well as Linda's Georgia driver's license in the hand of the last regent. I turned walking back to the podium where I began my argument minutes ago. Holding my arms our from each sides saying …if you believe my wife and I are not Georgia residents I implore you to tell me what state other than Georgia you believe we reside. I continued to say do I need to summarize calling out once more the trail of documents I placed as evidence in front of you?

Standing facing the regents with my arms still out to the side, I saw smiles I heard lots of chatter as they whispered to one and other. Maybe a mere couple of minutes after my last word the gentleman sitting center stood saying well done Mr. Bousquet, you have the regent's approval for in state Georgia tuition one third the cost of what you paid your freshman year. Congratulations

We did what was needed to make ends meet. We lived in a basement apartment off campus. In my junior year we made the change we upgraded for a view moving in the same building to second story apartment. We were on food stamps we ate well for a short while. That is until Linda got a raise unfortunately her slight boost in salary pushed us over the income limit, the food stamps became history. Times were hard surprisingly Linda and Jack were happy enjoying some of the best years of our life.

Dave Bazar to the rescue

Georgia Tech is my greatest accomplishment; business would be a snap by comparison. Like most things in life, I did not do this alone I had help; you see Linda gave me confidence that lovely lady believes in me even when I lacked confidence in myself. I was good in sports I was good with girls, I struggled with school. If not for Linda most likely I would have given in, missing out on my education.

Without a doubt another helped me when I needed help the most. My very first day, my very first class scared the crap out of me. I was certain I had made a huge mistake coming here. Can you believe my first class, a five-credit-hour course, was calculous? Talk about a subject that was over my head. Damn I had no idea what was going on. I, being away from school for so long, did not remember basic algebra. Actually, I never really held a grasp for algebra in high school. I got a D, so I took the class again the following year receiving a C. Yep, I did not put in the effort.

Dave Bazar was my dad's dear friend, a teacher he worked with at my high school. Dave, who at the time was in his early twenties, not that much older than me. Wednesdays at our home was Italian night, my mom would make ziti, spaghetti or maybe lasagna. My dad was known for bringing a young teacher someone he admired home on Italian night. You understand Wednesday supper was certain to have more than enough food already prepared for our family to share. So, one night my dad shows up with Dave a new math teacher. After that night we saw Dave often. He also joined the monthly Friday night teacher's poker game the other teachers all my dad's age, he enjoyed drinking beer, and he and my dad loved their conversations… mostly politics. Dave became my dad's closest friend.

After just one week, I knew I would fail so I decided to drop my Calculus class. I did however sign up for an Algebra class. Please note math at Tech starts with Calculus, my Algebra class was a refresher course a tune up I did not receive any credit for the class. I found eight other students in my algebra class, they as clueless as me. The class was extremely helpful I learned algebra. At the quarter's end, yes Tech is on a quarter systems not semesters. The courses are quick very fast one must be smart be focused this practice allows Tech to force more to their student education. The next quarter well the week prior I received a letter from my dad. My dad wrote about his conversation with Dave how Dave advised him willing to tutor me. Well now how in the hell can this work Dave a couple thousand miles north?

It all worked out perfectly Dave tutored me Tuesday and Thursday often for more than an hour each night. You see Linda employed by Trust Company Bank as a teller at one of the branch bank locations received approval from her manager with a key to access the main Trust Company offices downtown after hours. So each and every Tuesday and Thursday night for the following year and a half Linda and I would drive downtown, check in with the lobby guard take the elevator to one of the office floors. Linda would spend the time talking with her parents and friends by phone, me calling Dave. At the time Trust Company Bank used watts lines for long distance calls. The bank paid a monthly fee for long distance calls. That lovely lady I live with received approval to access the watts lines.

What a class guy giving up his nights twice a week for months to tutor me. At the beginning of the quarter while the other students purchased a calculus book Jack purchases two books, mailing one to Dave. My professors moved quickly, Dave taught me step by step.

I did okay, not great I received a C for the first and second calculus class I was delighted to receive a D yes a passing grade for my third and final calculus class. A 67 and one of the higher grades as many failed, you see this is the course Tech employed to weed out the students. We were told one student actually aced the test we all hated him.

The grade for my final calculus class was based purely on the final exam. We were tested periodically however the grades not counted just posted on the bulletin board in the hallway. The tests merely reflected our progress for learning. I failed the class once and dropped it another. Finally I passed with calculus now behind me I most certain I would graduate.

The final exam included only three questions. Students were allowed to bring 3 books and our calculator. Thank God for calculators I hated using my slide rule.it was awkward I had difficulty reading past two decimal points. I believe only one student used his slide rule?

The first question explain perpetual motion, good start this was easy as one of my three books I chose to include a physic book. So Jack starts off with a correct answer applying 33.3% towards my grade. The next two questions regrettably I had no clue none what so ever…the questions were beyond difficult actually light years over Jack's head.

The second question we were given information for a six sided glass box two brass balls in side 1/8 inches apart. The question if you release the vacuum in the box instantaneously how long for the brass balls to touch? I still do not know if the brass balls would even move. The third question was even more complicated. We were given basic plans for a rocket ship. The question, if the exterior skin of the spaceship is inessentially cooled by ten degrees what is your acceleration and what is the velocity? As you can imagine I was lost without clue.

We were given two hours for the exam, after merely fifteen minutes several students began walking out of the class. I could hear disgusted comments moans and groans. I was scared I began to panic. I have answered only one question so 33.3%, me thinking I failed a second time. What am I going to do I will have to drop out of Tech; maybe I can go to some the other university?

I cannot give up I must exercise any and all efforts available, unfortunately all I had was drive, knowledge to solve the questions escaped me. I composed calculus formulas for speed, acceleration, volume, and a couple of others randomly around the two daunting questions doing my best to make the effort appear positive. I hoped to show my professor I knew calculus I just do not comprehend how to use same to solve his questions.

Then I saw an extra credit question sitting precariously at the bottom of the page, this question worth ten points. If I can solve it, that would give me a 43.3 % still a failing grade but I was not willing to give up.

I saw ... Five symbols in sequence the question what is the next symbol? The question also provided a hint.... If you are able to find the next symbol you can sit here for an eternity coming up with symbol after symbols.

For the next hour I did my best to solve his extra credit question. I looked for space relationships, sexual connotations I even turned it upside down right next left hoping that might enlighten me and I had nothing absolutely nothing. The third symbol looked similar to the infinity sign however little else was apparent. So, Jack thought, what class is this ... a math class stupid then I thought what goes to infinity. Well, some say a piece of string; however, I never understood why. Then I said to myself only numbers go to infinity Jack. With that I immediately saw the answer. I looked around the class the test was killing most everyone.

But Jack knew the answer to the extra credit question he was smiling I felt like my mother just found a playboy magazine under my bed. The symbols were just numbers 1, 2, 3, 4, 5, with the mirror image in front of each combining the numbers creating the questioned symbol. The mirror image combined to the number made each look so very odd not at all like simple numbers. For example, the number 1 had a small slanted carrot on top with a solid line at the bottom; this should give you an idea of how the basic numbers were disguised.

For the remaining test time I composed a note on the top of my exam for my professor.

As you can see, I did not do very well on your test. That said you can also see I do understand calculus. I bet I am the only student in class who solved your extra credit question. I do not want an A, not even a B or C.... However, a D would be mighty nice.

I have a puzzle for you to solve, my puzzle also comes with a hint.

You are walking down the road when you come to a fork in the road, one direction will take you to fame and fortune, the other to sickness and poverty.one of two brothers is standing there, one of the brothers always lies the other brother always tells the truth. What is your question to figure out which way to go?

I run to the math building worrying about my grade feeling sick to my stomach, me believing I failed again. When I found my student number with my grade a 67 on the bulletin board in the hallway well I jumped in the air yelling yahoo. My physics professor was standing nearby talking with another facility member that quarter I received a B in his class; he approached me and asked Jack did you get an A in calculus? No I replied I got a D, I passed I have completed my calculus requirements. However a hand written note followed my grade post saying see me.

I walked quickly finding my professor sitting in his small office. When I knocked on the door he immediately saw me. Jack did you like your D? YES I replied, thank you. I asked if any other students solved his extra credit question. My professor replied, no, Jack, you are the only one, actually I have asked that question for several years you impressed me you are the only student to know the answer.

He went on to provide the correct answer for my puzzle... Jack concerning your puzzle, I go the opposite way, you ask which way your brother would say to go. Knowing the one who always lies would tell you the wrong way and the brother who always tells the truth would also say the wrong direction as his brother always lies. I asked him how long it took him to figure out the answer. His response surprised me, Jack I could not figure out your puzzle, I was at a wedding I asked all at the table for help, my twelve-year-old niece gave me the answer. My professor was a good egg.

Calculus required for my other courses was basic actually simple. Most important I understood calculus a tool that was necessary and required for my two physics classes, as well as my three engineering science and mechanics classes (the branch of mechanics concerned with bodies at rest and forces in equilibrium) of statics, of dynamics and finally of deformable bodies courses. Yep, engineering of liquid, this class was another challenge. I received B in the physics classes and C in all three engineering and science courses. I am eternally grateful to Dave, he changed my life. Dave became my friend in addition to my dad's friend.

I bought Dave a painting as gift which accompanied a thank you letter, looking back today the painting not very impressive, I possessing little or no money my gift lacked value it being well ... junk.

Many years later while developing my final project in Houston Linda and I traveled to Albuquerque her dream to see the balloons. Our trip absolutely spectacular, my Uncle Richard and Aunt Sandy joined us the second day making the event even more exciting and fun.

Years ago, Dave retired and moved to Albuquerque, Linda and I shared a lovely evening with Dave and his wife Linda that first night. My career being so much more than I could have dreamed for. I thanked Dave again as it would have been impossible for me to graduate without Dave's help. We spent the evening reminiscing about my dad, Dave and Linda learning of my stroke. My wife and I telling stories of how I overcame the issues. Interesting Dave's wife Linda also previously employed at the Morgan High School, she a teacher in my dad's business department. A lovely evening indeed, I hope to return one day with my grandchildren to see the balloons in flight and introduce them to my friends Dave and Linda Bazar.

Jack learns to think and it is outside the box

As I advised earlier, I never ever studied in high school. I had to essentially learn how to study. Learning how to study and managing my time was dire, as I found my classes to be most challenging. I find it critically imperative to employ a strategy; I must concentrate on Chemistry, Physics, Engineering Science& Mechanics, and Calculus. I must learn not merely memorize, once I came to this this realization well everything changed for me. I began to do better, much better. My other classes cannot deserve the same effort or I will fail.... A valuable lesson learned that I continued in my business life. For example in business I compartmentalized task in three categories, first what has to be done what I must know in detail, second what should be done what I need to know at a cursory level and third what I can merely understand and hope it doesn't come back bite me in the ass . Finally, never start a task unless you are certain you can finish it.

Well Jack studied for hours in hope to do well on my first Architectural History test; unfortunately my test scores a 72 so very close to a D. I must complete three Architectural History classes. The classes commence with the Egyptian Mastaba finish with today's modern architecture. I was certain I could not give up my time from more difficult courses studying as I had for an Architectural History test again.

About 100 students sit in a huge auditorium for fifty minutes three times each week. Our professor on the stage he teaches history with three plus photos of each building on the huge projection screen behind him. Huge question here for Jack, how can I do better, I cannot put in the same time or effort studying as my other classes would suffer. So I ask myself, what is important, what will be on the test, what knowledge and understanding is necessary, what is my strategy to succeed?

Each test, which covers at least fifty to seventy-five important historical significant buildings over a three-week period per test. Our professor would display the three plus slides previous shown from his earlier lecture for only five buildings. Five questions to answer the questions for all five- name the building, why was this building important then and why now as we approached modern architecture he also asked for the architect's name?

Yep, you are correct. Students were tested on only seven to ten percent of the buildings. If for example two answers are incorrect well the student gets 60% correct a fat D. However one could receive partial credit for example unaware of the building's name however grasps the significance of the architecture. We were allowed to use our notes for the test, however typically the class averaged a lowly 43 sometimes as high as a 57, so our grades always based on a curve. Now can you imagine the anxiety concerning the final exam, again just five buildings? My strategy functioned much better than I imagined every reaming test for all three classes I received a high grade with not a single minute of study time....

The subsequent class after a test while handing out our grades our professor would start with the class average then advise the curve amount. Moans and groans replied from the students. On one occasion in our third and final course he added, no matter how difficult I make the test that lover of architecture Jack Bousquet does well. At the course series end I was asked to be his teaching assistant, as honored as it was I turned down his request. You see I developed a strategy to succeed in his class, I did not believe me to be worthy to be his assistant. Interesting years later in business life I traveled to Europe two to three times each year to purchase marble and granite for my developments. I saw many of the historical building in person recalling his lesson for same.

I believed it best to keep my method close I could not divulge my strategy as I needed study time for my more difficult courses, I could not risk loose lips. Remember students have access to their notes so while all of us diligently writing as quickly as possible, I added additional information to my notes. Another key that escaped the other students, however these facts ever so clear. Our professor very proud that each and every slide photo he, our professor was the photographer. Lecturing to his students he would often articulate how he took the presented photo talking about the day and moment, a proud accomplished world traveler. So I could not afford the risk I kept my strategy to myself because the strategy dependent on his photos. If for example he substituted a library photo of the building in question, Jack's strategy fell apart.

My strategy so simple, I bet you could figure out my plan with a little time and effort. I created a chart, my chart including objects typically existing in the background of any photo. You see, I charted everything in a photo that is with the exception of the actual building. For example cars, people, birds, clocks were definitely my favorite.

So imagine a photo being displayed, I see a red Renault in the left corner, I search my chart for red cars that narrows the options to say five possible choices, next I see a woman in a short skirt in the center that could narrow the options down further for this example say two options, finally looking to the photo's right I see three birds in the sky. Ta-da! The correct answer Chateau de Chanbord, my favorite castle.

When I walked up to the castle so many years later on a stone purchasing trip I told the contractor Bruce Roberts my colleague and good friend the estimator who was traveling with me, this one had three birds in the sky as I pointe over there, my friend Bruce laughed.

If for example a photo included a clock I knew the answer immediately, license plates also helpful for immediate verification however most often the numbers not clear. I believe only two photos held a clear image of the car's license plate. My chart not perfect I learned to make it more simple and keep my penmanship tidy, also during a test while searching to limit options I had to stay calm photos only up for a short time, Jack stay calm, make notes- what do you see in the photo, you can come back to this later, Jack you do not want to compromise the next photo, pay attention stay calm. After the stroke similar practice /strategies enabled me to overcome my issues.

Our professor also required a perspective hand sketch due every Monday. Jack can draw with a straight edge that said I suck at drawing a three dimensional isometric sketches. One Sunday night while I was drawing Linda said, that is terrible. I replied yes it is, this is hard, let's see you do it smarty. To my surprise Linda made it look great, a little shading here some hard lines there. Wow, so the next morning I turned Linda's drawing in. Later that week when my professor returned my perspective drawing he said, nice to see your sketch work improving, this is so much better Jack. Unfortunately for Linda the remaining Sunday nights occupied her time sketching the required perspective. As you might expect Linda was so very happy when I completed the course series.

Solar energy competition 1977

Each year Engineering Universities across the country compete, a different challenge each year, this year's competition ... Solar Energy, design and construct a solar energy collector panel.

One afternoon while entering my cost estimating class, my professor met me at the door he requested I remain after class as he wanted to talk with me about something important. Well now my head began to race immediately I believed something was wrong, however I could not for the life of me figure it out. I was nervous, I was worried.

After class he began talking about solar energy, my professor asked me what I thought about it. I advised I find the concept fascinating unfortunately I know little if nothing about the notion.

He went on to tell me about this year's engineering competition. He elaborated to convey the strict rules, how this is a student competition, that professors are not allowed, actually forbidden to participate. He advised the Ga. Tech team could use my help. I believed he was nuts, I began to tell him same. My professor laughed, Jack if you join the team you will receive nine credit hours towards graduation. Well now that got my attention immediately, nine credit hours are three typical classes and classes I would not be required to pay for. Okay, I'm in … why me I asked? You worked construction before enrolling at Georgia Tech. I believe you possess practical skills that will add value for the team. I began to laugh; I am a drywall finisher a guy who walks around on stilts. My professor said they meet at 3:30 in the shop at the industrial engineering building, I told them you would stop by today. That is in less than a half of an hour I guess you knew I would go? Now he started laughing. Why do you think I can help them? Well Jack the team cannot figure out how to keep the apparatus upright, stop it from falling over, I believe you can figure it out.

I met the team that afternoon as requested. I found a very odd group of extremely smart students. Much smarter than me you must know these guys are brilliant, inventive so smart. They explained the engineering logic for the collector, well it to be way over my head and they knew it. Big attitudes, not the kind of guys you can go out and have a beer with, I also found them unfriendly they all came with that proverbial smart stick up their asses.

I had an answer to their dilemma in less than fifteen minutes; I was added to the team. As smart as they are, these students missed the basic logic of how to support weight. Their problem, the apparatus must fit in the back of a pickup truck for transport to Washington, DC to be set up on the National Mall for competition. What they designed was far too cumbersome to fit in the truck, or too flimsily to provide adequate support for the solar collector.

My idea, for the primary superstructure we design a tripod as three legs can easily support the collector. The legs include piano hinges this allows the superstructure to be easily folded and compact for transit. The foundation we use three resin rectangular low profile cubes with a cap on top for water to be added a small drain plug located on the bottom. I knew form my physics class water weights a little over 8 pounds per gallon. So this weight which could be added after transport which would provide a stable mass and ballast to support the apparatus above.

We just needed to do some quick math to figure out the dimensions for the rectangular cubes and the most optimal height for the tripod, while being light and easy to store for transit in the back of the pickup truck. The tripod was now simple to set up; easy to take down. So we had a plan the team spent the next several weeks finalizing the apparatus.

I was not invited to go to the competition, told funds were not available. I did not care; I did not expect to make the trip. I am so thrilled for the nine credit hours. Please be mindful, the student who designed the solar collect deserves all the credit. He used oil as his base liquid and a design that would cause the collector to rotate following the sun in one 180 degree pattern. I never understood or could comprehend his design; I just made sure the apparatus did not tip over.

A plaque hung in the physics building. Years later, while in Atlanta on a business trip for the Anguilla resort I decided to visit my school. The plaque was now no longer in place. I did purchase a Georgia Tech T-shirt at the book store visited my old mail box and enjoy an afternoon of memories while walking the campus.

CHAPTER 21
THAT NIGHT I WILL NEVER FORGET [1983]

Linda and I were looking forward to the birth of our second child, with each pregnancy we waited for the moment to see if a girl or boy would bless us. While I was constructing 3HC / Gulf Tower Ashley decided to arrive six weeks early.

Geoff, our firstborn arrived October 11, 1980. I remember the moment Linda told me she was expecting. I returned home to our apartment after a week working on site at the time. I was developing the Brown & Root satellite office complex in Lombard, Illinois.

Linda was waiting for me on our balcony. As I pulled in to park my car Linda ran down the stairs, we lived on the second story apartment; she greeted me as I was exiting my car. With a huge grin smiling from ear-to-ear Linda placed in my hand a little book with its blue and green hard cover Linda's favorite colors; she made a LOVE IS book, cutouts from the newspaper. At first, I was confused, trying my best to figure out why Linda was so happy and what the meaning of these cutouts meant? I flipped the pages reading each LOVE IS cartoon message wondering what is going on. The pages totaled at least ten to twelve. I did not have a clue. Why is she so happy, what is this book of cartoon cut outs for? Until I turned to the final page reading LOVE IS having your first baby. I looked up Linda with tears of joy in her eyes, I took Linda in my arms we kissed I held her tight, I spun Linda around. I asked we are having a baby? Yes, JP, isn't it wonderful? Life is good Linda and Jack are having a baby.

Now the pressure was on to find a home, our home, a place we own. We purchased a brand-new townhome in a development just minutes from Brown & Root's new office headquarters.

We decided to start our family just a couple of weeks before I returned from my trip. Nine months later Linda delivered Geoff without any medication the moment touching the moment blessed. Before Geoff was totally out in our world, we not knowing if the baby a girl or boy, Dr. Meyer lifted Geoff's head ever so slightly so Linda could see her babies face the image for me standing to the side surreal, as if our new baby and Linda looking at each other getting acquainted for the first time. Just prior to the final seconds before birth, Linda cried out that's my baby; I got tears running down my face. A second later we knew our first child a boy. We named him Geoffrey Normand Bousquet his middle name chosen to honor his grandfather, my dad.

This birth for Ashley very different set of circumstances from what we experienced with Geoff. Ashley birth terrifying, stressful we had to pray, I needed to hold our grip on hope.

We purchased our new townhome in her second trimester. On this night in the middle of the night, Linda woke me. She was crying however amazingly I found Linda in control.

Earlier she pushed her sleep away maybe twenty minutes before she woke me. Linda knew something to be wrong. Linda got out of bed and went to the bathroom once there she started bleeding badly. Linda phoned her doctor; he would be waiting for her at Memorial Hospital.

Jack, wake up something is very wrong. We must go to the hospital immediately. Linda's words moved the sleep from my eyes in seconds. I jumped out of bed got dressed grabbed Linda's overnight bag; we started driving to the hospital, well first we drove to Lil's home she took care of several babies including Geoff at her home during the day while Linda worked at IBM. That night Linda called Lil advising her that she was having a problem asking if Geoff could stay with her.

When we pulled into Lil's driveway, she came out from her door to greet me, taking Geoff in her arms Lil saying she will be sending prayers Linda's way not to worry Geoff will be in good hands.

Imagine two kids worrying actually scared to death about their baby while on a ride in the dark of night to the hospital. The drive at this time of night took me less than a half hour. Fortunately when we arrived at the hospital Linda stopped bleeding.

Linda's pregnancy six weeks early we found her condition called Placenta Previa; in addition, the cause of Linda's bleeding was due to her placenta pulling away. So now we could relax with Linda in safe hands at the hospital. We wait and wait nothing changes fortunately her bleeding ended. That said her doctor wanted Linda to remain at the hospital, Linda asked me to go home and get her some clean panties and her night gown.

I stopped to pick up Geoff on my way home it was great to see the little guy he brought calm back to my difficult day. Once I arrived at home just as I stepped through the door, I heard our kitchen phone ringing. I set Geoff down on the floor in our dining room with some of his toy cars; I answered the phone to find Linda on the other end. Jack, it's even worse; it is real bad this time; you need to hurry back; I'm scared; it's too early; they are going to deliver the baby now; hurry, Jack, hurry.

I called Lil I explained the circumstances the best a man can in this situation and asked if I could bring Geoff back to her home.

I sped this time traveling at rush hour to the hospital arriving in the nick of time finding Linda with tears we hugged. Everything was happening fast doctors and nurses moving like clockwork. I was introduced by Dr. Meyer to the neonatal team, a doctor and two specialized nurses as well as his nurse assisting with the C-section delivery and the anesthesiologists.

I was not certain the hospital would allow me in the operating room. Her doctor told me to hurry to follow him; he went on to say as we were walking along the side of Linda's bed rolling towards the operating room this will be different Jack you can make Linda feel safe, that said you must stay out of the way, do you have any questions? I responded no. I quickened my step in a matter of seconds we entered the operating room.

I stood at Linda's left side as this appeared to be the only place available for me, her doctor began to examine her. The anesthesiologist communicating with Linda's doctor while he placed a bag on the stand to Linda's right and connected the drip line to the IV port previously placed on Linda's arm. Across the small room the neonatal team began preparing items on a small table for our baby. I held Linda's hand I kissed her forehead she was so very scared. Her doctor told Linda in a calm soothing voice not to worry he will be taking great care of her and advised she will be going under soon, seconds later Linda was out.

This experience definitely different however I was impressed with Dr. Meyer's calm he continually talked to me and the others I became reassured all would be fine. I watched him cut… in my amazement I saw him lift a baby girl from Linda's belly. Immediately the neonatal doctor moved in place taking our daughter from Dr. Meyer's hands and quickly returned to the table on the other side of the room joining the two nurses.

I now watch Linda's doctor stich her up although I find myself constantly glancing at the neonatal team working on the baby girl, our baby is not crying they keep trying to get her to cry. I know something is very wrong I begin to feel panic I ask Dr. Meyer why she isn't crying is she all right? He does not answer … I hear her cry very faint a weak sound and the neonatal team simultaneously start cheering. Seconds later the neonatal team departs with our daughter taking her to another room.

My focus returns back to Linda. She has lost a lot of blood; they are giving her new blood. Dr. Meyer and his nurse tell me the baby is in good hands Linda needs to rest. Another nurse rolls Linda's bed to a recovery room. I follow I sit next to Linda's bed holding her hand she is not responding to me. Twice I walk down the hallway I look through a window and watch the neonatal team hovered around our daughter. The second time one of the nurse's smiles at me and waves giving the ok sign. She steps towards the door I move in the doors direction to meet her. She says your daughter is breathing however she is taking more breaths per minute than we would prefer. I ask is she all right? Yes, your daughter is a fighter; we just need to give her our attention.

I thank her and walk back to see Linda. After ten or so minutes, one of the nurses in the recovery room, says Jack your wife is heavily mediated she has no idea you are here I suggest you go home I know you have been here for well over twenty-four hours get some sleep come back in the morning. I ask, She is making moaning sounds. Is Linda okay?

Linda is fine. We're giving her Pitocin this is causing her to have more contractions the contractions will help stop her bleeding. AIDS was a new issue something we were not aware of at the time, donors not at the time checked for AIDS; fortunately, Linda did not receive any bad blood.

I walk down the hallway to see how our daughter is doing. I look in the window. I see her, I see a nurse, and she waves and smiles.

I find a bank of pay phones. I planned ahead; my pocket is full of quarters. I call my parents first. Next I call Linda's parents. I told them we are at the hospital. The baby decided to come early it's a girl. That said Linda is under anesthesia she does not know yet. Linda lost a lot of blood; however, she is doing fine; there are some complications our daughter was born today April 11, 1983. They heard concern in my voice. I tell them I will call in the morning to give them an update.

I walked back to see Linda and told the nurse that if she wakes, please call me; it does not matter what time. I left the hospital and drive home; it is too late to bother Lil so I return home without Geoff.

Like déjà vu…yep, it happened again, as I unlocked the door to our town-home the kitchen phone was ringing. I ran to the phone, a woman told me they are transporting the baby by helicopter to Herman Hospital. They do not know what is wrong, your daughter is struggling. A baby that was at Herman did not survive so that bed is now available for baby Bousquet. Jack you must go to Herman Hospital now as you we will be required to sign documents for baby Bousquet to be admitted.

Songs always bring me back to a specific point in time. On this night as I was pulling into the Herman Hospital parking lot, I could see a helicopter overhead positioning to land on the roof. The music playing loudly on car cassette player was Lunatic Fringe by Red Rider. To this day when I hear Lunatic Fringe it will always take me back to that precise moment.

Standing in the parking lot looking at the helicopter navigates to its final position. I thought about the building taking an elevator to the roof next trying to locate the roof access; when I noticed the fire escape just a couple hundred feet from where I was standing. I ran to the fire escape jumping up I grasp the bottom rung of the ladder I pulled the ladder down. I climbed the ladder arriving at the first platform, in minutes I was up on the roof. I know what you are thinking. I often ask the same to myself. Jeez, Jack why didn't you just go into the building.

On the roof I was immediately approached by hospital staff. I pointed to the helicopter and asked if that is the baby girl from Memorial Hospital continuing to tell them I am the father. I believe I need to sign some papers.

Yes, that is Ashley's helicopter. Please come with me. Now, I smiled, yep, my step quickened, my step with a little bounce returned. You see, I never told anyone baby Bousquet's name, you see, I was certain, I knew Linda told them her name. I knew Linda saw Ashley. We chose Sean for a boy and Ashley for a girl. I signed a thick stack of papers in seconds.

I later learned Dr. Meyer was concerned our baby might not make it through the night he wanted Linda to see her baby so he demanded they first bring baby Bousquet in an incubator to Linda so she could see her daughter and reach through the hand port to touch her.

Linda's memory, please understand, she was on lots of drugs, recalls Dr. Meyer showing Linda her daughter and Linda reaching to touch her baby saying Ashley. Linda recalls this moment being foggy. I applaud Dr. Meyer for his effort for his kind heart he was a good man.

The Herman Hospital neonatal clinic had bed stations for fourteen babies including Ashley. Each station manned twenty-four hours by a specific nurse. A small bed for the nurses at each station placed adjacent to the incubators in a sea of medical monitors, tubes, lines, and equipment.

I could visit Ashley anytime of the day or night. I was fortunate with Lil looking after Geoff. Lil provided me an opportunity to visit Linda and spend precious time with Ashley.

Linda had started to potty training Geoff, so picture if you will me driving a little Honda Accord a potty seat on the passenger floor with Geoff doing his duty, me pulling over to the side of the road to dump it out saying good job Geoff. I was not as diligent as Linda with the potty-training endeavor; she had to start all over when she got home.

Linda was placed in a room by herself a small pink heart cut out from pink construction paper with Herman written in the heart's center taped to her door. The heart advised all staff Linda had a girl and the baby is not with the mother, the baby is at Herman Hospital. The memorial staff, kind and considerate, provided Linda with a room to herself not to be sharing the room with another mother whose baby is on the premises.

I would visit Ashley early each morning before work, leaving work early first a visit to Linda, then drive across town to see Ashley. I ate at the hospital. Linda delivered Ashley on Monday April 11, 1983 Linda came home leaving Memorial Hospital the following Friday afternoon.

The doctors at Herman Hospital could not determine what was wrong with Ashley. Ashley's nurse argued with the doctors. She was certain she knew what was wrong with Ashley. The doctors believed the nurse was wrong and overreacting. Ashley's nurse was a young mother named Peggy, and she saved her.

I believe in fate. You see I believe I was supposed to meet Linda that day when we were just fifteen. Yes, I believe it prearranged. I also believe fate stepped in to play her hand to ensure it was Peggy's first day back to work after maternity leave, fate made certain Peggy was Ashley's nurse.

Peggy worked in a most stressful situation, her responsible for so many newborn lives. While pregnant she continued to work. When she delivered her baby, a little boy, her newborn son became a patient in the very same neonatal center.

Peggy's baby was the very first baby to live with this condition ... an infant form of pulmonary hypertension. The baby is born without the valves opening and the other not closing to the heart and to the lungs ... the infant continue to function as if the baby is still attached to the umbilical cord. The explanation to me from Peggy; when Linda's placenta broke away rupturing, foreign particles started floating in the amniotic fluid; if the baby swallowed these particles the baby would be poisoned. So as a defense mechanism the baby continues as if the umbilical cord remains providing oxygen.

Peggy kept telling the doctors this baby Ashley is suffering from the very same condition as her son. As you can imagine it being Peggy's first day back after a historical saving of her son believing the Ashley baby has the exact same condition, well Peggy's thoughts were discounted. The doctors believed Peggy to be stressed, incorrect and they were certain she returned back to work too early.

Ashley taking over 125 breaths per minute, she was failing. Early the next morning around 5:30 a priest came to see me just before I was about to go home to shower for work. The priest in his mid-forties I found him kind and sincere, the priest approaching said I understand you are catholic. I responded yes. he went on to say the doctors called me your baby girl Ashley is very sick, they do not believe her to make it through another day. Jack I can give your baby her last rights I am here to help you.

That was the first for me to understand the gravity of our Ashley's health. Without much thought actually little thought I responded, thank you father however that will not be necessary I am not ready to give up. You see I believe by doing so Ashley would lose hope.

I know what you are thinking however maybe it was me who needed to cling to hope. In the next 36 hours I was asked twice again if I wanted my daughter to receive last rights. I clung to hope.

I was not privy to any discussions or conversations so I do not know the details. One of the doctors told me Peggy's story and how she is the one responsible for diagnosing Ashley's condition the day Ashley turned the corner.

Fortunately, fate allowed for a bed at Herman Hospital Neonatal Center, fate having Peggy as Ashley's nurse and most important fortunate the doctors finally listened to Peggy. Yep, like I said earlier I believe in fate. Our daughter Ashley is the third baby to live with that condition, the second at Herman Hospital.

Ashley had an IV in each hand two in her chest and two in her forehead. Two IVs at a time that required replacing every 4hrs. The monitors showed her stress and failing whenever the IVs were changed, she did not like being stabbed with a new needle. I could reach into the glove on the incubator hand port to touch Ashley. Peggy showed me how to read the monitors and advised this touch relaxed Ashley we would watch her numbers go down. I would touch her face for hours, this helped she became relaxed.

As a preemie baby Ashley's hair extended from her eyebrows covering her head. After two or three weeks, the hair between her eyebrow and scalp disappeared exposing her forehead.

Ashley was placed on a ventilator. She suffered two pneumothoraxes, a condition where air escapes her lungs being trapped in her body cavity. I watched both pneumothorax the procedure required immediate resolve the procedure happening at her neonatal station. Each left a scar, one minor the second more severe. Ashley was stressing out taking so many breaths well over 125 each minute, this causing her brain to bleed one side a level 2 the second time on the other side measured level 3, fortunately, neither at level 4. Ashley was weak losing weight and not getting better. The doctor placed Ashley in a medically induced coma for forty-eight hours. This they hoped would allowed her valves to open and close without her experiencing more stress, longer than forty-eight hours could cause her not to wake.

On the fifth day for Linda a Friday she was able to leave Memorial Hospital, Dr. Meyer lectured us advising Linda must go home do not take her to Herman Hospital to see Ashley she needs to rest. We did not talk about it ... in the car I began to drive in the direction of Herman Hospital our townhome in the opposite direction. I said to Linda you want to see Ashley? YES was Linda's response we continued to drive straight to Herman. I parked the car, ran into the hospital returning with a wheelchair I found in one of the hallways.

I introduced Linda to Peggy. Linda met her daughter she placed her hands in the gloves and touched Ashley by way of the hand port. We kept her visit short. We picked up Geoff on our way home. The next day her parents traveled to Houston and upon arrival, I took them to meet Ashley.

Her mother Jerry helping Linda recover by doing house work and preparing meals. Most important this opportunity provided Linda significant daughter mother bonding time by just talking being together. Harold often accompanied me when I visited Ashley.

I only witnessed one other, a young single mother visiting one of the babies at the Neonatal Center. I asked Peggy why, where are the others? Why does no one come to visit these babies? Peggy advised it is hard for them to be here many came once they usually do not return and some we never see.

After 48 hours elapsed Peggy joined by Harold and I stood around Ashley's incubator watching her, hoping to see Ashley wake to see some movement. The three of us stood there for what seemed like an eternity. In absolute silence we saw nothing no movement I was beginning to worry. What if she does not come out of the coma?

When I said did you see that? Ashley moved her finger ever so slightly; did you see that, Peggy? We all looked closely at her hands and seconds later, we all saw Ashley move a finger this time. We cheered. I hugged Harold; next we both hugged Peggy. Ashley was born weighing 5 lbs. 2 oz. She now was at 4 lbs. 8 oz.

Two weeks later Linda held Ashley for the first time, she fed her a bottle just 1 ounce and it took over a half hour for Ashley to finish as she still weak. The very next day Peggy advised Ashley has turned the corner you can take your daughter home tomorrow. Peggy said once your daughter was the sickest baby in the center. Look at Ashley now. She will be going home with her mother. I believe it was Linda's, touch a mother's touch received by her baby that turned the corner; of course, the medically induced coma provided the initial step for Ashley's recovery. We are so fortunate for Peggy. She saved Ashley.

The doctors told us Ashley needs to be tested at several intervals to make certain there is no damage from the process that saved her, a schedule provided for Linda to return to the hospital for the tests. For example, they told us possibly she could be blind due to high levels of oxygen, with all her x-rays a concern that she may not be able to have babies. After ten months all tests were negative our daughter now chubby and healthy. We were so happy when Ashley got her first period. I wanted to take her out for an ice cream sundae ... Ashley thought her dad a bit odd.

That said, the doctors also did advise she might have learning difficulties due to the brain bleeds. Linda asked what kind of learning difficulties. The doctor responded she may have difficulties with math.

What kind of math? Linda asked.

With complicated math like algebra, the doctor responded.

Linda smiled and said, Hell, I never understood algebra, so that's not so bad.

When Ashley was in kindergarten, we told her story to her teacher as we wanted to confirm Ashley was progressing normally. We learned a huge lesson, the teacher got weird, giving our daughter special attention. We wanted Ashley to make it on her own; we wanted to give her the opportunity to fail as this would provide her the chance to succeed. So, we never discussed Ashley's story with a teacher again.

Interesting Ashley received the better grades then her brothers; she loved to read she excelled at school. In Ashley's senior year of high school she received an award from the Secretary of Education for scholastic excellence. Ashley did not want to attend the award ceremony she said everyone will think I am a brainer. Geoff responded, hell I would like people to think I am a brainer. We laughed Geoff broke the ice Ashley attended and received her certificate.

Until that night, I had doubts my faith was not strong like my mother's. Is God real? Are the stories in the bible true? That night I found myself praying, I no longer saddled with doubts.

Interesting thought just came to mind that I must share with you. When one is blessed with a baby it is a wonderful joyous event all the calls of congratulations received from friends and family, the gifts arriving for the new baby. Upon Ashley's arrival no calls were received and no gifts to unwrap. Years later someone who worked with me had a baby and unfortunately their son placed in the hospital's Neonatal Center. We sent a card and gift; I called to congratulate him and his wife. A couple of months later he advised we were the only ones to share in the birth of their son it gave him hope.

Thirty years later I returned to work and live once again in Houston; one Sunday afternoon Linda's first trip back to California I drove to Herman Hospital parked my car in the very same parking lot and played Lunatic Fringe. Sitting in the car alone I recalled that night saying out loud thank you Peggy.

CHAPTER 22
I LET HIM GO, I SAID GOODBYE... EARLY ANGUILLA DAYS [2004]

Anguilla, this little island is paradise right out of a story book you must go take a trip, how about a lovely vacation and see for yourself this charming island and its fascinating people. Walk along her sugar white sand beaches; see her clear blue skies, you can see the Milky Way at night with thousands of stars that twinkle in the sky. The restaurants have amazing delicious offerings you will come back again and again.

I love Anguilla one of my favorite places. I look back at my time working there as privilege. I have fond memories also very fortunate to find some close dear friends.

My confidence was waiting for me on that little island waiting for me to take it again. Maybe I just had to find the courage to take the step, put my fears in my pocket and find my way back to the game. Similar to learning how to walk again or maybe talk again, I took baby steps that seem insignificant at the time although the combination of steps makes all the difference between failure and success. YES, I beat the stroke, the stroke... well, now it did not beat me. Even with half a brain I made my way back. You see, I lost 40% of my brain to the stroke.

Believe in yourself, Jack, you can do it; you can do anything; never ever give up, but this was very different. I could not comprehend or even grasp this... you see, I did not know who I was. I know what you are thinking, what the hell does this mean, what is he talking about?

An interesting thought just came to mind as I sit here telling you how I made my way back, a journey for sure. I believe this is when I tell you the moment I found confidence. This moment was maybe a bit spiritual as I accepted myself. Believe in yourself, Jack. So yes, I have been waiting to share this with you. I could not find the correct place until I began telling the Anguilla story. You see I remember this moment just as if it were yesterday evening. I often think about this moment with a smile, the moment I could accept Jack.

I was in Anguilla traveling home after days of working on the island. I believe it was my third or fourth trip to Anguilla after my stroke. I was sitting on the front deck of a ferry boat alone from the other passengers below with the sun on my face riding the ferry to St. Maarten then catch a cab on the French side travel to the Dutch side where I would board my plane back to Los Angeles usually with a connection in Miami.

At the time it didn't appear to be noteworthy or significant I was simply enjoying another calm and tranquil Caribbean afternoon. I sat on the deck watching sail boats in the distance and my mind began to wonder. The sailboats were floating on the horizon darting through the sea. You see, I knew I could not keep him any longer, he is holding me back.

By now you know I often talk to myself, I guess I find myself in the best of company that way. So, picture, if you will, me sitting on the deck …You are doing great Jack, you are back. Yes, you had several issues to overcome however they were all minor compared to this. I always knew with time and a little luck and effort I could find the means to compensate and overcome my short comings after my stroke. However how can I deal with this?

The stroke did in fact leave its mark. Yes, the stroke changed me. I do not know this person, this Jack. Can you imagine not knowing yourself? I find someone else a strange person in my body, actually in my head. What happened to Jack where is he? I find an imposter, a poser; this new Jack stole his place. That said, no other can see or even comprehend this.

It is hard very difficult to articulate, I hope you understand. The only way I can try to tell you how different I am is with this odd analogy …you see I am Jack however I am no longer the Jack I knew. I think I act the same, I look the same, however I do not think the same, I do not feel the same; I do not know this Jack he is foreign to me.

Small things are easy to clarify and articulate for you. For example, I hated sushi and also, I hated peppers that said this Jack enjoys sushi and loves peppers. The Jack I knew could sing, he played guitar he sang in restaurants and bars, he sang at weddings and wedding receptions. On stage the old Jack had the lead in his high school play, Carousel. The following year he won the lead in a shoreline actor's group for the musical The Boy Friend. The Jack I find today not only can't carry a tune. Singing is an absolute impossibility. I know this may sound odd maybe even a bit silly? Those examples are definitely inconsequential. Yes, trivial compared to feeling like or as if you are a different person, well actually knowing you are someone else.

Who am I, who is this guy, where is Jack, why won't Jack come back?

Imagine, if you will, waking tomorrow morning to find … say, if you are a woman, you wake to find you are now a man, or if you are a man, you wake to find you are now a woman. That is how different Jack is. Is he the same, no he is not? Everyone else sees you unfortunately you cannot see yourself. To be clear I am a man and I am still a man. That said I am no longer me, the Jack I knew before my stroke that Jack he no longer exists Jack is gone.

Jack is not me; this Jack is not the one the same person who I was before. He is foreign to me; I do not know this Jack. I just cannot think of another way to explain how different I feel about myself. Things are very different I am very different. It is like stepping into someone's body and continuing on with that life. I hope my analogy was helpful so you can understand the conflict I have with myself.

While sitting on the deck with the sun on my face on that calm and tranquil afternoon enjoying my view of the Caribbean with the sailboats gliding so effortless in the distance, on the boat that day that moment what I am trying to explain to you is the instant I forced myself to become comfortable with this stranger the other Jack, the one who I was struggling to accept. I knew I couldn't change him back and it was best for me to accept me and move on. I knew I had to. I knew I had no other, absolutely no other choice. So, I did on that day that very moment what was best, if not I would go insane. I said goodbye. I let Jack go.

Design

As with all my projects, I always schedule an owner's design status meeting during the preconstruction phase with the architect, engineers, and consultants at the same time and location every two weeks. This provides information and options for owner decisions made at these meetings to push and shape the design progress. Typically, the design phase dependent on size and complexity will ensue for approximately twelve to fourteen months. We held these meetings at WATG's Newport, California office. That said for first couple of months the resort program and concept as well as the basic design notions were developed at meetings I held with Brad McNamee our architect, Richard Lis our civil engineer with Harris Engineering and Pierre Rousseau with Boyken International in my hotel room at the Cuisinart hotel in Anguilla.

Pierre is a consultant he is an expert concerning Caribbean resort development. Pierre helped me with island logistical issues, preconstruction budgets and contractor selection. I trusted his judgment and guidance; Pierre provided huge value to our effort. We became good friends. My first call to start the business day each and every morning for over two years was to Pierre. It did not matter where I was at the time. For example, if I was located in California, I called Pierre as soon as I started my car for the drive to the office. When traveling I made the call to Pierre before breakfast at whatever hotel's restaurant I was stayed at the night before.

These meeting in my room at the Cuisinart Hotel shaped the Viceroy Anguilla's design tone and galvanized our strategy for development.

Daddy

The islanders who knew me called me Mr. Jack. I interviewed over six separate demolition contractors. This basically included anyone on the island in the possession of heavy equipment an excavator and or bulldozer. The first phase of construction was demolition of the old and tired abandoned Cocoloba Resort.

I retained Daddy Construction a small company to provide demolition efforts. However, our agreement made certain that Daddy must include all of his competitors to assist with the effort. For example, we compiled a list of the required equipment - two excavators from one, a bulldozer and dump truck from another and four dump trucks from the next. I wanted the island and the island's people to be a part of our development. This allowed all to participate and most important I assigned Daddy as the big dog to oversee and manage the process. The largest equipment owner was already tied up on another resort development. I typically do not choice the largest firm I look for someone who is hungry and wants to grow, someone who will do whatever it takes to prove they were the right choice. Daddy was one of the smaller equipment owners at the time. I have made a career for myself by giving a chance to the smaller company. All on the island wear many hats as this is the only way to survive on this little island. For example Daddy, was the owner of Daddy construction, rental Car Company, pest control and Ace Hardware.

Daddy and I became close friends, Frank and I enjoyed our friendship and business relationship with him. When we first met, I started calling him Big Daddy. He replied my name is Fred Harrington. You can call me Fred if you prefer; however, all call me Daddy, not big daddy. The next night while enjoying an awesome dinner at Eats, I know what you are thinking; Yes, Eats is definitely silly name especially for a white tablecloth restaurant however the restaurant serves spectacular dishes. I saw on the menu a dish named after Daddy, so I had to meet the chef.

I asked my waitress to see if she could persuade the chef come to my table as I had some questions with the menu. Within a couple of minutes, the chef who I found from our subsequent conversation was also the restaurant's owner came to my table and asked if everything was all right? I introduced myself he replied I am Vernon most around here call me Val. I advise all is fine. I love this restaurant. Next, I asked about the Daddy dish and learned Fred was his friend.

To my surprise he said you are Mister Jack the one who is leading the new development to replace the old Cocoloba resort. He smiled and advised Anguilla is a small island everyone knows everyone here the islanders speak well of you. I learned a lot that night about the island I enjoyed our conversation. I told him I called Fred big daddy and he replied my name is Fred Harrington you can call me Fred if you prefer however all call me Daddy, not big daddy. Well as you can imagine I was curious to find how Fred got the name Daddy? Val motioned to one of the waitresses and she brought the two us another beer and he told the story. I felt foolish after and always called Fred daddy. My wife and children also know him as Daddy.

He began telling me a fascinating story.

Jack, many years ago Fred's father was traveling to St. Martin by small boat accompanied by two of his daughter's. One girl was ten, the other eleven or twelve. He wasn't certain. Unfortunately, the small boat capsized one daughter could swim the older child could swim but not very well. It was late in the afternoon so darkness would soon cover them. The sea current was strong. His father shed his shirt and some of his daughter's clothes to tie them all together as he did not want them to drift apart. Soon the sun vanished day disappeared to night. Three helpless bodies bobbed floating in the dark. Finally, his floating family was spotted by another boat and brought to safety back to Anguilla.

That night at his home all family and friends sat by his father's bedside and remained until morning. You see, his father had suffered a heart attack while saving his daughter's. You can picture his fear and concern. Family and friends were certain he would not live through the night. His father's last words as he placed his hand on his wife's eight-month pregnant belly: if it's a boy call him daddy. She named her baby Fred after his father; however, all from Anguilla know him as Daddy. Like I said earlier, my wife, children as well as my brother Gary and his family also know my dear friend as Daddy.

Val is an accomplished great chef I enjoyed his restaurant often.

Drew & Garrett

Many years later I traveled to Anguilla with my youngest son Drew and his friend Garrett the boys were sixteen at the time. Linda, Geoff and Ashley had on different earlier business trips joined me so they were familiar with the island. I wanted Drew to see Anguilla; plans were made for Drew's trip however things unraveled due to passport issues. So, years later on this particular trip I found things were different… as I no longer worked on the island. I was not important anymore; I could not offer islanders a job.

We flew from Los Angeles to San Juan. There are only two flights daily from San Juan to Anguilla American Airlines was the lone carrier. One flight lands in Anguilla at 1:30 P.M.; the other our flight at 7:00 P.M. To my surprise, we found seven or eight people waiting for us on the tarmac just outside the airport's lobby. The island's important people. Like Raymond who was in his seventies, I hired him to water the Marketing Center plants. Raymond did not speak English and unfortunately, I do not speak Spanish. His son Simon was with him. Simon always acted as our interpreter. The others were waiting to greet us ... Frank, Daddy, Pedro, and Michelle. I was humbled, the boys enjoyed our reception Drew was impressed, introductions with celebratory hugs and handshakes, I was back on the island I loved and missed so much.

My very first trip to Anguilla I drove from the airport to our site, to see the previous abandoned Cocoloba resort. As I pulled up to the main entrance, I noticed two men standing at the door to the lobby. The older men held a machete in his hand, partially out of sight; however, when I looked more closely... yep, Jack, you are correct, I said to myself, that is definitely a machete hanging from his right arm. Oh my gosh now he moves his arm forward holding the machete up and out in front of him. As you can imagine I did not expect this kind of welcome committee brandishing a machete. I opened the car door, while stepping out making direct eye contact with the older man holding the machete I said, I am Jack Bousquet from Los Angeles I represent the people who purchased the Cocoloba property.

The man without a machete places his hand on the other one grasping the machete he immediately began to smile he moved his arm holding the machete down and back to his side. He nodded his head and kept his big smile, lots of teeth. The younger man stepped forward holding both arms out to his sides and partially up like a minister in church. He began speaking with a thick Caribbean accent said I am Simon; this is my father Raymond as he steps to the other man and places his one arm around his shoulder. He doesn't speak any English, nice to meet you Mr. Jack. We were hired by the bank to keep the Cocoloba property safe. My father carries the machete to protect me. I smiled saying Raymond must be a good father. They both nodded and smiled. I stepped forward shaking hands all the while saying oh my lord what a gorgeous view, I love your island this is paradise. That was the first time I was called Mr. Jack. I became to like my new name, everyone absolutely everyone here called me Mr. Jack.

A couple of days later when I returned my rental car, as I walked in to the little structure to give up my keys the guy behind the desk said, "Mr. Jack, I hope you build a movie theater at the old Cocoloba hotel site. I responded I do not believe we have met; there was a different person here when I rented the car, and I am Jack Bousquet. Yes, Mr. Jack, our island is small we all know who you are. I advised we are planning to develop a new resort. He shook his head and said I was so hoping you guys would bring a movie theater to our island.

In time I hired Raymond to water the plants at the Marketing Center; I hired Simon to be our concierge for our temporary three key hotel. Simon was a kind man who worked very hard he was loved by all and provided huge value to our team. I later found he was a minister at one of the local churches. He also worked for another group as a man servant for VIP guest to the island, his most notable repeat client was none other than Robert DeNiro.

After the select demolition was complete, we refurbish three little villas added a swimming pool, converted a portion of the previous restaurant to our Marketing Center and converted an existing beach equipment rental structure to a beach bar.

Our sales team IMI would make arrangements with prospective buyers to stay on site at our three-room hotel to enjoy the island and experience... what the dream could be to own a piece of paradise. IMI sales team would convince our guests to make a deposit of $25K to hold their place for our future purchase of a room, suite, townhome, or villa. We ran the temporary hotel for five months. Each week three new guests would arrive. On the first sales date we sold over $172M.

Our first night in Anguilla 2008 I took Drew and Garrett to Eats'. I was surprised Val remembered me as I had not been back to the island for a couple of years. Val saw me and came over to our table to say hello, we talked for a couple of minutes I introduce the boys to Val. When Val stood to return to the kitchen he said, I remember you liked beer Jack, three beers for the table? I replied absolutely. The boys were excited; as you can imagine, this was my first drink with my son Drew and his friend Garrett. You see the drinking age in Anguilla is sixteen.

We need a plan

Daddy provided the heavy equipment for demolition I set up an additional contract to purchase earth moving equipment necessary for the new resort. You see I could not bring construction equipment on the island I would need special permits that would take forever to receive, maybe years. Daddy being an Anguilla resident did not require any special permit. So, I joined Daddy in a partnership with Kor Group. He held a percentage of the heavy earth moving equipment we elected to purchase and we established reduced rates for the equipment's use for construction. We also devised a plan so he could purchase Kor's share for full ownership when the resort construction was finalized.

I learned quickly that Daddy could manage earth moving operations that said he was struggling with the demolition of the old Cocoloba resort. I arrived on the island excited to see the first week of demolition progress. I took a cab to the site, dropped my bag at my apartment. The last structure scheduled for demolition was the old hideaway apartments; this is where my staff and our sales staff from IMI lived. My apartment was on the second level right above our construction office.

The old apartment structure was at Barnes Bay, I made the short walk to Meads Bay to see the demolition progress. I was shocked and dismayed as what I witnessed was chaos.

I found several excavators locked in the middle of demolition, no way for the excavators to load trucks to transport the debris to the dump. That night after dinner with Pierre, Frank, and our team Bill, Pedro, Michelle, and Aaron I could not sleep thinking about the chaos.

I got out of bed, found my notebook. I always use hard cover lab books to record my notes. You see I hold on to my note books as often I can use my thoughts to solve a problem on a future development. I have well over fifty lab composition books stored in the basement of my California home.

Well, after a couple of hours and several proposed applications, I developed a demolition plan. I met with Daddy in the morning told him the demolition to date was a huge mess as he had painted his equipment in a corner. I advised the operation requires a strategic plan for example trucks require pathways to enter as well as depart from the demolition area. Let's only move debris once verses relocating debris multiple times per the current plan. I shared my plan and strategy as we walked through the demolition. I also learned that daddy was good with the equipment however, he left the planning and supervision up to his staff and my staff unfortunately assumed the demolition crew knew what they were doing. Fortunately, we only lost a single day of time cleaning up the area to provide truck access/egress. The strategy for demolition efforts started at the east side moving west.

I returned to the island the following week, I was very pleased with our progress as the operation was moving smoothly and our demolition progress was working now ahead of schedule.

What did you do?

Jeanne Roccapriore my assistant joined me on this trip. Jeanne was also my assistant on the previous Trizec-Hahn Hollywood & Highland development; she followed me to Bousquet Dennis, and Associates as our office manager and now continued with Laura and me to the Kor Group. So, you see Jeanne and I had worked together for several years, and I trusted her judgment. Jeanne is a take charge woman who can think on her feet and make the impossible possible. I gave her a heroic task I asked Jeanne to set up our construction office and most important interview and find an assistant / office manager we as our team required a Jeanne in Anguilla.

We had nothing just an empty apartment that we wanted to convert to our construction office. Jeanne quickly found the island had limited supplies. She got what she could locally she mailed the reaming supplies and equipment. Her first miracle on her first day was phone and internet service. I knew she was the perfect choice to get our team's office set up. Jeanne took a car (Pierre located five or six white little Toyota cars that we used as company pool vehicles) to the valley the next day to interview several candidates for the office manage position.

That afternoon upon her return to the site she found me and asked, what in the hell did you do? As you can imagine I had no idea what she was talking about. Come on Jeanne you got to give me a clue as I have no idea what you are talking about. So what do you think I did? With that she said the dump trucks are racing on the roads they are driving fast.

Okay ... Jeanne, are they driving dangerously? Was there an accident? Jeanne replied no however, the truck drivers are traveling at a quickened pace and today I see several trucks actually many trucks on the road as compared to yesterday I noticed they were driving slowly yesterday, today they were driving much faster and I bet you have something to do with this?

Earlier that morning I asked Daddy to assemble all the truck drivers, I wanted to meet and talk with them. So, picture this if you will a lovely little island on a beautiful sunny day. Frank and I find about nine or ten drivers standing with Daddy with their back to the ocean, their trucks parked randomly between us and the group waiting for me. We are in Frank's little red truck a Toyota RAV 4 navigating through the parked dump trucks. As we drive through the parked trucks to join the drivers, I told Frank; oh my God do I love my job. He smiled and said yes this is going to be an amazing development a great resort.

I approached the drivers shook hands with Daddy and he introduced Frank and I to the driver's one at a time. I started to speak and advised that watching the progress yesterday I found the demolition progressing nicely actually ahead of what I had anticipated however the removal of debris is falling behind. At this pace we will never make our schedule. I continued to advise that I had kept track of truck tips and recorded same in my notes. I told the drivers most trucks only made two trips all day to the dump and a couple actually made three trips. They looked at me without concern; they actually appeared board and I though these men could not understand or comprehend why I was meeting with them not to mention my point.

I then asked how you drivers are being paid. This got their attention, now all eyes were looking in my direction, the ones who were sitting on the ground one or two with their back to me stood with the others. I believe they thought I was going to fire them, not certain however I got their focus and they now became engaged in my conversation. What do you mean Daddy replied and two of the drivers stepped forward and echoed him what do you mean Mr. Jack? Simple… I replied I am curious to find how you are being compensated? One man stepped forward and replied we get paid by the hour. The amount was $8 an hour rate. I replied I have an idea that I believe you guys will like and it should put more dollars in all your pockets. I want to change how you guys are being paid, effective immediately. From now on you will be paid $12 per trip. We found the drivers performance improved as they now had an incentive. Can you believe eight to nine trips per truck were recorded daily? The last trip required the trucks headlights to be on.

There is a speeding story. I was at my home in California my boss Brad with his wife Kelly and our marketing team on the island. Daddy called me: Jack we have a problem; the police want to arrest Brad. Why? What for? What did he do? I said. He was driving one of the black Range Rovers you purchased going exceptionally fast, they chased after him he would not stop. You know what Daddy Brad is always on his blackberry I bet he did not even know the police were behind him, chasing him. How do the police know it was Brad? They saw him when he turned into the Viceroy Resort construction site. They are trying to figure out what to do they know he is very important however he cannot drive like that on their island he could hurt someone. I asked Daddy, do they want him to pay a speeding ticket? Yes, Mr. Jack but most important Brad has to slow down. Okay. Daddy tell the police to write up a ticket, have them give it to you. I will talk with Brad. I will make him understand. I guarantee he will obey the island's rule for now. I ended telling Daddy I planned to travel to the island Monday morning. Let's meet for dinner at EATS give his ticket to me and I will pay it tomorrow I will give you the money at the restaurant.

I called Brad. I explained the issue. He said he did not know the police were behind him. Brad did slow down. He never had another incident. I believe the reason the police did not arrest Brad; you see I hired off duty police officers to provide security for the Viceroy Anguilla construction site. I knew them on a first name basis. At night after a day's work when I as on the island I would walk the beach ending up talking with the security guards I met along the way. The police also aware Daddy was the demolition/ excitation contractor and my friend.

Unfortunately, the dump was closed on the weekend. So, I drove to the dump one afternoon and asked the attendant at the dump if he could keep the dump open on Saturdays? He it has never been done before; we are open Monday through Friday unless a holiday occurs on one of those days. I advised I am certain we can come to an agreement. The attendant said, it will cost you. How much? I asked. He replied, a lot. How much is a lot? I asked. He said, $100 American dollar for the day. Oh my I thought this will work fine a mere $100 dollars and I get another 17% of disposal activity. The demolition phase was completed well ahead of schedule.

Peas and beans

Exclusive Resorts were interested in purchasing ten villas. This was huge for us to find a purchase from a five-star vacation company so early in the design process. We had to figure a way to make this happen. We definitely had a heroic problem. Please be mindful, the island was relatively flat this little island does not provide much variation in topography. The master plan included twenty-five villas located on a small bluff overlooking the beach below. For optimal views Exclusive Resorts wanted to add the ten villas locate seven on the second and three more on a third row. The second-row topography was elevated 35 feet and the third row was elevated 50 feet.

Our problem at the time was unnerving where do we find the fill material to modify the elevations and how could we provide a cost-effective strategy for the construction solution? Unfortunately, the only available quarry on Anguilla was closed. We ran cost scenarios to ship material from off island however the cost was definitely prohibited.

Frank by good fortune and his friendly charm and charisma by talking with some islanders located an unexpected source. Frank learned there was another quarry be it small, however the man who ran this little quarry did not provide material to others he used the material for himself and his excavating company to under bid his competition. Frank also learned the man's father owned the property; he was along in years and was now retired. Frank and I got to talking and we drove over to investigate the little quarry, we were pleased to see the operation and believed the source would more than adequately provide the fill material we needed. We decided to drive by the father's house on our way back. We found a nice modest home with a huge garden with rows of peas and beans. That gave us an idea, a strategy and most important hope. That night while enjoying another dinner with several glasses of wine at Mango Dave's Frank and I finalized our strategy.

I flew back to Los Angeles. The next morning Frank got in his little red Toyota RAV4 and took a drive to meet the dad. Frank parked on the side of the street in front of his home. He walked up to the front approached the door and knocked on the door panel then waiting for a response. To Franks surprise the door opened immediately. An elderly man greeted him and asked what can I do for you? Frank responded I saw your peas and beans and I have a few questions. Frank found the elderly man with a lot of time on his hands. The two talked for most of the day their conversation started around farming peas and beans when the man said you are the one who runs the construction at the old Cocoloba Resort. So you know who I am? My son says the man who runs construction is a big man a very big man who drives a little red truck that has to be you. What do you want Frank, why are you here today?

Frank's version of the story that night while we were talking on the phone ... he said he started with the peas and beans then talking about his pizza restaurant back in New York. He went on and on about the sauce and how Italian sausage provides the spice and flavor. Frank learned that the father and son often have disagreements. Upon days end Frank had a verbal agreement from the father for our team to purchase raw cut material.

It would be our responsibility to supply the trucks to transport the material to our site and also our responsibility to crush the material and place same in six-inch lifts to modify the elevations. This was huge, Francis did it, and I was impressed I loved this man. So now we could move forward with the ten villa sales as well as have a prestigious internationally known partner in Exclusive Resorts. I called Brad gave him the good news, he was happy.

The impossible was no longer impossible. That said we now had another issue although be it easy to resolve by comparison. You see one doesn't have a rock crusher handy or available. I called Daddy; we already had an agreement to jointly own equipment, so we found with the assistance from Daddy's son Enrick Harington who is a used construction equipment broker. In addition to the rock crusher, we also purchased a couple dump trucks and a D6 bulldozer. The D6 dozer was an easy find. You see an international contractor from Scotland had just finalized the renovation to lengthen the runway at the Anguillan airport; we found they would prefer to sell the D6 than transport it back home to Scotland.

Weeks later we purchased a mobile concrete batch plant along with a couple used concrete ready-mix trucks. A month later two Pettibone (like a fork lift with an exceptionally long reach) to get materials out of the shipping containers

Just think about what just happened. It all started over a great dinner and a couple of beers and one or two glasses of wine at Mango Dave's restaurant. That was the night Frank began to tell me the story of the new found small quarry. I miss my dear friend, Frank and I went through many battles together we fought the odds several times these odds were never on our side ... we were a great team. I am proud to call Frank friend, I only wish he was still here with us. Everyone who had the pleasure to know Francis loved him. Frank was the kindest man I ever met.

October 13, 2008 we lost our dear friend. Frank passed on the island after suffering a severe a heart attack. This was such a difficult day for me. I was sitting in my office in Dallas. About a half hour before Michelle called to tell me we lost our friend, Linda called to tell me her mother passed. Jerry was very ill she lived long life ninety-three years. We knew she was failing and this day would soon come, it still hit hard when she passed. Linda and I cried on the phone although we were happy for her as Jerry struggled in the end. You see her heart was so very week. What a morning to lose two so close.

Frank was a dear friend and a valued colleague; I sat back in my chair with tears again in my eyes remembering our last time together.

My last trip to the island Linda and I wanted to share the experience with our dear friends from California Jon and Vicki Yudin. I had recently obtained a new position to develop a resort in Playa Del Carmen, One Resort Two Hotels. I was enjoying an awesome lunch and wine with Frank at his island restaurant Un Amore. Frank was a great host I was fascinated watching him go from table to table the night before greeting guests and giving all a personal touch.

Frank wanted to follow me he hoped I would hire him again. I asked what about your restaurant, he replied my daughter Christine can run it while I am gone. Christine had moved to the island in the early years of construction. Michelle on our construction team took great care of Frank she was like a daughter to him. That said Michelle lost that position when Christine arrived.

Unfortunately, since then his weight had ballooned; Frank would lose weight, gain weight, lose weight and gain more sometimes well over 100 pounds in each direction. Although now he was larger than ever, Frank could barely walk five feet, this was now a struggle for him even with his hand on my shoulder. I thought back to that moment remembering our conversation, telling him he has to get into shape I can't have him on the team when he can't walk. I saw the pain on his face. I saw his disappointment. However, he put out a big Francis smile; Frank said good bye Jack gave me a big Frank hug. He said wait till we meet again I will be in fighting shape next time.

Now only three or four months later, Michelle called, that was my last trip to Anguilla. Unfortunately, that was my last conversation with Frank. I got to go back to Anguilla. I miss that little island. I miss my dear friend Frank.

Asked to leave, yep fired

Couple of years earlier Brad and I started having strong differences in direction. On several developments however the straw that broke the camel's back was mainly our resort in Anguilla. For example, he wanted me to use the plant propagation site about a half-acre area for labor housing. We did not have an RO system (reverse osmosis) for clean drinking water or a waste water plant. I believed this would be like the grapes of wrath for the workers and hurt our efforts. I could not imagine a couple of hundred workers living there. I told him I gave my word to the government that we would do this right; a man is only as good as his word. I wanted to lease a property...an old hotel a couple of miles away that was damaged and abandoned several years ago by hurricane to house the workers. I believed we could reenergize the RO and waste water plants, bus the employees back and forth to our site. There were several other issues also causing friction it was clear that we could no longer work together, I was asked to leave.

Tulum

Around a year later a new property the Tulum project became a huge problem. With assistance/direction from that Dallas consultant who specialized in Mexico development logistics, Brad purchased a small palapa hotel in Tulum not far from the famous Mayan ruins. Only to find out the government would not allow the property to be redeveloped you see the hotel was on government land. Millions lost, most important Lubert Adler Brad's financial partner became disenchanted.

The Anguillan government called me

About ten months later I received two separate calls both just minutes apart from members of the Anguillan government. Easy to recall as this my daughter Ashley's wedding day. I always kept my Blackberry close, habit from constantly working. I stepped out to the balcony as the noise inside the Robinson Ranch Country Club prevented me from hearing the call.

So now standing on the balcony looking out over the golf course the caller advised well over 100 Indian workers from the Viceroy Construction site walked to the Anguillan business center they are demanding their return to Bangladesh. I was certain things had to be very bad as who would demand to be returned to Bangladesh? I advised I'm no long employed by the Kor Group and haven't for almost a year. I am certain Randy the new led, advising he is the one who took my place can manage this issue, however have you called Frank?

Some were sick due to unsanitary accommodations. As you can imagine a new focus spotlighted the Viceroy Construction site. I am not certain what happened next. I do know the issue was resolved, after a couple of month's apparent calm returned. The project continued on however the budget a bust the schedule lost. The resort fell in receivership.

Jacks Cove

Starwood Capital Group controlled the property. Remember earlier my excitement for me and my partners Jack's Cove who invested in that two bed lock off? Yep, we purchased $1.75M hotel condo unit created a Bahamian corporation Jacks Cove. Our investment now lost as Starwood is trying to sell our unit.

So, I fought back, I led the effort keeping Vince ever so close as Vince became the lead partner. After a long battle the new financial team Starwood advised they will honor the previous agreement. However only to a single entity; they will not recolonize Jacks Cove Corporation.

Vince believes his company could use the property to entertain prospective clients. The property held a two-year sale restriction. Our plan in two years Vince would buy me and the three others out. I with my brother Gary still hopeful to build the two homes with Daddy on his hillside beach property at shoals bay with the profits. Vince now held ten shares as he purchased Frank's two shares as well as the others with the exception of my two shares my friend and attorney Jon Yudin, my brother Gary as well as the architect Brad McNamee who elected to stay in.

Unfortunately, Vince's divorce ended our partnership as Vince advised him no longer available to shoulder the purchase contract. I talked with Brad,

Jon and Gary I felt terrible they lost their investment. Interesting all sad it did not work out. Each advised they could have and maybe should have sold when Starwood changed the game as Vince was purchasing shares. Not one angry not one distant each believes it all unfortunate and each fond of the opportunity missed.

CHAPTER 23
EXCITED TO HAVE A PROJECT
IN HAWAII. [2007]

More than ten years earlier while at the time working for the mouse Linda and I enjoyed a fabulous Hawaiian vacation with our children. It was great to get away, enjoy some family time and leave work to my DDC team. We seldom took family vacations so this was a very exceptional time for our family. Unfortunately, we can count family vacations on one hand. On this Hawaiian vacation my sons Geoff and Drew learned how to surf. We discovered waterfalls beautiful jungles and enjoyed many delicious meals.

One day while walking on the beach in Maui I came across a huge resort under construction. I saw tower cranes erecting the structure, scores of workers placing material. The development majestically reaching for the sky.

My mind began to wonder and be hopeful that I could have a project on a beach at a sexy location one day, I couldn't help myself I was fascinated with the notion. Why can't I do this, oh gee whiz I thought development here would be exciting... sexy. I got to do this one day, yes and hopefully soon.

My legs hurt from the dermatomyositis as I had walked a long way not bad but definitely feeling weak. I could use a rest and I was fascinated with the construction. So, for about fifteen minutes I stopped to watch the high-rise construction in progress. I sat on the sand I took out and lit a cigarette, actually two; I dreamed that this could be my future. I decided that one day very soon I will be fortunate to lead the development for a project in Hawaii. Heck of a dream wouldn't you say?

In March of 2007 I joined Fifield in their Costa Mesa office. Traffic in California is daunting. The trip to my office in Costa Mesa from my home was well over a two-hour drive, at rush hour even greater. I was fortunate to have an apartment included with my employment agreement.

I was responsible for the design and construction for our West Coast Developments. All projects were ground up condominium developments. They included a sixty-seven-story tower in San Francisco, twin thirty six story towers in Costa Mesa, a twenty six story tower in Beverly Hills and the prize the reason why I accepted the position a twenty eight story tower in Waikiki Hawaii. Yep that dream came true. When I accepted the position, I smiled and remembered my cigarette on the beach. It is good to wonder and great to dream. I was pleased to find this dream was realized actually several times ... Playa del Carmen Mexico (twice another adventure in the future), Anguilla and now Hawaii.

All four Fifield projects were in the initial concept phase, so yes, I was extremely fortunate to be hired when the developments were at the initial step of the development process.

I enjoy the preconstruction design phase the most. I actually believe the construction phase is the easiest part of the development process. Projects are made and lost with the decisions here in the preconstruction phases. The design notion and all the complex engineering decisions, creating the design documents, the marketing idea, who is our customer, what does our customer want, how will we embrace the idea, walking the design through the city to finalize the necessary building permits and securing financing is by far the riskiest and most exciting time for me, hundreds of decisions are made every day you can make a huge mistake... I enjoy the risk.

One week each month I traveled to Hawaii for design meetings, two or three days in San Francisco a week in Beverly Hills and the remainder of the month at my office in Costa Mesa. I drove home on Friday nights returning to my apartment late every Sunday night.

Unfortunately, the San Francisco and Costa Mesa developments never progressed beyond the Design Development phase. That said the other two projects in Beverly Hills and Waikiki were built. It is so very difficult to walk a real estate development to the finish line. You would be surprised to find how many developments die on the drawing board.

A pair of Kahunas

I love traditions and I have always been fascinated with the beliefs, customs, and practices of different cultures. I found the following Hawaiian tradition most interesting as well as a fascinating challenge.

Before construction can commence in Waikiki one must schedule a ceremony to have a Kahuna bless the property. Construction workers will not step on the construction site until the property is properly blessed. The islanders believe terrible things will occur … bad luck and misfortune for workers to proceed with construction without the traditional ceremony.

I did a little research and found opposing ideas. Some believe a man is better served as the kahuna while others disagree. They advised a woman is a more spiritual kahuna. Well, I thought, what the heck? I will cover all bases and retain both a woman and man for the event. To my surprise I got a lot of resistance, the woman did not want to include the male Kahuna and the man refused to include the female Kahuna.

I can be very convincing; however this task took me three separate discussions with both Kahuna's at our meetings to finalize and come to an agreement for the female and male Kahuna to work together. The female kahuna wanted the lead she could not see herself as an equal Kahuna to the male. Finally, everything, yes all issues previously discussed for example payment, ceremony protocol and ceremony customs and practices was worked out we had an agreement when … are you kidding me, the female Kahuna demands that the male Kahuna walk behind her. Luckily at our third and final pre-meeting the male Kahuna acquiesced to her demand. Looking back I believe the male Kahuna didn't want to forfeit his fee. You see I agree to pay both a bonus to work together and they each received the standing ceremony fee rate.

At first, I felt like I was in a *Saturday Night Live* skit. However that initial impression disappeared quickly. The Kahuna's were very serious. Lots of dancing, chanting and local island historical ceremony.

The event was fascinating, interesting, and very spiritual. It was a privilege to be a part of the event. Our ceremony began early in the morning; traditional food as well as typical breakfast items were served to the guests and participants. The male Kahuna believe something like champagne was appropriate the female kahuna believe no alcohol however she did want orange and also

257

pineapple juice served. I actually got them to agree to all beverages and some could be combined. I felt like a seasoned diplomat. I thought hell I am the guy who lost forty percent of his brain, so yep I worked the problem with half a brain to an agreed conclusion with two very difficult and demanding parties… . Isn't that special?

The kahuna's first blessed our celebration, the meal and drink, I and my team and next huge jugs of water with bowls and aspergils made from palm tree proms.

The Kahuna's requested that I participate and walk with them. I was honored to be included that said the female Kahuna stepped in close she gave me a hug and requested in my ear in a soft whisper that I walk by her side with the male kahuna behind us. Oh my, I began to laugh and pull back … well now I said how about we walk together with me in the middle I responded. She touched my cheek; smiled and said as you wish Jack this is your project. I was actually shocked by her quick agreement.

The blessing began at one corner of the property facing the sun and we walked back and forth for the length of the property while the Kahuna's chanted, danced continually spraying water on the ground as we walked making certain every square inch of the property was blessed. Certainly an enlightening experience… the day and moment I shall never forget and will always cherish.

So, I guess you may wonder why the ceremony became a tradition and why the ceremony is required, why are the construction workers hesitant to commence before the property is blessed?

When Captain James Cook found Hawaii, he bought more to the islands than he imagined. Measles were a daunting epidemic in Europe at the time. Even the Royal Family in England was not spared from this deadly illness. Unknown to all traveling on his ship in hiding was more than one could possibly imagine. Captain Cook brought the measles to the Hawaiians. Nearly nine thousand of the Hawaii inhabitants fell to death from this newly exposed disease.

Unfortunately, that was just the beginning you see upon Captain Cook's return a few years later he brought something with him again this time he exposed the islanders to the flu and pertussis (whooping cough). The flu with its diarrhea was far more deadly by nearly nine times than the islander's lives previously lost to the measles. Unfortunately, anywhere from a low of ten percent to a high of thirty three percent of the islanders died on the various Hawaiian Islands. At Waikiki where we were developing our condo development thirty three percent of the islanders perish.

So many of the islanders were lost, the custom at the time attributed to bind the deceased neck to the ankles so the remains were placed in the ground in a crescent shape. Waikiki is the original location for the main island settlement, five original families date back to the beginning.

When one develops real estate in Waikiki you find a demand from the five families to make arrangements in the design notion to keep any found remains undisturbed. If that is impossible an area in advance must be designated to replace same. We chose a flower garden for our potential relocation area. However, this is a difficult task to find approvals and requires time, concern, and patience.

The water table is very shallow this requires isolated dewatering practices to construct the foundations. Fortunately a rather slow and laborious process this allowed our construction field team to watch carefully for any remains.

We found our first remains confirmed in the crescent shape just a day into construction. We met with the families. Ironically the remains were already in the preplanned area. All was fine no concern from the family's council.

The second discovery was a much different concern. The remains were located at a critical column for the structure, actually the most critical column for the entire development the column and subsequent beams bridge the condo structure to the parking garage structure.

We exhausted all efforts with our design team to relocate the column. Regrettably, the column could not be relocated without changing our basic design notion.

Another meeting was scheduled with the council, two of the five family representatives were concerned and demanded that the remains stay as is and not relocated to the garden area. This was an impossible request. A major redesign would have to take place. Millions would be lost with time delays being the enemy....

So, I began to ask a few careful questions. For example, how close could we get to the remains? They advised as close as you can without actually touching the remains and they reiterated relocation of the remains was definitely not a consideration for discussion. I asked could we get as close as say the thickness of a piece of paper that I held in my hand as a prop. Yes was their response as close as that ... just do not touch the remains. That response got me thinking.

My architect and structural engineer were attending the meeting; I asked if I could step in the hallway with my design team for a couple of minutes to discuss a possible solution. The request was fine with the council they advised they would wait for our return. We departed from the council and began discussing the issue in the hallway. Certainly the column cannot be relocated however the remains were not under the proposed column the remains would be in the foundation area that supported the column. So, what about designing an eccentric foundation? (Short in length on one side however much longer on the other)

Fortunately, Joe Farrell was an accomplished Architect and Michael Kawaharada a creative engineer. I believe we may have a solution I just need one more question answered from the council. My team and I returned to the meeting. How much dirt can be disturbed around the remains I asked. They replied you can do as you like as long as you do not touch the remains or cause the remains to shift or settle.

I apologized for my example that I was about to say in advance. I went on to a say I do not want to be thought of as being disrespectful; unfortunately, I can't think of a better example. They said go ahead. If we find your idea curt or rude, we will certainly stop you.

I stood and began walking towards the council's table speaking as I moved. I have found from previous meetings like this that by standing and approaching the council it actually gave me an advantage as all eyes in the room would now be on me and I would hold their undivided attention.

I began by saying when I was a child. I would catch lighting bugs and put them in a jar. I asked if any of the council members captured any lighting bugs as a child, they responded no. Jack, there are no fireflies in Hawaii.

Well, I continued my discussion, I imagine when you were children you may have trapped a bug on the ground with a glass or jar? Yes, they smiled hesitantly. I continued by saying please be patient with me I believe you will find my solution more than acceptable. Think of that glass or jar you held as a child to encase the bug. In lieu of the jar to encase the remains what if we dug a perfect circle around the remains to allow the soil to be lower than the remains resting elevation. Next, we could place five or six foot circular concrete storm sewer culvert section vertically with the remains undisturbed in the center, the top of the concrete culvert just a hair above the undisturbed remains. The construction team will place a concrete cap on the culvert section closing the top. The ground floor slab will be placed or should I say poured over same. We will retain an approved historical consultant by the council to watch and monitor our progress. We will also place a historical brass plaque at the column noting the remains and the historical significance for same at this location as well as the remains previously found in the garden area. The council began to shake their heads and clap their hands in approval. A formal vote received a unanimous approval for the idea

We found the two remains early within weeks after construction commencement; fortunately, no additional remains were ever discovered. Like I said above, I enjoy working in new places discovering traditions, customs, and local practices.

After the meeting I returned to the Halekulani Hotel, got a beer by the beach looked at the stars the skies here are awesome you can see the Milky Way and celebrated a great day by myself. I thought about my stroke I recalled the debilitating days when I could no longer walk or talk. I smiled, today was a good day Jack... I ordered another beer.

Without trust

I was close to finalizing the negotiation for the construction agreement with Pankow Construction for the Club View development in Beverly Hills. Different construction teams however Pankow was the same General Contractor for our Hawaii and Beverly Hills projects.

Club View our Beverly Hills tower has spectacular views over the adjacent Los Angeles Country Club housing only two condominium units per floor. The top two levels each held a massive single suite unit per floor. Without a doubt a luxury first class and top shelf Richard Keating design.

All the difficult issues that usually put rocks in the road to secure a construction agreement were previously resolved and agreed to. Construction contracts are always difficult and often issues concerning indemnity and risk require a careful hand. Having a template made the process a bit easier to manage. After five weeks of discussions the final day of negotiating the contract language was coming to an end late at night at Pankow's Pasadena office.

We began to shake hands and talk about how awesome the development would be when ... Dave Eichten Vice President and Regional Manager for Pankow pulled me aside and asked what are you doing? He usually is a calm and happy go lucky person, this moment concern and a serious nature engulfed his demeanor. I asked Dave what are you talking about what is your concern? Dave said we know your company has already sold the property, so as you can imagine we do not understand why you continue to portray that you guys are still in the driver's seat. The conversation continued for several minutes Dave providing insight and detail concerning the new owner. He advised one of the clerical assistants in his office is married to a banker and her husband informed his wife concerning the sale. I knew nothing of this, I was certain he was mistaken.

However, as I began to drive away from the Pankow Construction office a little after nine that night I called Tim O'Brien my boss who I worked for and relayed my conversation. I was assured that I would have been the first to know if in fact the property had been sold. Don't worry, Jack, we are looking forward to you leading the construction effort just as successfully as you have led the design/pre-construction phase. Please be assured we would have confided with you Jack if we were intending to sell the property.

We began construction, bought out all the trades. The construction effort was progressing smoothly all was going quite fine. That is until four months later I received a call. I was told: sorry we could not confide in you, we wanted to make sure the details of the deal were finalized first. That said we had sold the Club View development when we talked previously. They want us to complete construction for them. Jack it really does not matter if we or someone else is the owner we are looking to you to deliver Club View.

I guess I should have been surprised. I understand why the profit would be rewarding there was also at the time discussions on the news that the economy was beginning to slow actually faultier in some sections.

For me if I had been advised of the sale when I called and questioned the rumor all would have been fine. I know and can appreciate the secrecy and silence concerning a monumental transaction like this. That said for me trust is most important it is just about everything and I no longer held their trust. So,

I decided to search for another position. My decision to move on should have been harder, maybe I could have taken more time, maybe I should have given them a break; you see, if I leave, I would also forfeit my phantom equity. At the time that did not concern me. I gave my two weeks' notice.

I made one final trip to Hawaii. This time I swam in the ocean. I was ready to check out from my hotel room and find a cab to the airport when I thought I have never jumped in the ocean. So, I returned to my room and put on my bathing suit and enjoyed a short swim in the Waikiki surf.

Chapter 24
Oh My Gosh Cancer It Is [2008]

While I was near the end of working on the Fifield projects things changed for me again health wise. I should have paid attention. About six months later working for a new group trying to develop a huge project in Las Vegas I got bad news, very bad news.

I was at Dr. Hartzel's office (my dentist) when he said to his assistant, Oh my God. Look at this. Jesus Christ. Oh crap, I do not like what I am seeing.

I responded you have one hell of a bedside manner. You're scaring me.

He said you have a nasty place on your tongue, Jack. It looks very … yes, very bad.

I said, Remember when I was here six months ago you saw that place on my tongue and you sent me to have an oral surgeon to have a look at it?

The dentist turned to his assistant and said, Write that down… that I told him to have it checked. With that I started laughing. Did you see him? What did he say?

I responded the best I could with his dental mirror still partially in my mouth. He said it is not a concern. However, we should watch it, see if it changes.

Oh dear, the dentist responded. I will never send anyone to him again. Jack, you need to see an ENT immediately. I will give you contact information for Dr. Saadat. He is an ENT also a surgeon. I asked what an ENT is. Jack, ear nose and throat specialist, he responded. And I will call him and tell him you will be calling. Well, as you can imagine, I was very nervous. Previously the oral surgeon took a biopsy and advised it was negative. However, the place is now an ulcer; I would hold spiced rum in my mouth to dull the pain. Yea I agree this was not a smart move on my part. Maybe I was trying to fool myself hopeful all would be fine, hell the oral surgeon believed same, so why shouldn't I?

I called to make the appointment when I returned home just a fifteen-minute drive from Dr. Hartzel's office. I found Dr. Saadat had already received a call about my condition. He set an appointment for the next day.

My mind was racing I was thinking the worst as Linda and I drove to his office. My wait in the reception room was very short. I was directed to a small well-appointed medical room. When Dr. Saadat arrived I introduced myself and told him about the oral surgeon as well as my previous biopsy and status being negative. I advise that the place has worsened most recently. He stopped me there advised he was glad my dentist saw it and with that Dr. Saadat looked in my mouth. He responded almost immediately, definitely within seconds, this does not look good, Jack. I want to take a biopsy. He then advised, However, let's talk about surgery and possible next steps as I believe surgery will be required. I think it is cancer.

Well, now as I look back and think about the situation, fear, uncertainty I was hoping for doubt, however cancer never entered my thoughts. I listened to Dr. Saadat he articulated next steps, I want you to get a CT and PT scan so surgery could take place as soon as possible. The additional the biopsy analysis and tests were promptly scheduled for the next day. As I began to drive home all was quiet for a while, I said he believes it is cancer …when Linda reached over touched my hand gave me a kiss on the check she said if it is cancer, I know you can do this, Jack. Everything will be fine the doctor said it was found early. You can do this. I know you can, Jack.

The next afternoon I received a call from Dr. Saadat he advised cancer was found and he already scheduled surgery for the end of the week, the earliest available date.

So, I have cancer that hated word. Being told that is like having a ton of bricks fall on my head. Dr. Saadat advised that I should still be able to talk that the area to be cut on the left edge side of my tongue close to the center in length is about the size of a nickel coin. He drew a diagram to show me where and how the surgery would take place, step by step. He advised, in addition to the localized area he would also cut and remove further areas slicing the top as well as the bottom of my tongue inward towards the center.

When he removed a small ulcer piece for biopsy the pain was intense not at all like the biopsy six month earlier. I knew for sure things were very different this time.

All the arrangements were scheduled and I thought if this is in fact cancer well now, I was actually looking forward to being free of it.

I had cancer before. That' said it was skin cancer on my chest where the top button of my shirt remains open. Years of working outside in the sun took its toll. That said to me I believed this was minor you see I know it was cancer however I did not believe this to be serious.

Tongue cancer is a horse of a different color. Tongue cancer is serious, what if he has to cut more to make certain he got the margins, what if I can't talk. I know it to be silly to worry absolutely nothing about worrying will help me; only get my head to spin. I need to keep my thoughts clear and positive. So, I put the cancer as well as the upcoming surgery out of my mind. Linda did her best to try and keep me positive. Well, it did not work well it did not work at all. I was fine blocking cancer issue during the day that said at night while waiting to fall to sleep the cancer scare kept occupying my thoughts. The cancer thoughts took command to a point where I needed a sleeping pill.

Surgery was scheduled early in the morning at eight at an outpatient surgery facility not too far from our home. Linda stayed with me right up to the moment the nurses wheeled my bed into the surgery room.

We talked about how she had prepared things for my recovery. Linda made several flavors of Jell-O some chocolate pudding and she also found small containers of apple sauce. In addition Linda purchased a small white board and a couple of colored markers that I could carry and use to communicate with her. Dr. Saadat advised if all goes well and hopefully as planned that I most likely will not be able to talk for a couple of days after that he believed I would recover. With a kiss and a touch to my face Linda smiled and said it will be ok Jack.

I remember the anesthesiologist telling me to count backwards from one hundred and seeing the lights overhead, nurses appeared to be jockeying into position.

I woke not certain how long I had been out. I was in the recovery room a nurse was standing over me smiling. I tried to say is it done? Not certain if she could understand me, she shook her saying don't try to talk Jack. You did great the surgery was a success. The nurse asked if I was in any pain if yes give me a thumbs down if no please give me a thumbs up? I was surprised my mouth was not in pain, I could not feel anything all was numb. I gave her a thumb up and she smiled and told me in addition to the anesthesia, I received a lot of Novocain. Shortly after Linda came into the room to help me get ready to leave for home.

Everything was sailing smoothly; this was so much better than I had imagined. I was so hungry from fasting for my surgery I tried a bit of Jell-O. I was also due to take my pain pill. The pill was hard to swallow Linda cut it into smaller pieces. That worked better the pill was much easier to swallow.

I would write on the whiteboard and Linda would respond. Communication was working and Linda laughed and said can you imagine if we had an argument Jack there is no way you could keep up with me. I wrote … Actually, this isn't bad I was just worrying for nothing. Yep, this isn't bad at all.

Maybe ten or fifteen minutes later the pain hit me hard, I guess the Novocain wore off exposing me to a strong dose of reality. The pain was intense, sharp, strong, and pulsating. With my whiteboard in my hand I wrote DRUGS and ran downstairs to find Linda. She was standing in the kitchen. I held up my whiteboard and pointed to what I wrote. Linda said you just had drugs and you can't take it again so soon. I wrote on top of the whiteboard stronger drugs. I am dying of PAIN. Again I wiped the whiteboard clean with my hand and wrote it feels like a truck is parked on my tongue. We need stronger DRUGS.

Linda made the call for a stronger drug, it helped ever so slightly. The next day things were not much better. I had to do something to get my mind off the pain. I went into my garage found an unopened can of paint, a roll of masking tape and a paint brush. I occupied my time this day painting one of our bathrooms. This painting work in tight, small areas definitely helped thinking of something other than the pain. Unfortunately, it not diminishes however time passed quicker and I now had a new focus. The next morning and for the next couple of days I found a new focus, I striped and refinished a wood clothes dresser.

The pain began to weaken and I found with a little effort that I could talk. The next day I could talk without any pain. This was an awesome moment; I knew all would be fine. Linda was a princess among women always there to help and take care of me.

I stayed home to recover for a week and a half. When I returned to work Dan stopped me in the hallway to my office, he asked how I was doing and said it is great to have you back Jack. I responded fine actually I am doing great the recovery was faster than I thought it would be. Lucky, I guess. Dan said we weren't certain you would be able to talk appears you are doing just fine.

About a week or two weeks later I was told someone else was hired to replace me. They hired a guy who had previously worked for Robert. I am not certain why Robert asked me to leave... was he concerned about my operation and effects from same, did he prefer to work with someone from his past; I also knew the project would never be realized, the World Jewelry Center a very unique and challenging undertaking for sure. WJC concept was a huge mixed-use project in Las Vegas all about jewelry and only jewelry. Only jewelry tenants in the retail center as well as only jewelry businesses in office condo tower with residential condo space at the highest twelve levels for the jewelry retailors and jewelry manufactures to purchase. The design was in the preconstruction phase we were just shy of completing the fifty percent Design Development phase package. The economy was beginning to fail the jewelry market felt the recession first. I did not see the economy failing in any other economic sectors or financial markets. Shortly after the world stopped spinning, the economy crashed. Unfortunately, I was correct about a couple of months later the development ended. Robert lost millions.

CHAPTER 25
THE OTHER FRANK CALLED ME [2009]

I started working on a very exciting development in Beverly Hills more or less as a consultant. They hired me as part of the team that said I had an advisory role. I was not directing or responsible for the project.

The development was interesting, complicated and a challenge; I found the team young but smart. I have always enjoyed working with smart and capable people. However, I also found the team a bit out of sync and rather dysfunctional as this was a spread sheet management team. To be clear, I do not manage projects from a spreadsheet. I use spreadsheets for information. The team was consumed by updating various spreadsheets, often losing sight of the issues at hand. I believe there are two groups of managers; one group keeps track of what is happening with documentation to articulate same, the other group, a much smaller number of managers, actually ... can make things happen, move and guide the development process forward.

At the time I was working for a consulting firm Gardiner and Theobald a London based firm who was managing the development for their client Candy and Candy a developer who was also based out of London. I was there for a short time maybe a mere four or five months.

From left field totally out of the blue one lazy Sunday afternoon I received a phone call.

Hello Jack this is Frank... Frank Gehry. Who is this I replied? Is this you Jon? It's Frank he answered. I was certain my friend Jon Yudin was pulling my leg. He again responded this is Frank. Now my mind began to race, could this actually be Frank Gehry on the call? It is not like he calls me all the time; actually, he only called me at home once previously to advise that I would not be working on the Disney Concert Hall, at that time he said some people must really like you or maybe they hate you. They advise you are very sick. Frank went on to say he was told if he continues to talk to me about the position Michael will remove his donation for the Walt Disney Concert Hall development. I was disappointed.

You see I was very sick at the time with dermatomyositis. Frank requested that Disney give me a leave of absence so I could manage the Walt Disney Concert Hall development. The Walt Disney company was not the developer or responsible for the concert hall. Eli Broad one of the wealthiest men in Los Angeles was leading the funding effort and he was the big dog in charge. He was hopeful to find someone to manage the design and construction. On Frank's recommendation I met with Eli, we actually met twice. I found Eli to be a very powerful man during our first discussion he had to excuse himself to take a call from the governor. Yep you can imagine how insignificant I felt.

> Our conversation was very positive however we did have one moment of friction I guess more like confrontation, yes definitely confrontation. You see Eli advised that he wanted me to recommend to the board that the project continue as a design/ build effort with contractor holding the primary contract with Frank's design agreement under the contractor's umbrella. I thought about his request for a minute or so ... I was sure how to respond that said I was hopeful to find a way to make Eli understand and not be angry that I did not agree with his notion. I began speaking all the while making certain to look Eli in the eye. I said I believe Frank designed your home? Eli responded yes. I continued to say your home is lovely and worth millions, unfortunately because you had it constructed as a design/build with the contractor holding the primary contract and you looked for the contractor to make design decisions during construction I believe that Frank does not take credit for the design. He actually has gone on record to advise your home is not his design that your contractor designed your home. Yes Eli responded. If you had entered into a traditional agreement with Frank as the designer your home would be worth twice as much as it is now due to his name. Yes, Frank has disappointed me he does not take or want the credit for the design of my home he actually

272

goes out of his way to say he did not design my home. Eli, I know you are trying to control costs; you can do that without taking away Frank's control. I have worked with him several times the projects were delivered on time and on budget. I believe if you go design /build a similar response would most definitely occur here I believe that would tarnish the Disney Concert Hall. At the time I believed Eli understood. Later I learned I was incorrect.

The first call occurred years ago a couple of days before Christmas, as you can imagine like I said above I was extremely disappointed. The Disney Concert Hall was a signature project and I wanted the opportunity to work with Frank once more.

So, if it is Frank on the other end of this phone call, it would be huge as we had not spoken in well at least four or five years. Well now, with that thought I said to myself you better listen and focus Jack. Is this Frank's voice, yep maybe I should I let Frank speak uninterrupted what the hell could this actually be Frank Gehry?

That worked I could now hear him clearly and was certain this caller was Frank. And crystal clear as I knew for certain when the voice on the other end of my call said JACK this is Frank fucking Gehry. I want to talk to you. I have several, actually four clients who do not have a clue. They do not know what they are doing. I want to introduce you to them; have you travel with me and you decide who you want to work for. We talked for a couple more minutes and we ended our conversation when Frank asked … Jack can you come to my office for lunch Tuesday? Absolutely I responded, Frank I look forward to seeing you again.

I met Frank maybe seven or eight weeks after I was recruited by Disney. I joined Disney Development Company (DDC) in Burbank, California on April 1, 1991.

I became the Director of Development and Design for our west coast DDC team. My job was beyond fascinating, I found the projects exciting and the pace fast. Most enjoyable I found our DDC team smart and capable; they all made a difference a team one could count on … a strong team indeed. I was responsible for the massive a $650M Walt Disney Studio renovation and expansion, all California corporate developments, NYC corporate developments and Pacific Rim second generation tenant improvements (interior office improvements at properties Disney leased in the Southern California as well as the various Pacific Rim locations).

My corner office was located on the top floor of the Disney Channel Building in Burbank, California, less than a five-minute drive to Walt Disney Studios.

One day I walked into one of our conference rooms where several from our team had just finished a meeting. I was curious to find information concerning a model resting on a table in the back of the room that was covered by a canvas tarp. The night before I was working late, on my way out I stepped into the room and I removed the tarp. What I discovered was like no other building I had seen before. The model was amazing, I found the building façades were twisted and bent at acute angels. I thought what a phenomenal design concept. I wanted to have a role in the design meetings, I wanted to construct this design; I wanted to have a role in making this project happen.

So, I walked towards the people sitting at the conference table, DDC team members from our theme park development group and asked does anyone know who the architect is responsible for that model under the tarp? I pointed towards the tarp, the one over there in the corner on the table as I began to walk towards the back corner?

Someone responded some guy named Frank Gehry is the architect; his office is in Santa Monica. Jack that model has been there for more than a year, that project will never get approved it will never be built.

Hmm… well now I was even more curious. Why I asked? They responded actually two reasons first someone has to put together a list of who should occupy and why they require a new office investment, create a Capital Authorization Request and issue same for approval. That is relatively easy as there is a huge office requirement and need for the Team Disneyland groups in Anaheim. They advised we believe another architect will be selected to create a design that works.

Second, several speaking simultaneously began to clarify… The proposed property for a new Disneyland office is located at Disneyland theme park; the site adjoins the back of the house support area just north of the theme park. That said they went on to advise the real issue is unsolvable. Well, there is an answer for everything, nothing is impossible I responded.

My Disney colleagues started talking again at the same time. They began to explain to me the design strategy and specific requirements concerning how each and every Disney theme park is designed.

Jack, if you have ever been a guest to one of the Disney theme parks throughout the world you already know that an earth berm encircles the theme park. This visible landscaped barrier ensures that all of our guests at grade level within the park can never see the outside world while enjoying our theme park. So, I asked what about when one is on a ride in the air above grade or at a second level terrace or on a higher structured elevation? How could you block that view to the outside world? They responded that is all right to see the outside world when one is above grade however at grade all protected views to the outside world are critical.

Jack, the model under the tarp doesn't fit the Disney criteria, if that concept was built it would certainly compromise views, the structure could be seen from most of the northern area at grade locations, the adjoining area that the Imagineers are creating the new addition to Disneyland called Toon Town.

I continued walking over to the table in the corner and I removed the tarp. We began talking about the design strategy and I learned specific details and dimensions for the berm.

At the time I was in my mid 30's and I believed I could do anything. I find with age one tends to become more practicable and a bit more cautious and maybe not so out spoken. Definitely more reserved and less bold.

I called Frank's office and requested a meeting with Frank ... I advised I had an idea ... our meeting would be concerning the Team Disneyland proposed project that had been shelved previously. I advised I was most certain Frank would enjoy discussing and the topic. The woman I was talking with said, Frank was traveling out of the country. However, I was told he would be arriving back the following week and just like that... our meeting was scheduled.

When I arrived at the Frank Gehry office early, I was surprised to find several odd and different sights. I have visited many architect offices that said I found Frank's office different and rather unique, For example a few architectural models were displayed on tables however several other architectural models were attached to the walls and also many models were actually displayed by hanging upside-down from the ceiling. The most fascinating to discover was cardboard chairs and table in the waiting room area. The cardboard furniture was tattered and worn but that appeared to heighten the furniture's character and charm.

With-in a short time I was taken to Frank's office and we were introduced. I was surprised to see Frank had a duplicate Team Disneyland office building model sitting on a table close to his desk. After greetings and the traditional hand shake, Frank pointed to the model saying I had my guys place the model here in my office I understand this is what you want to talk about? I doubt I would be so bold today to request a meeting like this, you see at the time I was young and as noted above I believe anything and everything is possible.

I began advising Frank I was new to DDC, that I was impressed with his design notion. I went on to tell him that I had never seen a concept like this. I told him that I believe I have a solution that can get the team Disneyland project moving forward and actually built. Frank sat there looking at me he gave me his time however he was certainly a little preoccupied. We talked about the Disney requirements for theme park design and how his concept in-terfered with same. I thought the conversation was progressing smoothly, I believed I had his attention, so I began to tell him my idea for a redesign. Yes, I suggested a redesign was required and most necessary for the development to move forward.

I stood and stepped closer to his model on the adjacent table while he re-mained seated behind his desk; Frank I believe the redesign is actually a very simple effort. I continued explaining all you have to do is flatten the structure out. Just eliminate one level and increase the building concept footprint ac-cordingly. Move this over here and maybe spread this area out over there as I pointed to his model.

Frank hadn't spoken for a while he was more than ready to say something now. Looking me in the eye he stood and moved towards me... Frank said who in the fuck are you? I smiled keeping eye contact and responded, Frank I am nobody. That said we can get your design built.

A relationship was cemented that day. Of all the architects I have had the great fortune to work with Frank Gehry is definitely my favorite. I was most fortunate to work with Frank three times. Also, I came ever so close to working for him; I will talk about that later.

So, getting back to his phone call, I was looking forward to seeing Frank again on Tuesday. Can you believe the next day that Monday, I well I gave no-tice to resign? Linda thought I was crazy. What if his clients do not want you to join their team? Jack, she said don't you think it wise to see what happens first? To meet his four proposed clients I needed time and I believed this would be impossible if I continued working. I wanted to be responsible for a project again; I was not enamored with a consulting role. Most important I wanted to work with Frank again. I believed I was bullet proof; I was not worried about a job. Looking back now that I have more years behind me and this occurred prior to the financial crisis I can see how my youthful logic was misguided. I guess my confidence level after my stroke remained high for myself.

Over the next couple of weeks, I met with the three clients Frank suggested. The fourth was located in the Middle East and at the time I did not see myself living there.

The most intriguing of the choices was Russian Investments owned by Janna Bullock. RI a real estate development company was located in Moscow. Janna a very pretty Russian woman leading a real estate development company who was looking to hire someone to lead the design and construction effort for an extraordinary hotel project that Frank was designing in Moscow. She also talked about another hotel in Switzerland that she had recently purchased and wanted to remodel. In addition to the two projects, we discussed she advised that she was hopeful to create a new boutique hotel chain, with many hotels at key destination cities around the world. Janna definitely was dreaming big.

Janna and I first talked by phone her vision sounded exciting as you can imagine she definitely held my curiosity. She requested we continue the conversation and meet at her apartment in Manhattan.

I traveled to New York the following week. Janna, I found indeed rather fascinating. She definitely came off as a wealthy woman one who enjoyed the sweet tasting good life, well actually more like a very rich woman who appeared focused and determined to make her mark in the real estate business world. I did some research in advance where I found many articles and photos of Janna and celebrities enjoying the New York night life, art and museums, parties. She already became known in Manhattan frequenting shows and making significant donations to the arts.

After we met, I believed her to be the most interesting option for me. Her apartment was in an upscale conservative location, the neighborhood looked of old money; our discussion lasted over three and a half hours. Janna wanted me to move to Moscow our conversation was very positive.

I found her to be very fascinating. We ended by discussed my role and possible timing. Janna advised she wanted to remain close to her business, she then asked if things would be my way or the highway? I told her I am not a yes man, if I disagreed with her direction or choice, I would tell her. She would always know my opinion and thoughts. That said I told her, Janna, RI is your company if we disagree the final word is most definitely yours.

I had talked about the resort I developed in Anguilla; so, to my surprise, Janna asked if I was familiar with the Malliouhana Hotel? Absolutely I responded the Malliouhana Hotel is located at the same cove as my project, just at the opposite point. Janna advised she was hopeful to purchase the Malliouhana resort.

Janna asked if I would be willing to take on some consulting in advance of finalizing an employment agreement. Janna talked about her desire to add a condo hotel component to the property and renovate the Malliouhana Hotel. On her behalf she requested that I meet with the existing owner confirm the development rights for potential expansion. She also requested a simplistic design and construction budget for the proposed development.

Janna asked that I meet one of her senior advisors who were located in Switzerland. I believe his role was to check me out. We met in Anguilla; Reto Gaudengi was an odd man I did not care much for him. I made a reservation at the Malliouhana and scheduled several meetings with the hotel owner who was in his eighties so he asked that I meet with his son. I wanted to talk with the owner first tour the property next confirm the development entitlements status with the government and circle back to have a follow up discussion with the owner. I assumed Reto and I would meet there.

I also assumed Reto would attend the meetings. Reto made reservations at Cap Juluca, at the time the finest hotel on the island. We had very little time together dinner one night and a discussion after breakfast the following morning. I advised Reto what I had learned of the development rights and provided an estimate for what I believe the cost efforts would entail to add the improvements Janna desired. Reto talked about me meeting the remaining RI team in Moscow he also advised that I should relocate to Switzerland not Moscow.

My relationship with Janna however short eventually fell apart; I never relocated to Moscow to work for Janna. Before the relationship fell apart, I finalized the consulting effort as she requested.

My meetings with the Anguilla government as well as owner of the Malliouhana Resort were very informative. I found that there was indeed a huge opportunity to add a condo hotel component, the property held several additional development rights. The property was underutilized so no new approvals from the Anguillan Government were needed. Information I obtained held all the necessary data to finalize my report for Janna, I was returning home on a Sunday, actually it was Father's Day... Yep, not the best day to be alone traveling home.

In Anguilla cell phone service at the time was extremely limited most often I did not receive any emails while visiting on the island. I flew from the little Anguillan Airport to San Juan. From there I would catch a flight to Miami, then another to Los Angeles, definitely a long day of traveling.

When I arrived in San Juan on a lovely Sunday, like I said above actually Father's Day, my phone connected to the internet again. I found several e-mails from Frank Gehry. He advised that I should not take the position with Janna, he had a crazy idea that I should go to work for him. Gehry Technologies was not performing as he had hoped; Frank believed that I could provide the necessary leadership to turn Gehry Technologies around. He asked for me to forward to his attention a brief outline regarding my notion to take Gehry Technology in a different direction.

I was scheduled to travel with Frank to Moscow for a meeting with Janna and her team concerning the Moscow hotel. Jill Konek, Frank's assistant, purchased a ticket and she also obtained a Russian travel visa for me

Reto advised Janna wanted me to come a week earlier... that did not accommodate my visa, well things just fell apart. I never made the trip to Moscow. As you can imagine that lovely lady I live with, Linda Bousquet well now she was beyond pleased to learn that we were not relocating to Moscow.

A couple of years later I learned of Janna's husband presumed embezzlement issue with the Russian government. I now understood where and how Janna obtained her funds for RI. Fortunately for me the relationship ended with Janna.

A couple of weeks after I returned home from Anguilla Frank's assistant Jill set up another meeting at his office. This time the subject was Gehry Technologies. I arrived at Frank's office to find several of Frank's team waiting for me.

Frank introduced his design team; in addition, also joining us was Stuart Jacobson who led Gehry Technology. Frank stood by my side and introduced me. I received the most complementary complement ever from Frank, I was beyond humbled. Frank stood next to me and addressed his team: This is my friend Jack Bousquet I think he can make Gehry Technologies more profitable. I have seen Jack make it rain and I believe he can do it again.

Then Frank turned to face me, what happened next was a bit awkward. Actually, very awkward I was surprised not certain what to do or how to respond next. Frank went on to say Jack, me and my team will be in the conference room we had lunch brought in for us. I will leave you and Stuart here to talk, when you are done, please join us for lunch.

Well as you can imagine my conversation with Stuart was short, very short. He runs Gehry Technology why would Stuart want to talk with me and consider my opinion to secure greater profits and or run a more efficient company? I believe the total discussion ended in less than fifteen minutes. I talked about my notion he had little to contribute. I asked for a future meeting where Stuart could explain in great detail the concept and practices for Gehry Technologies. Stuart was a gentleman. I am certain he had to be concerned and fearful for his position. That said our conversation was calm and polite.

We joined Frank and his team in the conference room for lunch. His architectural team talked about several new designs and clients Frank was working for.

The following week I met with Stuart a couple of times. The information gained concerning Gehry Technologies provided huge value for me. They worked and billed similar to google providing access by a licensing agreement, billing hourly to provide assistance.

Frank purchased from NASA a version of the CATIA software and formed Gehry Technologies as a separate company. This state-of-the-art software would allow Frank to map his design concepts for the first time he could now explore his notions to create extraordinary complex designs and find the information on paper.

I will try to articulate the concept in a simplistic explanation ... well basically his team would construct a three-dimensional model. Next, they would touch a wand at key points of the model. The CATIA software would transpose the three-dimensional data to a two-dimensional drawing.

The first time frank used CATIA was on my DDC project the Team Disneyland Office project. The Gehry staff worked out the bugs and learned how to utilize the system to achieve extraordinary designs for example Balboa Museum in Spain and The Disney Concert Hall in Los Angeles. Without CATIA these developments would not have happened.

I met with Stuart twice. I tried several times; unfortunately, I found it impossible to connect with Frank. After three weeks I was more than concerned that I had made a mistake by resigning from my consulting position, I also began to question myself and wonder about recreating a relationship with Janna. Please understand, that I no longer was receiving compensation, the consultant fee from Janna for my work on the Malliouhana Resort was small. Linda was definitely questioning my judgment, Jack how do we pay the mortgage, pay our insurance, and put food on the table? I questioned my post stroke judgment and decision-making abilities.

Not certain what to do? I recovered from my stroke however; unfortunately, I took a huge risk when I quit my job to follow Frank,; I began to worry should I begin searching for a job, how do I earn money, and most definitely concerned that Frank has gone silent for such an extended period of time.

Well, now they, whoever they are say God works in mysterious ways; I find it funny maybe better said ironic how circumstances can take care of their self. I received a call from a head hunter she advised Jack your name has surfaced from several of her contacts about a very challenging, exciting, and dynamic proposed development in Playa del Carmen, Mexico. I know Playa well, like the back of my hand having worked on several sites in Playa and the Rivera Maya beach sites about 40 miles south from Cancun and just north from Playa during my previous time working at the Kor Group.

Four real estate developers—ICON from Mexico City, Walton Street Capital from Chicago, Circa Capital from Dallas and Carvel the real-estate arm of Cargill the parent company that controls most of the food in the world combined forces to create a new resort development in Playa del Carmen… Two Hotels One Resort.

The headhunter advised they wanted me to travel to Playa to see the two existing hotels that would be demolished have the site scrapped to create the proposed new resort development. She set up a meeting actually an interview with Gilberto Riojas an executive from the Icon team.

I found the site fascinating I believed it an opportunity of a lifetime to have the prospect of being considered to lead this exciting development.

I felt blessed; I thought of my stroke and looked back on the memories of what I had to do and all my struggles to get back. I do my best to forget my stroke and not let it occupy my thoughts; however, I still have shortcomings that keep the stroke front and center. For example, can't feel my left hand or left side of my face and most definitely my short-term memory issue is most difficult for me to forget.

I arrived at the property in the early evening I could not believe my good fortune, I was pleasantly shocked as well as delighted to find the proposed development property abut one of the Kor Group beach vacant lots that I was very familiar with.

The Kor Group lot was rather shallow the two abutting lots with existing palapa style hotels were twice a deep and occupied more than three times greater beach frontage. I found my imagination wandering thinking of the possibilities for development amazing.

I walked the two existing hotels Mahekal and Las Palapas. At one point I actually began to laugh out loud I could not believe my good fortune. From my previous experience in Playa with the Kor Group, I knew the people, understood the protocol for the city building department, I had some good friends here. I believed the location to be one of a handful of the very best development opportunities Playa had to offer. I was hopeful to be hired and believed I could create an amazing new multistory destination resort with the opportunity

In the morning I met with Gilberto Riojas at the Las Palapa restaurant for breakfast. I found Gilberto to be a confident fellow and very likable. Our discussion was very positive. He advised they are searching for someone to lead the development; Gilberto talked about the four-development-company team how the partners communicated and painted a clear concept of what the partners desired for the proposed development. A meeting was scheduled in Dallas at Circa Capitals office to meet and be interviewed by the other partners.

The following week I traveled to Dallas. When I stepped from my taxi and entered the ground level lobby my phone rang it was Frank Gehry calling. Please be mindful, it has been over two months since my last conversation with

Frank. My bank account was beyond skinny, I was definitely in need of a job. I found a seat in the lobby on a planter we talked for a very short time maybe ten minutes at most. I told Frank that I was on a follow up interview in Dallas. Frank advised that he was in New York and would be back to his office in a couple of weeks.

The interview was beyond positive I was certain and most hopeful to be hired to lead this fascinating development.

The following week Linda and I traveled to Richmond, Indiana to visit her parents. We had a layover in Kanas City. While there I received my contract the agreement for the Playa del Carmen resort development. It was difficult to read on my blackberry however I am thrilled to be back to work and on such an exciting development.

When we returned home, I called Frank; unfortunately, we were not able to connect. I was uncertain how he would react; however, per our quick phone conversation while I was in Dallas, he knew that I was hopeful to entertain an offer for employment. So, I wrote Frank an email advising that I had accepted the position. I never received a response. I did learn a month or so later that Frank's daughter was very ill struggling with cancer unfortunately he lost his daughter. No wonder Frank went silent. I thought I can't imagine what he went through as a father; Frank must have been in unbearable grief and sorrow. Now I understood no wonder Frank did not return my calls. Years later I tried to see Frank I sent an email I suggested I could stop in his office and we could catch up. Unfortunately, we never talked again. I was ever so fortunate to have the opportunity to work with Frank and on several developments. Frank is definitely my favorite architect.

In 2008 Linda and I drove to Dallas. We secured a lovely two-bedroom apartment in a high-rise apartment tower next door to my new office. Our view of the city at night was spectacular. Typically, I occupied my time a week in Dallas another in New York and the remaining time at the property in Playa del Carmen. Life was good actually awesome, I enjoyed working with the Dallas partners Frank Aldridge and Lamont Meek. They had a silent partner Harold Stream who I also enjoyed they called Harold ...SPOOK as he was born on Halloween.

The financial crisis was looming I was actually in New York City enjoying dinner at a Wall Street restaurant in mid-September with Frank and Lamont when the crisis began. Lots of buzz in the restaurant that night, I did not grasp the gravity of the financial crisis for another week or so when Lehman Brothers failed.

At the time Mexico was dealing with all the bad press concerning the Mexican border drug problem and now a worldwide financial crisis. The cherry on the top, or what I could say that proverb…the straw that broke our development's back occurred a few months later, the flu epidemic the 2009 swine flu, H1N1 flu that originated in pigs from a small region in central Mexico. Well this was too much for the development to bear, which ended the project as it would be impossible for any lender to back our development now. Without funds we had no hope.

Fortunately, I had negotiated a clause in my agreement…if the project ended I was due one year salary. A blessing and smart move on my part yes, that said the payment received in December, a significant huge loss to taxes with no income my bank account disappeared fast.

I assumed that upon returning home to California I could easily find another development position. I found this not to be the case. There were no jobs no one was working not Architects, not engineers and my contractor friends were all on hard difficult times, the world stopped spinning. My world definitely stopped spinning income wise. So, Linda and I packed up and moved back to our home in California.

CHAPTER 26
THE LEAN YEARS [2010–12]

Financial crisis

Our world stopped spinning when the financial crisis became a reality. The next couple of years were hard, very difficult times. At one point I thought we were going to lose our home. I took a loan on my life insurance $40K; this got us by for a little longer.

Our life style changed drastically. We did nothing, spent nothing we worked hard on surviving. We did what we could to get by. Times were hard indeed. No one was hiring, I desperately needed an income.

Our son Drew and at the time his girlfriend Rachel sat with Linda and I on my birthday to advise a baby was on the way. Difficult times as finances were short however exciting news for our family.

Our daughter Ashley delivered our first grandchild Hayden October 19, 2010 about a year and a half earlier.

Knox Jack Bousquet blessed the new family May 25, 2012, I bet you can imagine how honored I felt for Knox to have my middle name? Drew and Rachel were already living at our home. Rachel was a beautician working until it was difficult for her to stand for long periods of time, Drew held a minimum wage job working for MB2 a go-kart racing adventure in a big box warehouse. Drew was attending College of the Canyons at the time; he later transferred, making the big move to a four-year university. He attended Cal State Northridge pursuing a degree in Business.

Drew's future father-in-law was a teamster who worked for the movie industry; Drew took Mike's advice and began the necessary steps to become a teamster himself. Drew enrolled in a truck driving school he also enrolled in a bus driving course.

His plan and hope were to be hired by Universal Studios Hollywood to be a driver for the Universal Studios Tour. A signature attraction at the park, and goes into a working film studio, with various film sets on the universal studio lot.

I knew Universal only hired two new drivers each year so his notion may be thin. Fortunately, the woman who interviewed Drew hired him on the spot. Drew signed a two-year contract. The agreement had strict provisions he could only miss a small number of days one more beyond the designated number and he would breach the agreement. So the job gave him a direction and the position had great insurance benefits. With a baby on the way health insurance was a godsend.

Sadly, the job was seasonal. It was impossible for Drew to make ends meet; fortunately, they lived with Linda and I that made the difference for their new family to enjoy a secure start. During the second December of his agreement he was taking four classes at Cal State Northridge. He was forced to miss his classes due to the Universal work schedule. He could not jeopardize his contract so he dropped out of school.

Now I thought for sure that would be the end of Drew's college studies. He asked what I thought about his idea to continue studies at the online University of Phoenix. I told him that was a great idea however with his job and family I imagine he would find it impossible to earn his degree. He met the challenge and graduated from University of Phoenix. I was very proud of Drew I believed it amazing accomplishment especially due to all the constraints.

I asked favors for my son and secured a few job interviews for Project Engineer position from a couple of the construction firms' general contractors and specialty subcontractors. Construction companies I had hired during my previous lifetime, firms I had worked with previously. I was certain due to all the work I previously gave them that they would find an entry position for my son. Unfortunately, work was slow and no offers were made for his employment. I was disappointed... hell Drew was extremely disappointed.

Drew focused on the movie trucking business he secured a couple of day driving opportunities (daily assignments) for the movie industry and this paid off. Teamsters start as a three, you see ones are hired first, then twos and if needed threes. Three's seldom work he found it impossible for threes to keep steady working hours.

While doing day work, he completed a long day of over sixteen hours; the trucking job captain asked if he could return the next day. Drew responded I need the work you do not have to pay overtime. You see the movie business requires an eight-hour turnaround from day to day if less than eight hours the next day the driver is paid time and a half. He worked the next day as requested, at day's end he stopped at the office to find his paycheck

So as fate would have it while walking back to his pickup truck to return home … when Drew opened the envelope and saw is paycheck, he was surprised he realized they had paid him time and a half for the second day. He immediately turned around and walked back to the office. Drew entered the office approached the payroll manager and said, I believe there is a mistake on my paycheck. I told the job captain I need the work I said that straight time was fine with me there is a mistake here you paid me time and a half for today.

Consequently, this conversation was relayed to the job captain and to the owners of the trucking company. They were impressed with Drew's character. More important they offered Drew a position on their show. This was huge very huge as it meant steady work, which is as long as the show runs for the season. Drew elected not to renew his contract at Universal. The decision was wise Drew took a major step forward.

Our family is growing we find so many grandchildren joining us, life I good. Our daughter Ashley gave birth to our first grandchild Hayden on Oct. 19, 2010 just shy of two years before Knox arrived. Ashley and our other daughter in law Jeimi also became pregnant while Rachel was caring Knox. This was the most fascinating time for our family to have three babies on the way. Ashley's daughter Taylor arrived after Knox on June 14, 2012 and Jeimi's daughter Scarlett four months later arrived October 26, 2012. A year and a half later, Rachel delivered our third baby granddaughter Savanna, (Savi) Oct. 10, 2014. Linda and I were fortunate we were blessed with six grandchildren, including Geoff and Jeimi's daughter Layla who would soon become a teenager.

Riyadh

Early 2010 I became aware of an international construction management firm headquartered in Toronto called Projacs the owners were searching for an executive to lead the Riyadh office. The lion's share of Projacs's business contracted in the Middle East. The two owners held a Ga. Tech background, one a previous professor the other his student. The business financed by a third wealthy Middle Eastern business man.

I met the previous student he a little older than I in Toronto my interview more than promising it looks like I will be relocating to the opposite side of the world. A trip scheduled for me to Riyadh. I told Linda if I decide to stay mail me my things, needless to say Linda was nervous, actually she did not want me to take the trip.

During my previous lifetime just a few years earlier while employed by the Kor Group I traveled to Dubai and Oman. I was searching for a General Contractor to construct the Viceroy Anguilla Resort. The construction market at the time strong the economy boundless, I asked Pierre Rousseau to put together a list of potential contractors familiar with the Caribbean construction challenges. I was hopeful to find a contractor that was hungry believing my project a key to their future success. Unfortunately, I learned most on the list already consumed with work, for example Blunt Brothers recently entered into a contract with the US government renovating embassies throughout the world, Perini contracted for the massive City Center development in Vegas. One GC that I believed might be what I was looking for Carillion out of London; they had a strong position in the Caribbean however mainly industrial however Carillion possessed a solid hospitality group constructing resorts in the Middle East. So, me and Carla Romero from my team took a trip, an investigation trip to check out the projects, most importantly this would allow us to meet their construction hospitality team.

I was hopeful Pierre to join us; unfortunately, he was not comfortable traveling to the Middle East. You see Pierre is from Jamaica on a previous occasion we were traveling to Anguilla on the French side of St Marten going through customs when the customs officials removed Pierre out of line taking him to a small building. I waited and waited sitting on a bench outside the customs building. Pierre finally stepped out. Me? Well, I was worried. He advised this happens as they see I am from Jamaica so they believe I might have drugs and think they need to question me. Can you believe I sat on that same bench waiting for Pierre two additional times. I certainly understood why Pierre was fearful to make the trip to Riyadh.

I found Dubai was like Vegas on steroids without the casinos, Oman was like being in an Indiana Jones movie.

Lady luck touched me again yep… I can split the work to make the budget pencil; upon return from my trip and review of the bids I realized a perfect game plan. You see after weeks of investigating Pierre and I found two General Contractors desperately in need for my development to change their future.

I hired Dick Construction from Pittsburg for Anguilla Viceroy Resort for the first phase to construct all below grade disciplines for example foundations, retaining walls and underground utilities. Dick recently lost millions due to their contracts with ENRON; the day of the interview at their office I also witnessed an auction for their heavy equipment taking place in their parking lot. Dick struggling facing hard times can you believe a bank official actually sitting in on the interview. Dick was low bidder, substantially for the first phase. Interesting extremely high for the vertical construction.

I hired Carillion low bidder for the second phase to build the super structure, exterior skin, and interior finishes. I was impressed with Carillion's resort construction quality more importantly found their construction team strong and resourceful. Due to our Middle East trip with accompanying associated interviews with their onsite construction staff at several projects we assembled a Carillion team for Anguilla; I want this guy here that guy there and the tall guy from that other resort, a handpicked team. A strong team assembled to construct our Viceroy Anguilla resort.

I entered into separate contracts the same day with both Dick and Carillion providing the necessary reciprocal language with the contractors to allow for a seamless transition from phase one to phase two. Dick employing /providing labor from Mexico, while Carillion employing/providing their labor force from India.

Do I stay or do I go?

Traveling internationally after my stroke always created tension for me, this trip to Riyadh obviously I am alone so as you might imagine anxiety is my fear and yes anxiety took its hold. It did not help knowing Linda was worried, my daughter worried, my mom worried and my three sisters worried, they did not want me to make this trip. An American traveling to the Middle East, a guy who fights the effects caused from his stroke... come on, Jack, you can do it, think, and be smart, yep, I can do it.

This was one crazy visit; I flew to Hamburg with a six-hour layover waiting for my flight to Riyadh. I slept in a chair at the airport the best I could. My itinerary made arrangements for travel I was advised someone would provide further direction at the hotel. The taxi dropped me at my hotel around seven in the morning; I was so very tired. I asked for any messages, none were found. I took the elevator to my room and jumped in bed.

I got a call just before nine, advising my driver was in the lobby waiting for me, a team has been assembled at the office to meet me. With that, I took a very quick shower put on my suit however no tie and of we go. Business suit is my uniform; early years always included a tie, which is until after Disney days unless I am giving a speech addressing an audience, however in Mexico, Anguilla, and Hawaii hot humid weather my business uniform transgressed to white khaki trousers and a casual shirt.

Kalhial was my driver for the next week and a half, Kalhial took me everywhere. Not certain what he would do while I was in meetings that said he would appear when it was time to go and he always was well informed where he needed to take me and who I would be meeting with. However, I found he was not privy to the agenda.

I want to introduce Jack he will be the led for our Riyadh office. So, I am standing at the door to the Projacs conference room their entire business executive's assembled, after that introduction I find the men smiling and I know they are talking about me. I look down and smile, so my fly isn't open ... I hold my hands out wide and look at them ... I know you are talking about me, could you be so kind to include me in your conversation, does anyone speak English?

A guy at the end of the table stands and says ... we have to compete with those blue eyed American and Canadian bastards; we are pleased to see we now have our own blue-eyed bastard.

I was there for ten days; I was expected to sign my agreement on day ten. The last two days my driver and I toured potential housing locations in addition I visited the shopping center as well as the museum. They were not pleased when I advised I will not take the position and I am leaving in the morning. It was too harsh there. I cannot have Linda visit me here definitely not my daughter not certain even for my sons.

The girl needs help

Returning to my hotel one evening, I found a young lady with 6 luggage bags struggling to pass through the entrance revolving door. She was wearing traditional attire all you could see was her eyes and shoes. I knew she was young as she as wearing cool shoes. Over a dozen men also wearing traditional attire passed her by. She didn't speak English. I helped her get her bags through the door. I was fearful I might get in some sort of trouble, hell I did not know. Once I placed all six bags inside the bell hop came to her rescue, interesting he also watcher her struggle.

In the lobby, I found tea and figs; I was the only one in western attire. After twenty or so minutes, I started towards the elevator. I noticed her bags were loaded on a cart in the elevator lobby.

I started to enter an open elevator cab, when to my surprise I saw six women wearing black burkas. All I could see were twelve eyes. I hesitated; they waved me to come in. I asked do any of you ladies speak English. One looked down the other five shook their heads no. I stepped in … to my surprise the call buttons were on the left side not on the front panel. So now I had to navigate my hand through a sea of black to reach button #16 providing all efforts available to not touch the ladies hidden beneath. Upon pressing my floor call button, I saw below the same shoes earlier, an interesting day indeed.

My son Geoff called me on Skype one morning it was so nice to talk with him via video chat.

Don't touch that

I did enjoy my time with Kalhial he spoke English he asked if a friend could join us at the museum, his friend also spoke English. The three of us enjoyed the afternoon at the museum and the shopping district ending the day with a fabulous dinner.

At the museum I was pleased to find most of the storyline for the artifacts also in English. I learned how Getty discovered oil, he was going bust all wells dry when at number nine oil well he took a risk and drilled additional 150 meters deeper. YEP, I bet you know he hit the motherload.

Only guns and knives are behind glass everything else accessible out in the open. Kalhial shocked the hell out of me I did not see this coming; a small bowl the label in front read 350 BC. So, can you imagine my fear and trepidation when he picked the bowl up with only his thumb and finger and placed the ancient piece in my hand? My left hand, oh crap. My nice hand yes the other one went into emergency mode immediately to make certain I would not drop this priceless item made before Jesus visited our world. What are you doing? Are you crazy? I said as I placed the bowl back on the table as carefully as I could. It's okay. This is for the people; we can touch them, he said. Well, how about we just keep our hands in our pockets? Please do not do that again.

So Kalhial and I got along famously I found him very likable. He was so helpful showing me options for expat housing some came with a safe room all gated with what looked like teenage guards at key points around the perimeter walls holding AK-47s. Everything imaginable on the compound, restaurants, swimming, pools tennis, convenience store barber shop and to my surprise at the more expensive options even a liquor bar. I was expected to select my choice for living be mindful one must pay a year in advance, the company provided allowance if I chose a residence that cost more that would be on my dime, less I could pocket the change.

The morning Kalhial drove me to the airport to return home. Something odd occurred, I think I read too many spy novels; maybe my imagination got the better of me. In view of the airport maybe just a minute from pulling in Kalhial asked me if I like Range Rovers. I replied yes, they are great cars; I purchase two for the guests at a resort I developed in Anguilla. With that he turned to look at me and handed a Range Rover DVD. The print in his language, my initial thought, well this is KUL a nice souvenir.

My second thought made me nervous, why did he give this to me just as we are entering the airport, he could have given it to me any time why now? Oops the seal is broken, is this bomb, Jack you have a crazy vivid immigration stop it. He pulled up to a parking area to let me out, retrieving my luggage we shook hands gave our good byes. Kalhial gave me a big hug, said he would have continued as my driver if I had not turned down the position. Walking to the airport door I saw a trash can about five feet from the entrance. So yep, I tossed the DVD in the trash. I should have kept his gift, today I am certain the DVD was not a bomb, yes my immigration got the best of me.

Bousquet International Ltd.

From the original four Playa firms the new company to develop the resort would have been called Bousquet International. So I used the name Bousquet International to start my consulting company. I created a California Corporation, built a website, and began networking with previous colleagues. Work was not what I imagined. The first year was slim, very slim however the second year I did well. My stroke is now a distance memory. I have definitely learned how to cope and accommodate for the shortcomings the stroke left me. I cannot worry about my stroke anymore I must take care of my family. I have to be a financial success.

I secured an agreement with a southern California savings and loan, Luther Burbank Savings who were interested in investing with a northern California adaptive reuse development. Another client, Antioch University, who were looking or a new home for their campus. A financial investor Invesco retained me because they wanted to make certain there were no significant issues. Don Prohaska, who I met years before when he was retained by the Club View development lender to review the monthly financial status, Don recommended me to oversee the Invesco project, one project became five. This was a very odd position; my job was to attend design and construction meetings and report my view of same. They wanted my point of view ... how were they doing, were they making mistakes? I was Darth Vader when I entered the conference room all became quiet. I was not responsible or accountable, I would say things like did you ever think about this, or perhaps you guys should try that.

One assignment that I enjoyed, Barton Myers a talented local architect retained me, the city of Orlando were short raising funds. Barton asked me to help him salvage his design for the Phillips Performing Arts Center in Orlando.

Steve and Paul Matt who I had the pleasure of hiring several times in my previous lifetime before the financial crisis were a huge help. As the owners' representative at Disney Development Company and Trizec-Hahn, I hired

Matt Construction for six important developments, all on time and under budget, each development a huge success.

February 10, 2012 on this night I was humbled. I was in the audience with my peers. We came to hear a great builder, a man who we all respect remiss about his brilliant career. He told stories about great architects, incredible projects, impossible challenges … and then to my surprise he talked about me. Paul the most respected in the Los Angeles construction market talked about me, a humbling endorsement calling my name with accolades for my leadership ability to manage difficult and risky projects

If not for this assignment with Matt Construction I am certain I would have not have been able to make ends meet. Steve and Paul retained me to assist and provide insight with the owner's point of view. The work was exciting, challenging and I learned much concerning the practices and policies as well as risks from the General Contractor's point of view. Pac-12 studio, Cal Tech Child Care Center, pre-construction for a Hockey Center in Santa Barbara. As well, as various proposed developments, they were hopeful to secure the construction agreement.

I also worked on several proposed developments that never saw the day of light. A couple opportunities with friends and former colleagues from my Trizec day's architect Steve Nakada and Jack Iles he a most creative visionary the projects were remarkable; unfortunately, our team did not win the development prize. I also worked with others as well we teamed to win a proposed development contract providing my time for well over a year. Some of the proposed developments were promising and some were not. That said the work for the most part was random, we got by, we made ends meet.

CHAPTER 27
BACK TO THE BEGINNING [2013]

Thirty-six years later, I found Houston calling me once more.

On a Sunday August 2013 afternoon I received a curious call, at the time I was watching a preseason football game. I was contacted by Bob Cavoto a headhunter who I was not familiar with. Bob advised that my name came up several times from various sources who believed I was the perfect choice to lead a new ground up mixed-use development in Houston. The conversation was intriguing I was not certain that I wanted the position? That said, my consultant work I found not very exciting.

Bob asked if I would travel to Houston. He wanted me to see and check out the site for the proposed development; why not I thought, as I have not returned to Houston since we moved to Virginia in 1984. I thought the trip would give me an opportunity to check out a couple of developments from my previous life time.

Two days later I flew to Houston, arriving at the property I walked around the proposed site more than once… actually three times. I was impressed in point of fact I was very impressed. Standing on Kirby Dr. with my back to the property just short of a half mile south of River Oaks I began to smile. This could be another extraordinary opportunity; yep my mind began to race thinking of the possibilities for development. River Oaks is the Texas version of Beverly Hills. The neighborhood includes street after street of huge mansions for the wealthy….

The morning after I returned home, Bob called me he was curious to see what my trip taught me. I advised real estate is based on location; this site definitely has huge potential. I told him I was very excited about the opportunity. We talked a bit longer; a trip to New York was scheduled for the following week Wednesday September 3rd to meet with the owner, Thor Equities a company I was not familiar with. I also was told I needed to have a telephone interview with another Thor Executive Vice President Kurt Reich. The call was short and uneventful. The next morning, I flew to New York.

I love New York City it was wonderful to be back. For over five years in my previous life time (Disney days) I traveled to NYC every other week. I took a cab from the airport to the Hilton midtown on Avenue of the Americas. That night I walked to Times Square to see a couple of my old projects from my previous life time. I was exhilarated to be back in Times Square, the crowds, the fast pace the excitement was a rush. I first walked to 42nd Street to see the New Amsterdam Theater. She is definitely my favorite. Then back through Times Square to gaze upon ABC Studios. My head was filled with fond memories and reminisce of all who were on my team. Francis Faranda my dear friend occupied my mind, I sure miss my friend. I thought of Laura, Norm and my friend and former colleague Vince DeSimone and all the moments we shared with Frank, I called Laura... next Norm to advise I was standing in front of the Theater unfortunately we were not able to connect. So yes, I enjoyed the evening reminiscing.

In the morning of September 4th, I woke took the elevator down to the lobby. At the pastry stand I chose a cinnamon roll and a coke. I walked around the corner and found a seat at an area adjacent to the closed bar. I thought about the upcoming interview, I thought about my stroke how far I have come; I hoped I would land the position.

I took a short cab ride to Thor Equities office at 25 West 39th St. Thor's office occupied several floors of the building that said the 11th executive floor was the previous office location for Tommy Hilfiger a KUL interior design and Thor kept the design exactly as it was from the previous tenant. I was directed to the main conference room where I met Melissa Gliatta who was responsible for operations and Phil Maguire a Vice President for the development team who reported to Melissa.

The conversation was positive we talked for over an hour and a half. I asked what they had in mind for the development. Melissa talked about a mixed-use development including retail, office and residential with 300–350 apartments.

I responded that they have a unique and very special opportunity that their proposed Houston development should be exclusive with no more than 200 apartment units. I believed a larger component of apartments would be a mistake. Melissa requested that I explain what I mean by exclusive?

Well, I said valet parking as well as valet bicycle parking for the residents and then I thought of Club 33. So, I paused for a second or so, I decided to respond with a story from my Disney days. I went on to tell the Club 33 story.

Melissa we were meeting with Michael about Club 33. I advised Club 33 was a notion of Walt's to provide a private and most exclusive club for the original 33 Disneyland sponsors, for example companies like Carnation and Nestle. You see Walt was the first to have business pay to sponsor; in this case they paid for their name on a theme park ride providing Disney with handsome sums on a yearly basis for the advertising brand opportunity. .

The club was very exclusive located at Disneyland in New Orleans Square. The entrance was simple door with only an oval marker displaying the number 33 to identify the entrance. One needed a secrete password to gain entrance. With a knock on the door saying something like bears like honey, on the other side someone would respond Mini Mouse loves her shoes. Next the one requiring access would respond Mickey is my friend. With that access to the club was gained. The guest would enter to enjoy a fabulous dinner experience.

Most guests at Disneyland had no idea what the door led to. You see, the arrival point just blended in to the scenery... not too far from Pirates of the Caribbean ride. Club 33 offered alcoholic drinks at the time this practice triggered the club to be exclusive. However, over the years Disney hotels as well as all the hotels around Disneyland also offered alcoholic beverages, so unfortunately now the club no longer was exclusive.

I went on to tell Melissa and Phil I scheduled dinners at Club 33 several times to celebrate and thank a Contractor or one of the Architecture teams for a job well done. I was always surprised to find how Club 33 was under-utilized. Meeting with Michael we were certain the club would be abandoned and changed to another use. Michael asked how much does it cost to be a member of Club 33. I responded $5K each year. What Michael said next shocked me, let's make it $25K each year and provide special perks. I responded we will lose all the members. Michael laughed and said Jack we already have, Club 33 is not exclusive anymore, and it is no longer special.

I went on to advise Melissa that today Club 33 has a long waiting list of people who want to join. Melissa and Phil just looked at me neither said a word not a single word. A young woman walked into the conference room and advised Melissa that her party had already arrived for her next meeting; they were waiting for her in another conference room.

I took the train to Clinton, Connecticut to see my mom and family for the weekend with plans to fly back to California Sunday night. I called to tell my wife how things were going… Linda asked if I got the position, I responded, no I told them I disagreed with their idea for their project. Linda laughed and said why didn't you just go along and tell them their idea sounds great?

The next morning while I was visiting my sister Jill a Principal at a local elementary school Melissa called me, she offered me the position. I excused myself from Jill and some of her staff we were standing outside of Jill's office my sister said go ahead you can use my office for your call. I stepped into Jill's office and took a seat at her desk.

I asked Melissa what she wanted for the project and Melissa advised what you said; make the development great, exclusive, top shelf. We discussed my contract and agreed October 1st as my start date. I wanted to get a jump on the development and advised I would like to travel to Houston next week to meet with the architect to engage Gensler to commence with a concept plan. Melissa thought that was a good idea she approved the notion advised Phil would join the meeting and added she will also travel to Houston meeting me the next day to introduce me to Blake Tart. She explained Blake had an awesome office less than a mile from the site and explained he was the broker who assembled the property; Melissa advised she made arrangements for me to office there.

First time

So back to the beginning or should I say back to the future. Thirty-six years earlier my business carrier began in Houston, the day after graduation from Georgia Tech we moved from Atlanta to Houston.

I started interviewing in my junior year to make certain I had a job. To my surprise knowing I had a year remaining at school I received four job offers. A sales position I was not interested in for US Gypsum, an assistant project manager position for a general contractor Whiting Turner located in Baltimore, an estimating position for Blunt Brothers a general contractor located in Montgomery, I also received an offer Cost Engineer from Brown & Root to work overseas with initial training in Houston.

I chose Brown & Root. I graduated June 10, 1978 I held an offer letter from a year earlier advising to commence my first day June 19, 1978 arriving at the disclosed address in Houston. We found an apartment within minutes from the office.

On my first day I got a huge surprise a major disappointment. I arrived at my new office actually twenty minutes early; the woman sitting at the reception desk asked if she could help me. I said hello I am Jack Bousquet reporting for my first day. She looked down at some papers on her desk and said wait here I believe you have been transferred. With that she began to walk down the hallway turning back to look at me, take a seat Jack someone will be coming to talk with you she said as she disappeared down the corridor. About an hour later a man walked up to me and asked are you Jack? I was told I was no longer part of this group that a month or so earlier I had been transferred to the real estate development group. All righty then hmm ...what does that mean, I was wondering why they did not tell me in advance.

I was not happy at all my office now would be at the main Brown & Root corporate complex located at Clinton Dr. on the other side of Houston. If you have never been to Houston well the traffic is daunting the freeways move at a snail's pace during rush hour. So now I had over an hour drive to work in lieu of five minutes. My main concern was I would not be working overseas. To me the overseas assignment sounded exotic and exciting. I kept thinking I should have taken the Baltimore position with Whiting Turner. I wondered should I call them. Ralph Pass head of the office, he drove me to the airport after my interview Ralph kept me in his car for over forty-five minutes at the Baltimore Airport doing his best to convince me to join his team. However with the position being offered over a year earlier and turned down I assumed my call would fall deaf ears.

I wrote a letter to my dad sharing my disappointment, upon his death my mom returned all my letters back to me, I still have them today.

The B&R development group was responsible for all real estate activities for the Haliburton Corporation, an energy conglomerate consisting of thirty-two companies. With time actually a very short period of days I realized my being transferred was by far the best thing for me. I was actually fortunate, extremely lucky to be selected for this exclusive team. My office was a little cubicle that said my office was located on the executive floor of the main building; you see I began my career at the top of the real estate /construction food chain. Yes, my office being a small cubical however I traveled every other week, so my time in the cubical was minimal to say the least. In my future I learned to enjoy the prestigious corner offices with a sofa and TV including the breathtaking spectacular views.

As construction manager I was assigned two developments, an office building in Dallas, Texas for the Life Insurance Company of the Southwest and a satellite Brown & Root office complex in Lombard, Illinois, a short drive from Chicago. I was extremely fortunate and learned quickly. I started at the top finding myself involved in every aspect of the real estate business for example, land purchases, to receiving a background education and protocol strategy dealing with architects who were out of control or contractors who missed the required budgetary mark also exposed to building trade councils who represented the labor unions calling for strike. I was involved in each and every aspect of real estate development.

Being transferred to the development team was by far an opportunity that set my carrier journey to excel to a quickened pace. After working for just three months my boss Tom Robinson the head of our department who was Vice President of Development for all Haliburton properties surprised me with a complementary letter advising he was pleased to give me a sizable 20% raise in salary from $15,600 to $18,720 per year, he advised that I was contributing faster than imagined already providing value. My carrier could have not begun any better. You see previously I always worked with my hands, I was rather nervous school was a difficult challenge for me, could I be successful thinker? I had many doubts, I was always afraid of failure. I believe this fear pushed me. Yep, my fear of failure drove me to success

Back to Houston

So indeed we are going back to the beginning, I told Linda let's start our trip to Houston September 28th the day after my birthday. What I did not know,

Linda had organized a party at our home for my 60th birthday September 27, 2013 ... eleven years to the day after my stroke. I told her we can have dinner with the kids on my birthday and leave for Houston the next morning.

With that well ... so Linda came clean. She said, I planned a surprise party for you, so it appears you want me cancel? We can't have a huge party and just leave a mess for the kids. Well now I thought a party for my birthday hmm... this can also be a going away party for us. I advised a party sounds perfect and what the hell the kids can take care of clean up this will be an awesome way to say goodbye. Linda talked with our kids they said no problem we can clean up you can count on us mom. I think they were a little disappointed the party was no longer a surprise. However earlier in the afternoon before the party Doug, Geoff and Drew kept our plans for us to go to a local sports bar for drinks to celebrate my birthday.

The party was great including friends from our baseball years; I was also pleased to see as well that Linda invited a couple of business colleagues from work—Jack Illes, Paul Stockwell, Kevin, Laura /Norm and so many more attend. We enjoyed a lovely evening

We began our journey early the next morning. My expectations for the Houston development were high; Melissa previously advised Thor equities called the project Kirby Collection. She told me I could change the name that said I believed Kirby Collection to be a great choice to name the development as the property was located on Kirby Dr. in addition the project will be a mixed-use development including office, retail and residential. With that I saw Kirby Collection as a collection of uses ... live, work and play. I was anxious to create the new development. Thor Equities arranged an executive apartment for the first month while we searched for an apartment. In just two weeks we found an apartment located less than half of a mile to the site.

Concept

The architect Gensler chose a very young woman named Anna Deans to be my primary contact. Anna was on maternity leave when I first met the Gensler team in September. My first meeting with Gensler after relocating to Houston included several seasoned architects an impressive group. I scheduled weekly meetings commencing the first week of October to measure and follow progress for the concept package.

However, to my surprise only Anna was available to meet with me during the subsequent times. I found myself creating the concept, please be mindful, I believe I can make things happen better than anyone that said I know I am not a creative guy. I did, however, enjoy my meetings with Anna. I found her to be very smart and she had talents that escaped someone of my age, you see she was in command of the computer arranging, moving, and putting a magical touch on the graphics to articulate my thoughts. In a matter of minutes Anna could control the concept story and make revisions and alterations as we scrubbed and analyzed the consultant reports. I was very impressed with her. I also enjoyed working with Anna she is very likable and I so enjoy working with smart people. The two of us toured Houston for several weeks to see and understand the competition.

Anna and I started to develop the basic design concept upon; receipt of the requested reports from specialty consultants. Previously I requested traffic analysis, market demographic survey data for the area, geotechnical reports, and city parking requirements for all three uses and city protocol as well as city design guidelines for setback requirements. The work was fascinating, I loved my job. I did my best to keep my stroke form occupying my thoughts that said I was reminded when my left hand would act up and do something strange.

The concept package was easy to conceptualize you see the property showed me what to do how to create an exclusive development. For example the traffic report confirmed only one arrival point from Kirby Dr. limited to one specific location. I wanted an exclusive development so the residential component required a separate access and sense of arrival point; I located the residential lobby on the back side corner of the property adjacent to the existing residential neighborhood. To create an exclusive residential experience, I kept residential parking gated in addition to being gated I made certain to isolate the experience from the office and retail parking requirements.

Residential parking could be isolated to the below grade parking. Soil reports confirmed only one below grade level was financially feasible. I wanted to include town homes at the back side of the property to become a common thread with the existing residential neighborhood. Parking requirements set the limits for the building heights. A shading study showed only one area to locate the swimming pool for afternoon sun a huge requirement for a first-class development.

You see from my previous travels I found lakes have an exclusive as well as ordinary side on each lake. Homes on the ordinary side receive morning sun that said homes on the exclusive expensive side receive afternoon sun. So, like I said earlier the site told me how to organize the retail, office, and residential components how to park same I created a plaza level at the sixth floor which became the glue that held all the uses together. The plaza was a huge gamble requiring a ground level as well as sixth floor office lobby. In addition, the elevated design feature would not generate any income however this sixth level plaza design notion would set our development above and apart from the competition.

After one of our concept design meetings while Anna was walking me to the elevator bank we happened to come across her boss as well as a few Gensler architects who attended the initial meeting where they introduced me to Anna. They asked how things were progressing and how I was doing. We exchanged pleasantries and said our goodbyes. That said when my elevator arrived and I walked in I started thinking… Jack you are not a creative person. Yes, the concept package is great however the property told you what to do. My mind kept racing, so what if Gensler continues to ignore Kirby Collection to not provide staff and direction. Jack, you want extraordinary and you cannot continue as the creative lead. By the time I arrived at my car just minutes from our recent, how are ya doing, well I was certain it best to make a change and select another architect.

Change the architect

That afternoon I scheduled interviews with several Houston architects. None met my notion for an extraordinary architect, so I started thinking I could have two architects—one as the design architect and the other as architect of record, creating production drawings, the construction documents.

During my Disney days most projects included a black cape designer architect and a production architect to create the construction documents. This idea would allow me to find a designer outside of Houston someone I was certain to provide an extraordinary design I was not interested in a box that looks like all the other boxes one find with most architecture. However I was certain, I needed a local architect from Houston who would be familiar with the building department and local protocols to create the construction documents.

So I placed a call to Rick Keating a talented architect who I had worked with previously, I was confident Rick could create the WOW design I was looking for. Rick is not an easy guy to work with but I was certain I could control him. With Rick on the phone we talked about the design competition and advised I was enamored with his designs; I said to Rick, I needed Rick not that evil twin brother Skipper. Rick responded he did not know what I was talking about. So I went on to say that I believe he may be the most self-destructive person I know, if he wins the prize and we have an issue let's talk about it without drama. I continued to advise I am looking to him as an option to be the design architect that I did not believe his firm should provide the construction documents. Rick began his career decades ago in Houston to return where he began would be an interesting notion, similar to me.

I called Melissa unfortunately we did not connect; she has a taxing schedule and was unavailable. Fortunately, late that night around 10:00 P.M. my time, 11:00 New York time, Melissa returned my call, I told her that I wanted to make certain Kirby Collection would be the extraordinary development promised; I shared my notion to have a competition with several designers including Gensler the architectural firm she previously selected. Melissa was beginning to trust my judgment she thought the idea of a design competition is wise.

Wedding dress

I set up a design competition with several local architects including Gensler as well as Rick Keating. With the concept package in hand articulating basic masterplan criteria I requested a preview of the architect's thoughts for design. Each independently asked what I wanted the building to look like. I responded I want an extraordinary design. All but Rick were confused, each requesting guidance.

So, at each meeting I gave all the same response. First, I asked if they had a daughter, fortunately everyone responded yes. With all having a daughter I continued with ... so on your daughter's wedding day everything is special for her perfect day that said one thing will be the most important to ensure your daughter's wedding is extraordinary. You see your daughter must find her perfect wedding dress.

Your daughter is not sure what that desired dress looks like; maybe it is strapless, maybe long or short, maybe spaghetti straps and possibly lace and satin. However, when she sees the right dress for her she will want that dress as well as know her wedding day will be all she has dreamed. I ended with … give me my perfect wedding dress.

I am sure they must have thought I was being a smart ass; however, I was looking for a special creative design I was hopeful to create a spectacular extraordinary development, I wanted Houston to take notice of the new developer entering the Houston market, Thor equities. The wedding dress analogy was the best I could offer to express my hopes for an extraordinary top shelf development to set Kirby Collection above and beyond all other Houston architecture.

I requested the competition to be in two phases or parts, first two weeks to submit their fee proposal second an additional two weeks' time for the design notion. The day to see the design for my wedding dress came with each architectural firm giving me an hour presentation. I was hopeful Gensler would step up and surprise me. Rick was scheduled first the other two design firms in the middle with Gensler presenting last. Actually, I asked Gensler where they prefer and as suspected the Gensler team chose the coveted spot to be the final presenter.

Unfortunately, the Gensler design reminded me of all the buildings along the Houston energy corridor. They did add a couple of concepts like solar energy in hopes to convince me they were thinking outside of the box; however a box notion it was. Don't get me wrong these buildings along the energy corridor are nice that said they all look the same, pleasant decorated boxes all in a row along the 10 freeway.

After meetings I always walk my guests to the door, on this day I walked a bit further. While walking the Gensler team to their cars after their presentation I advised that I would be selecting a different architect for Kirby Collection. I thanked them for their efforts I also asked if they would be interested in being the architect of record working with Rick Keating as designer. They advised that they would think about it. While shaking hands and saying goodbye I added you know you have a very smart and most talented employee in Anna Deans. They responded yes, she is young we see potential in Anna; I went on to say I want to give you a heads-up as I intend to hire her. They all laughed smiled while saying goodbye.

By requesting the fee proposals in advance, I confirmed my thoughts that having one architect as designer with the other as architect of record would cause the architectural design fee to be more expensive. I also needed to find a local architect of record. With preliminary fee proposals in hand, I confirmed my fears.

I scheduled a meeting with Melissa and traveled back to New York. At our meeting Phil joined the discussion. I presented a breakdown of fees and associated cost for the architects, including a comprehensive pre-construction budget (what our business calls a Proforma). In addition to the pre-construction proforma I also presented a pre-construction scheduled. The budget package was inclusive of all and any anticipated cost for example all design, primary consultants (MEP/structural) specialty consultants, preconstruction assistance from General Contractor and legal, taxes, city building department t fees, everything from soup to nuts.

I explained to Melissa if we change architects our fees increase substantially. Melisa looked me in the eye and said I am not afraid to spend more money to get something special. With that she approved the preconstruction budget and schedule. I knew Kirby Collection would now be top shelf another development that I can be proud to call mine.

I hired Rick Keating as design architect, Kirksey a local Houston group as architect of record, also from Houston Walter P Moore structural engineer, Wylie consultants MEP engineer, WGA civil engineer. To ensure a top shelf design I also retained dear friend and extraordinary interior designer Dianna Wong from Los Angeles. I added McCarthy Building Companies to the team as preconstruction contractor.

To ensure a positive start I wanted to oversee each and every detail intimately with that I decided to work alone and do everything myself for the first five months, building the proforma cost an income side to ensure desired returns Thor expected, leading Kirby Collection through the concept phase and schematic Design.

My team

When we started the Design Development phase I decided to build my team, I reached out to my dear friend and former colleague Sheila Nelson we had worked together several times previously. Without a doubt Sheila is by far the best at controlling costs and keeping track of the money. I convinced Sheila to become my cost controller to work with me once again. This was a huge decision for Sheila as she would have to relocate to Houston with her husband Lyle leaving her home and family behind in California.

I also placed a call to Anna Deans; remember I told the senior people at Gensler that I believed Anna has promise, potential ... I believe she can become a star. I was delighted for Anna to join my team. I gave her the tile Project Manager that said I made Anna my second. You see I had a hunch that this young woman was special I believed I could coach her, I believed Anna would provide huge value. I believed she could excel and become a leader; I knew I could make her a star. So, Anna went everywhere with me. I exposed this young woman to each and every aspect and challenge. A year later I changed her tile Director of Development, in addition to her promotion Anna received a substantial raise.

When I called her, Anna joked that her boss told her what I said to him after the presentation that I was going to hire her, Anna went on to say that he would on occasion ask if Jack called yet. Anna said she was flattered by my kind words however she never expected that I was serious and that I would actually call to invite her to join my team. I told Anna how she impressed me while we were working together. One never knows what the future will hold; always do your absolute best you never know who is watching you.

They did not tell me this

David Crockett Homeowners Association became my first significant Kirby Collection problem; a challenging obstacle I initially feared could end the development before we even began. Thor Equities was remiss to disclose the previous law suit and subsequent legal restrictions between Thor Equities and the David Crockett HOA. Prior to my joining Thor the developer allowed a night club to occupy one of the several structures on the site. Previously a funeral home occupied the structure. The nightclub was very popular with the young crowd. So popular parking was an issue, many parked in the adjacent residential streets. When leaving the club in the early morning hours the young partyers would continue to party while walking to their cars, talking loud, leaving beer cans and empty liquor bottles on the manicured home lawns, and often urinating in the streets or on the neighborhood lawns.

At the trial's conclusion, be mindful after Thor spent $1.8M on attorney fees the legal battle to close the night club was lost by the HOA. However, the court ruled in the future if any modifications and or improvements to the property, all of the property area owned by Thor if said improvements totaling over $100K prior to construction commencing Thor must present the concept to the David Crockett HOA Design Committee for approval. There is more. Yep, the hits keep coming, here is the knife that I believed could kill my project I could not believe how anyone could possibly agree to this. The design committee has approval of any and all exterior colors, materials, and design notion.

I knew from my previous lifetime Cadillac Fairview days while working in Houston when we developed the fifty-two-story Gulf Oil Tower that the city does not abide by typical zoning concepts or zoning laws. Houston development is based on plat deed system, these deeds totaling in the thousands throughout the city could be initiated and recorded as City deed requirements however most often the deeds are defined to a smaller precise areas established and recorded as homeowner association requirements. The Kirby collection property I learned was included as an integral piece of land which was defined and the plat requirements are governed by the David Crockett homeowners' association.

I know from my previous experience it is important to know your audience. So, I investigated to find the backgrounds of the HOA design Committee. I learned the design committee included a team of five all but one was an attorney. I was curious as this surprised me, why with so many attorneys would they elect the only non-attorney to lead this committee. I found one of the members Bill Mathews previously lead this team, I also learned he led as well as organized the residents in law suit fighting Thor.

So, I started with Bill, I will begin this story by advising over time Bill and I developed a friendship. Now, this surprised me as well. You see, I liked Bill. A couple of years later while we were constructing Kirby Collection, Bill became very sick. He had to be hospitalized twice. We would talk, share some stories, and catch up on life whenever I called to check in to see how Bill was doing.

So, my first call was to Bill to set up a meeting introducing myself and discussing my vision for Kirby Collection. Bill was quick to advise the restrictions and requirements also making certain I knew he was no longer the President of the design committee ... I thought it interesting Bill was not an angry man, I saw him to be smart, very articulate and one who wanted the best for his community. We met twice before Bill introduced me to the Design Committee members and Paul the committee's leader. I met with the committee several times.

With the Design Development Documents now 100% complete I scheduled a presentation. On a Friday afternoon I presented the concept to the David Crockett design committee. I was pleased to see they believed Kirby Collection would enhance their neighborhood providing great value to the residences they also knew their property values would definitely increase. At the close of my presentation, I presented a copy of the Design development Documents to the committee, Paul advised within a week to ten days they will respond with an approval or rejection however the design looks wonderful we are very impressed.

The following Monday Paul called me I was shocked to hear him advise the committee wanted to add a couple additional restrictions and he also advise the committee could not approve or reject Kirby Collection based on Design Development Documents, he went on to say I would need to submit the final Construction Documents for approval at a later time.

So, this was not what Jack was expecting. I do not like delays I submitted the Design Development Documents for approval to ensure this issue was behind me I needed to make certain I could commence construction when I wanted to. If I wait for Construct Documents that would require another presentation and give the committee leverage to delay my start to construct.

My response to Paul even surprised me. Standing in my office with Paul on the phone while looking out the window at my jobsite a block away, I heard myself a say ... Paul I want to make certain you understand I am making myself clear ... I will not entertain any more restrictions; you can approve or reject Kirby Collection based on my presentation based on the associated Design Development Documents I gave to you last Friday.

I continued you are being foolish Kirby Collection will enhance your community all the residents will see an increase to the value of their homes. I said a man is only as good as his word, last Friday after my presentation you advise Jack your concept for Kirby Collection looks wonderful. We are impressed.

Then I crossed the line, I said it is interesting maybe even fascinating when you know and see the exact moment someone plateaus, an opportunity is missed, the precise moment when one fails as a leader, Paul this is your moment. I said goodbye Paul. Well, he next responded goodbye to you Jack.

The line went dead Paul hung up. I stared out the window gazing at the project site. As you can imagine I instantly began to question my response to Paul. What do I do now, how can I explain this to Melissa jeez Jack what is next? Jack sometimes you push too far.

About fifteen minutes later my phone rang, Paul was calling. I answer the phone Paul advised he talked to the committee and he had a couple of questions for me. First he wanted my word. I responded all who know me know I am a man of my word. Paul said will you guarantee the design you presented will not change during the Construction Document process? Absolutely, I responded I will create what I presented. About ten or fifteen seconds went by without a word from Paul or me… at the time his silence seamed unnerving. Paul next asked if I would give a presentation to all in the community so they also can see Kirby Collection through my eyes, I responded, Paul I will not address a hostile crowd I will only give a presentation if it is understood that Kirby Collection has already been approved by the Design Committee.

So if you give me approval in writing based on the Design Development Documents I would be pleased to present Kirby Collection to your neighborhood. I will also invite the architect Richard Keating he will certainly give a better presentation then me. I will make the presentation an event with wine, soft drinks and hors d'oeuvres; a top-shelf event for a top shelf development. Before we ended our conversation his approval letter came across my computer screen. Smiling I thought you still can make things happen Jack, or maybe you are just lucky?

The presentation was perfect Richard charmed the audience. Some initially voiced concerns that the construction workers might park on their streets. I advised I had made provisions actual arrangements for construction parking, you have my word this will not be a concern. Several from the audience also questioned the parking garage lighting will it be bright and bother them at night? I responded the light system works on motion detectors so at night after hours lights will only function when motion causes same, residential parking is below grade the upper levels will be empty. The garage should be dark most of the night. They were thrilled and began clapping to show appreciation.

However one resident became curt and belligerent, I stepped away from the podium and began walking acknowledging the audience moving close and in the direction to the rude resident while I deflected his impolite behavior with humor. The presentation's end the homeowners stood and clapped thankful for Kirby Collection to join their David Crockett community. The homeowners departed that night excited and anxious for construction to commence. Many lingering to have a chance to talk with Richard and me in the parking lot. Not a bad night for a guy who has only half a brain.

Budget bust

I programed several estimates with our contractor McCarthy to confirm Kirby Collection is tracking to my budget. (Concept, Schematic Design phase, 50% Design Development, 100% Design Development, Construction Documents, Permit Set and finally 100% Construction Documents).

Our progress at this time took us to the Schematic Design package. I meet with the design team every two weeks this practice allows me to follow progress intimately and make the various necessary decisions to further our design. I push the design in an effort to achieve the most for the development. During pre-construction I acquiesce to the designers that said during construction my decisions favor the contractor and construction team. This strategy works well for me to deliver a top shelf development at or below budget and most often ahead of schedule.

Well it appears I pushed too hard, when Anna and I met with the McCarthy pre-construction team accompanied by our designers to review the Schematic Design estimate… well you see I found the shock of my life. Yep this is one of those moments that never escape you.

We walked into their conference room to find estimate packages were already placed strategically around the conference room table. We made our pleasantries exchanged the morning greetings advised donuts and coffee waiting on an adjacent table. While the others in the meeting, continued to share small talk and grab a coffee also finding a donut of choice, I took my seat, I immediately turned to the last page of the estimate package and looked at the bottom right corner to find the estimate total.

These words came out of my mouth without hesitation or thought. Holly crap... I feel like I just fell from my seat, my head has hit the table on my way down... I find myself lying here on the floor dying. What the hell is this?

With that everyone stopped talking and found a seat, the chaos was like musical chairs. The room is now silent all attention focused on me and waiting for my next word. I continue to address the McCarthy pre-construction team I did not yell you must understand I never yell I spoke with a soft tone however an extremely pointed direct manner...what is wrong with you guys? You sit with me and our design team every two weeks so what in the hell do you think you are invited for? You do not have the balls to talk with me in advance of this estimate you do not have the backbone to advise the budget is severely in jeopardy? All heads dropped no one looked me in the eye.

You see Kirby Collection was a $235M development all in soup to nuts with Construction cost estimated at $136.5M. Highlighted and in bold font nefariously placed on that last page of the estimate package I found the number at the bottom right-hand corner displaying a $32.5M cost overrun.

Please be mindful the previous concept estimate was on target that said I was assuming a $4–5M problem. I came prepared to show all how to correct same and get Kirby collection back in the black and on target. Unfortunately, a budget bust over $32M is an intimidating problem. My mind raced can Kirby Collection survive this, I have to correct this, and can I correct this, how do I correct this? Maybe it is due to my stroke; maybe just maybe I have lost my edge. Maybe I am over my skis; maybe I should throw in the towel?

But no, I said to myself no Jack you can fix this. Do not quit never ever give in. Stop and think Jack you can do this come on stupid focus roll up your sleeves and get to work.... With that I turned to Bobby Campbell McCarthy's senior estimator, I asked Bobby to walk me through his estimate leaving no detail unturned.

So, the remainder of the day was difficult and laborious. At meetings end I advised the designers that I expect the design process to continue forward without delay. I followed up giving that direction in writing. What about the cost overrun? Scott Tibelliti, the project manager with Kirksey architects, responded. I advised I will fix the budget bust. I expect the design to continue as time is of the essence. We cannot delay we will miss our market window.

I went on to also advise in separate meetings lead by me and Anna I will meet with McCarthy to rectify this cost overrun. I also advised that I intend to engage another General Contractor to confirm the costs and subsequent budget overrun. Scott questioned my logic he believed the design team should also attend my meetings to fix the cost bust. I told them I had to move fast to fix this problem they would slow the process and I cannot afford delays. I continue to say all will be transparent I plan to keep you all advised of my progress. I believe most in the room were certain Kirby Collection would die on the drawing board never to see a commencement for construction.

Most in the room believed my strategy to engage another contractor a huge mistake they advised me of same later in emails or phone discussions as well as in person. They were fearful that the subcontractors would pull their bids if the General Contractor decision was changing and not clear.

For me I had to be certain the estimate was accurate. I also lost trust with McCarthy you see an issue with costs overrun so high warrants a conversation a discussion this is not something a contractor keeps to their self and surprises the owner later. If there is a cost issue speaks up this is why they are invited to the design meetings. I have McCarthy attend and be a party to each and every design meeting, their role is to provide cost, schedule, and logistics. I have no tolerance for yes men. I want my team to speak up. I like people who have opinions, they do not have to agree with me, I need thoughts and opinions I need people who are not afraid to speak up. McCarthy failed me.

At meetings end while walking to our cars I told Anna we need to concentrate to focus and investigate each and every notion to find a solution to rectify this cost overrun. I have some ideas. I then smiled and said I do not believe you should buy anything in your personal life until we find a way to fix this. Anna understood the situation and effort needed. Don't buy anything she said. Jack is Kirby Collection done? Do you believe we can fix this? Absolutely we can fix this, however be smart in your personal life until we do, I responded

Four months previously I directed a deliberate and detailed process to find a General Contractor to be added to our team. After all the interviews and presentations during a design meeting I asked each and every member of our design team sitting at the table who they believed we should choose. All advised EE Reed, the team was very impressed with Richard Milby the EE Reed proposed superintendent, and he definitely stood out from the rest. You see, usually superintendents are not articulate, Richard was most impressive. The design team also liked David Rasch EE Reed proposed Project Executive, you see when I asked what would keep them up at night what aspects of our design are you afraid of... well David was the only one from all construction teams presenting who listed the very same issues that also concerned me. All other General Contractors responded nothing concerned them.

I was impressed with EE Reed however I decided to go with McCarthy as I had a previous relationship having worked on several projects totaling over a billion dollars of construction costs. I believed that hiring a Contractor that I had a previous relationship could provide huge value if and when issues began to surface.

Please understand my McCarthy relationship was with several California staff and the President who worked out of St. Louis. This Houston McCarthy team was new to me. Interesting turn of events I was not certain which contractor to choose EE Reed or McCarthy. You see the night prior to the date for a decision concerning General Contractor I was at my Houston apartment watching the Academy Awards. McCarthy was my contractor for Hollywood & Highland/Kodak Theater project. I was so impressed with McCarthy response on that difficult project I am certain no other contractor could match their effort. So, while watching the 2014 Academy Awards, I kept recalling The Kodak Theater design and construction, and it occurred to me that I should hire McCarthy for Kirby Collection. The next morning at our design meeting I advised McCarthy won the contractor prize. McCarthy was added to our team all seemed to be going smoothly that is until the alarming schematic estimate presentation.

So, I began value engineering process meeting several times with McCarthy I also engaged EE Reed conducting additional cost meetings with their team all these meetings and detail provided huge value. At the time I was still uncertain do I replace McCarthy or not?

With estimate background and detailed cost information and subsequent analysis Anna and I turned over every rock we looked at each and every design aspect and we challenged all of my previous decisions. We exhausted all efforts available. We ran several meetings with McCarthy and EE Reed. We traveled to Los Angeles to meet with Rick Keating, Ryan Davis, and Dianna Wong. Rick is an accomplished designer and Ryan a designer who is also a great problem-solver Ryan's insight was most valuable. Dianna as well provided value an insight. We went down a few rabbit holes however the day was well worth the effort.

I was able to get the horrific cost budget problem back to a manageable issue. I now had a mere $100K exposure to my budget. At the schematic phase this is meaningless as the drawings are weak. Without going into laborious detail, the problem was easier to resolve then I had imagined. I cut some material frills, added leasable area to the residential tower to increase the profit side of my proforma and cleaned up some of the more complicated design notions.

Melissa has a taxing schedule she works even longer hours than I and she travels often usually twice a month to Europe. Melissa is impossible to talk with during the day. I learned when I need her to send a text message after nine, her time ten at night; if she is available, she will respond can you call me now on my cell phone?

Stakeholders

I called Melissa with the good news, I advised Melissa that we were back on track the budget problem is no longer a concern. Melissa was pleased, she said I knew you would do it…. However, what she said next caught me by surprise, Jack I just finished our meeting with the shareholders they have been here for the past week, the good news Kirby Collection is moving forward they approved the development. That said unfortunately for you what was necessary to make this work and get them all on board (slight pause in our conversation) she advised, your construction budget is $1.5M lower $135M in lieu of $136.5M previously approved…. Your construction budget is now at $135M, will that work for you? As you can imagine finding out $1.5M was no longer in my control to make Kirby collection a top shelf development made my job even more difficult. However, I understood why Melissa believed it best to make that call. I also trust and hold Melissa in the highest regard. So, I responded I am glad your presentation went well, Melissa. You can be assured Kirby Collection will be extraordinary. I will deliver Kirby Collection beyond your expectations.

In the morning I brought Anna up to speed concerning my conversation with Melissa. She asked what that would mean…. after what we just went through this is a huge loss to our budget. I responded most likely we must omit the tile at the sixth level plaza and now use colored concrete in place of the tile. Most likely we will have to do with something other than designer kitchen cabinets, something more economical. I went on to say all will be fine, and then I smiled and said did you tell your husband Scott that I told you not to make any purchases? Anna laughed and yes. Well now I responded you can buy things no worry anymore. You did great Anna I so enjoy working with you. We solved our budget issue. We are moving on.

Rick lobbied for me to keep McCarthy, Scott with Kirksey as well. That said I believed EE Reed to be the better choice as McCarthy also at the eleventh hour compromised the contract discussion by requiring certain legal demands concerning the apartment component that could not be resolved moving forward (fearful the apartments could become condos in the future).

So, I made the change to engage EE Reed and never looked back. The key consideration in our decision to build Kirby Collection was getting the project into the marketplace ahead of the competition. To achieve this, we knew we would need to bring a contractor on board early to analyze systems, finalize budgets, and operate in a design assist mode during the fast-track construction process. In light of these considerations and latest challenge I chose E.E. Reed Construction, I decide to change General Contractors

EE Reed by comparison was a much smaller contractor, their paper work lacked finesse and business acumen however their paperwork was well, adequate. During the remainder of the pre-construction phase; E.E. Reed provided spot on budget information to allow our firm to perform the necessary feasibility studies to proceed with the project. They worked hand in hand with the designers to optimize systems and components that were ultimately selected for the project. Furthermore, they were instrumental in prioritizing the effort to make the process a success. During the course of construction, E.E. Reed's experience, resources and team approach contributed significantly to the successful completion of the project.

EE Reed brought a high level of leadership, experience, and technical expertise to their projects. Their ability to foster team work and arrive at timely decisions is key elements in their approach to guiding the project delivery team to success. They understand our business, a company and individuals whose honesty and integrity are the foundation of their service.

The key to our success was Richard Milby his leadership directing field operations provided huge value. Richard and I became friends seeing each other out side of work enjoying many evenings with our wives. In addition David Rasch's ability to bring an A-team of subcontractors to the project provided great value. To my surprise and a young Matt Lang's tireless work ethic also provide huge value to Kirby Collections success. I watched Matt grow to become a leader. One Saturday afternoon I found Matt at the site office. We talked for a while, I advised that I believe him to be smart and most capable; however, if he does not learn to delegate and help make the people reporting to him smarter, he will never grow.

The best worst idea

So what happened next caught me by surprise. Please be mindful for the previous six to eight weeks while finalizing a course and strategy to correct the budget bust I continued to meet with our design team to further our progress every two weeks. As time was of the essence I needed to get my development under construction ahead of the market competition, timing meant success or failure. Unfortunately, Doug Hamell the partner in charge for Kirksey directed the design team to pause as he believed the budget bust would not be corrected; you see Doug believed my notion for the development would not be feasible, he believed Rick Keating's design to be unrealistic financially. Doug thought we were wasting our time he believed we should design a box a basic concept similar to all the existing box shaped developments that lined the freeways in Houston. Kirby Collection was unique to the Houston market, a mammoth vertically stacked mixed use development occupying 3.2 acres including 1.5-acre landscaped plaza located at the sixth level, the elevated plaza is the design glue that holds the development together.

I told Scott Kirksey's project manager verbally also in writing to continue that said Doug directed the team to pause. So now I was faced with another issue a timing problem that I believed could drastically hurt my development. I asked for a meeting with Doug, Scott and all Kirksey partners I wanted the Kirksey partners to know I was disappointed, I wanted the partners to know my project was now in jeopardy, I wanted the partners to know I gave explicit direction to continue. I came ever so close to firing Kirksey however I did not believe my development could take another blow. You see if I were to change the architect of record the new team would have to catch up I could actually lose more time.

Doug never attended another meeting. He remained in the background appearing by phone on occasion to voice billing concerns that for the most part he misunderstood. Unfortunately, Scott lost his mentor I believe the Kirksey partners were remiss they should have moved Doug from my project and replace him with another partner. Scott is a hard worker who was very likable that said Kirby Collection was a challenge. I would work with Scott again in a New York minute.

So, I developed several schedule scenarios' all based on three concepts. Using the permit set to push the schedule, relying on the 100% construction documents package to clean up any holes or problems by moving so quickly and engaging subcontractors earlier than typical to gain subcontractor thoughts and input to assist our designers while finalize the construction documents. I scheduled an all hands on deck meeting with our complete design team as well as our General contractor EE Reed. At the meeting in an effort to make up for the lost time I presented three potential possible design schedules. I closed my discussion advising I have no choice we must beat our competition it is important that we choose a schedule to regain the time lost. It is imperative that we come together as a team it is essential that we over communicate for Kirby Collection to be a success. I advised it is a privilege for me as well as anyone on the team to be associated with Kirby Collection just saying you were part of this team will lift everyone's future, all of Houston is talking about Kirby Collection and I bet we get national attention. I went on to say what do you believe is the best worst idea for our schedule? At the conclusion of an all-day discussion scrubbing the various schedule alternatives my team selected what they believed the best worst idea.

As I drove back to my apartment I smiled and thought with just half of a brain you still can make things happen (make the impossible possible) Jack. Once during the meeting at a critical point I got confused while articulating the schedule strategies .I saw concern and a bit of confusion on the faces of my design team, so immediately I stopped talking. With one hand in my pocket the other pointing I walked back to the white board where Anna had previously wrote the basic conditions. I turned to the team smiling saying I know this is complicated as you can see I made an error explaining same to you … with that I went on to say I got derailed off the track a second, so team let's get this train back on the tracks. I continued to discuss the options pointing to the list of pros and cons listed on the white board. As a team we choose the best worst idea. It actually worked Kirby Collection got back on a successful path.

You already know I am so fearful that someone will know I suffered a serious stroke. I have to constantly coach myself to keep my secret. I am fearful the wheels will come of if someone finds my secret.

David a great addition

The design process got back on track we gained lost time I was pleased that our construction documents were coming together nicely.

I needed to find additional staff for my development team to ensure we were ready for the upcoming construction phase. So I found a seasoned construction manager named Richard, well it did not take long to realize that Richard was a poor choice. I pride myself on finding the smartest and best to put around me.

After a short time, I asked Richard to come to my office I shut the door I walked back to my desk he took a seat on my sofa, With a short pause I looked Richard in the eye Richard I said, I do not believe this is working for you or me … I believe it best for you to move on. With that Richard a tall man much taller than I, well he jumped up from his seat with his arms flailing he began to lurch towards me. So as you can imagine I believe Richard was angry well I was dead wrong. At the last second Richard held his hand out to shake mine and he said you expect too much there is no way I can do what you need, it just is not in me, I was trying to figure out a way to tell you I should move on , thank you Jack.

Shortly after I hired J.J. Minicamp a Texas gentleman around my age, JJ a very likeable guy had many contacts in the Houston area. I also retained David Rendon a young man close to Anna's age he had previous contractor as well as owner experience I held high hopes for David as I believed he had great potential. So now I had my development team, Sheila our Cost Controller, Anna the Project Manager, JJ the Construction Manager responsible for the office tower and parking garage construction and David the Construction

Manager responsible for the residential tower, retail and offsite construction. I thought JJ could assist me by mentoring the younger David, within a relatively short time it was apparent that David was head and shoulders above JJ. He was lazy unfortunately he never possessed the experience he portrayed by contrast David was very smart, creative and ambitious.

David worked well with the design team he could lead the construction team and most important David got along and worked well with Anna and Sheila. By contrast JJ was not a leader. David however became a strong leader, a key to our success.

About eight months before we finalized the construction for Kirby Collection I asked JJ to move on. It was neither difficult nor easy. You see like I said JJ was a very likable guy he has a bubbly personality. He just holds a more relaxed work ethic. In retrospect I should have made the move earlier.

About a year before completion I hire a young intern Khaled Noun. Khaled he reported to David. I have a habit of finding young interns at the close of the development I believe this to be a great chance for finding future talent. In Khaled's case he provided value to our team a very nice and likable guy. At the completion of Kirby collection Khaled transferred to work at our home office in New York City.

With my team in place and the Kirksey unfortunate schedule bust behind us Kirby Collection was progressing smoothly we find the development substantially under budget and a couple of months ahead of schedule.

As a rule of thumb for each and every development I press construction to advance as fast as appropriate as well as plausible. I look to the future and try my best to get ahead of schedule before the construction tops out (reaches the highest level) During early construction one works with a small number of subcontractors however once the development is topped out now the skin and interior subcontractor commence at this point of construction scores of subcontractors occupy the site, the project is more complicated too many subcontractors are dependent on one and other. Typically, I find I lose half the time we previously gain on the schedule after top out to completion. For example, if at top out we are four weeks ahead of schedule most often we will end up no better than two weeks ahead at completion. That said, if the project is mismanaged, we could find the development late and miss our schedule all together.

Construction is risky for example often circumstances rise from left field that one finds absolutely no control no immediate answer…you just have to stay confident and do your very best to work through the dark empty days. For Kirby Collection the oil and gas market decided to test our resolve

Oil market falls

When I commenced the design effort oil sold for $105 per barrel the oil and gas market was hot Houston being the energy center for America was definitely thriving over one hundred and twenty-five thousand people were moving to Houston each year. During this boom Houston grew to become the fourth largest city in America surpassing Philadelphia. With the Design Development documents finalized we began the exercise to secure financing. Regrettably the oil market was in a free fall dropping to a besieged $45 per barrel; the Houston economy market struggling to stay afloat. As you can imagine Exxon, Shell, BBP every oil company in town announced huge layoffs and the independent oil companies struggled to keep their names on the door.

So our future looked dim. What do we do? Should we throw in the towel? Is Kirby Collection dead?

I believed our competition would wane, I also believe I could command favorable bids for construction while finding the best of construction talent finding actual A-teams to construct Kirby Collection. Thor Equities missed the development wave last time could they afford to wait again? Could the shareholders afford not to move forward? I traveled to New York I met with Melissa and key parties from Thor. With very little hesitation Melissa elected to move forward. She is a strong woman who can quickly rasp the situation and make her way through the complicated and intricate murky analysis.

So that was the good news, now we wait to see if we can attract financing. Without financial backing Kirby Collection would never get off the drawing table.

After meeting with a couple financial brokers we chose Jones Lang La-Salle. JLL proved to be an impressive team securing a lender as well as a mezzanine loan. However there was one catch. As the office market disappeared over night along with the oil profits the investors were not interested and had no appetite to fund the office tower. Please be mindful, Kirby Collection is a vertically integrated mixed-use development. At the sixth level a landscaped plaza ties all uses together. This meant it was necessary to construct the office tower at least to the plaza level. So, yes, the investors elected to fund the office tower as well, but only to level six, a huge obstacle another problem to work around.

I worked tirelessly with my team so very pleased Anna and David stepped up providing huge value on this effort. We created graphic package including associate cost for a couple alternatives. We scheduled a meeting in New York with Melissa and her team. After long analysis I believed we had one of two strategies. We could build the office tower to level six and stop or we could continue the shell and core tower to top out. The graphic rendition showing the office stopping at level six brought the issue to hand immediately. As it would be certain the residential and retail components would suffer due to the unfinished office tower. The second option to continue shell and core construction disciplines leaving interior finishes out proved to be the less risky option for Kirby Collection. That meant Thor Equities would have to pay forward eight million dollars of additional equity. Once the office market recovers the paid forward equity in question could be reimbursed by the bank. This pay forward strategy I proposed was found acceptable. It was not easy initially rejected before I could finish my presentation; I just started my discussion over from the beginning continuing to sell my pay it forward strategy. Fortunately this time I got Melissa's attention she saw she understood she made the tough decision. Melissa a strong woman a most capable leader, I wish I found this woman earlier in my career I so enjoyed working for Melissa.

The lenders made a provision to accommodate my strategy they created two parts two distinct financial considerations to the loan. The office tower including level seven through thirteen as well as all subsequent interior finishes in the second loan phase, requiring 35% pre lease trigger to fund the second phase.

We moved forward with construction achieving the 35% pre-leasing although three months later than I had assumed. That said we did it we made it work this strategy enabled Kirby Collection to commence construction and become the success she is today.

Interesting as it may we commenced construction October 5, 2015 the meeting to choose a construction strategy occurred November 15, 2015. That was the last time we met with Melissa and New York. From that point to completion we moved Kirby collection to the finish line continuing to provide Melissa a weekly report. From that point on I had Anna and David author the weekly reports to Melissa with assistance from Sheila and JJ.

Jack is back, I was on cloud nine my confidence obviously returned my stroke still a secret however that mishap becoming more and more a distant memory. Please be mindful I still have issues, short term memory is a challenge as well as the assortment of other problems I discussed with you earlier. No one knows I have half a brain yep I mastered my deficiencies I found ways to compensate and work around my short comings.

We go to court

One of our adjacent property owners a rather difficult gentleman filed a court order injunction he hoped to disrupt our construction he wanted any and all construction access as well as egress to not occur on the street fronting his property. The office tower crane's tail end that housed the counter weights the jib swung over his property however our contractor made certain the front end lifting items for construction never moved over his property.

His attorney attacked the office tower crane placement they demanded we take the crane down and accommodate his wishes abandoning construction activity on the street that provides access to his retail property. My attorney Mark Guthrie believed I should negotiate, that said I believed that to be a mistake as time and associated cost would seriously jeopardize my development. The buck stops with me it's my decision so we went to court, we found experts we studied and organized a team to respond and fight his attack. Mark built a most impressive case.

Anna wears many hats on my team one of which made Anna the face and voice to the neighborhood community; she was the one to advise homeowners and business owners of all road closing and difficult deliveries. This hat unfortunately required that the young woman be the one to represent Thor Equities on the stand in court. David Rasch represented our contractor EE Reed a hand full of experts assisted Anna and David. We won. The crane remained as designed we lost a couple of weeks effort on the office tower fighting the injunction however we were able to continue construction on the residential and retail components while we fought our legal battle.

Our advisory was so confident he posted $100K bond in cash to fight us. I could have kept it all. That said I entered into a separate agreement with him that basically required me to refund $90K with my advisory guarantying he would not cause future injunctions and or harm to my efforts to construct Kirby Collection.

I was so very proud of Anna our advisory's attorney tried several times to trip up this young lady, Anna prove to be capable, smart and charismatic she won the judges consideration. I told her I felt like a proud father watching her shine. A couple of months later Linda and I met Anna's parents. We became friends often enjoying dinner together and weekend travels. Her dad so enjoyed me is telling him the story of how his daughter turned the court to our favor.

What happened to the concrete?

I often have been known to joke saying, be careful when things are going well much better than anticipated ... well now that is when one must pay attention, one must make sure you are smart enough to make certain all is well. In construction if something can go wrong most often it will? Construction is complicated a problem will quickly alter and spoil your short moment of bliss.

So picture if you will ...The office and residential tower construction's vertical erection was taking its place on the skyline. Kirby Collection supported three majestic tower cranes on the horizon erecting the retail, office and residential mixed use components. Kirby Collection is becoming the talk of Houston; better yet we were substantially under budget and more than two months ahead of schedule. AND THEN.

One Friday afternoon our construction team placed concrete at three exterior columns on the fourteenth floor of the residential tower. In addition, they placed half of the tenth floor elevated slab of the office tower. The office tower deck a huge footprint is rather complicated comprised of a composite structural design included a waffle slab with integral posttension concrete beams.

Early the following Monday morning I received a call from David Rasch the project executive for EE Reed. David most often is laid back and calm however on this morning his voice commanded concern and worry. David went on to advise that when our subcontractor Keystone Concrete stripped the residential tower forms the concrete fell to a dry moist pile exposing the columns reinforcing steel skeleton above. While talking David forward a photo to my cell phone, definitely a startling image. With that David advised the elevated tenth level office tower slab also not curing. He said he could write on the slab surface with his fingers. Obviously this is alarming something is terribly wrong however no one has witnessed the occurrence like this previously.

David had already notified the concrete ready mix concrete supplier, several representatives from Campbell Concrete had arrived to the site, and currently they were in the process of running an investigation at their batch plant. While talking with David my independent testing company ECS were calling me on my other line and simultaneously Jose Diaz sent me an email advising that the concrete test cylinders for Friday's pour were displaying critically low results. I put David on hold advised I had ECS on the other line.

Talking with ECS I found they were also baffled. I advised I had David on the other line and reiterated my conversation with David. I asked Jose to go to the batch plant to see what they could find.

The previous Friday we placed the questionable concrete the Houston weather was well like most Houston days during this time of year... three to four days a week the weather is hot, muggy with scattered light rain. I got back to my call with David it was still early in the morning just before nine. We talked about the possibility of waiting a day or two to see how the concrete reacts maybe the concrete would cure, maybe not? Without hesitation we concurred it is best to remove the concrete and begin the process immediately. Please be mindful, we could not strip the forms as that would be too dangerous for the construction workers. Concrete removal must commence form the elevated slab's top surface.

Next, I placed a call to our structural engineer Ricardo Martinez with Walter P. Moore. Ricardo was already driving to the jobsite he advised he was just minutes away. Ricardo is a very smart and creative engineer I trust his judgment and guidance

As it turned out the problem was too much fly ash in the concrete recipe. Fly ash is a common additive used in high humid locations to slow down the concrete curing process. Typically fly ash comprises 15% or less is added to the recipe. Alarmingly in our case tests found a sporadic range anywhere from 55% on the low side and as much as to 85% to the high. No one was certain how this happened that said the ready-mix supplier believed either a faulty valve which kept getting stuck or a computer error. We stopped receiving concrete from the questioned batch plant until they were certain the issue was corrected. This particular ready-mix company had several batch plants in the Houston area. Most often concrete was delivered form several batch plants depending on the need and demand for the day. Fortunately, in our case all the concrete placed that Friday came from the same batch plant.

The demo process took two weeks we worked ten hours each day, with guidance from Ricardo our structural engineer and leadership from Richard Milby EE Reed superintendent we were able to save the reinforcement steel and post tension cables. The noise was daunting ten to twelve hand held jack hammers and six robotic jack hammers working simultaneously. The robotic jack hammers about the size of a VW Bug were extremely precise. The construction workers controlled the robotic jack hammer remotely with an IPAD. Their precision and control was most impressive. As the problem was the fault of the concrete ready mix supplier their insurance paid for all costs to remove the faulty concrete. From the onset they took responsibility never a question; I was impressed with the leadership at Campbell Concrete. I would work with Campbell again in a New York minute.

On that Friday when we placed the concrete due to the possibility of inclement weather forecast that particular day only four other projects received concrete from the questionable batch plant. All four projects received a faulty mix. We chose to remove the concrete and began the effort immediately the other four developers elected to wait and pray the concrete cures at the required design strength. That proved to be a huge mistake as the time allowed the concrete mix to further cure however never coming close and never achieving acceptable strength. Their wait caused a more heroic effort and time to remove the faulty concrete.

China trip

We purchased wood flooring, tile and quartz counter tops a $1.1M savings from state bound manufactures through our subcontractor BGT Interior Solutions from sources in China. So, with approximately 10–15% of our product fabricated I scheduled a trip to China, you see I wanted to make certain the material met our standards.

I made dozens of trips in my previous life time to Italy or Spain for marble and granite Canada for glue laminated beams and millwork, however this would be my first time visiting China.

Three representatives James Clark, Keith Wagner, Luis Aguilar from our subcontractor BGT Interior Solutions David Rendon and me made plans for the trip. Unfortunately, our General Contractor EE Reed was small minded they did not understand nor comprehend the value subsequent discussions with Chinese Manufactures could provide, so they chose to send at the very last moment their young project engineer John Socha.

So, imagine this just out of college John flew to Shanghai to join up with us the day after our arrival in China. BGT sent an email to John with the following direction… on arrival he should go to the Burger King at the airport and ask for Wang, he will connect you with your party,

Can you imagine a young man an American walking around the Shanghai airport questioning random people, are you Wang? I had little confidence in this plan so I requested that we go to the airport to find John. The drive to the airport was crazy the freeway traffic moved at a snail's pace. We did find John standing outside a short distance from one of the airport entrances at the airport a couple of hours after he landed; I believe it was a miracle. I can't imagine having the confidence to do what john did.

I liked john he was very smart a quick learner I believed he would have a promising career. John made our trip fun his youthful outlook was priceless. In addition to visiting the scheduled manufactures to confirm our products acceptable we attended the Canton Fair, twelve million sf of building material all under roof. This was impressive very impressive to say the least. On previous occasions the BGT team made many trips to China they understood the country, hired a Chinese logistics manager who resided in Shanghai, most important they had vetted many manufactures, knew them well establishing strong working relationship with several factories.

I found one issue with the quartz countertops… the plant manager organized his team to solve my concern; I was pleased and impressed with his corrective response I liked what we saw.

The next day while touring the Canton Fair I came across maybe fifty kitchen /cabinet manufactures a huge area where several factories displayed their product. I found the quality to be similar to our Canadian manufacture's mock up at my office.

About a month prior to our China trip I approved the contract for a Canadian company to fabricate our kitchen and bathroom cabinetry. I had the subcontractor construct a mock up at my office. One Saturday afternoon I went to my office to clean the mock up making certain all was presentable for a meeting with the designers the following Monday. While cleaning the mock up being ever so close to the cabinetry I realized many imperfections, to say the least I was definitely disappointed.

So, walking around all these displays at the Canton Fair I happened to find one manufacturer that was head and shoulders above the competition. Immediately I was impressed and curious. I jockeyed through the crowd to get closer, inspecting the smallest details. I stumbled across a great product although China made the cabinetry a white lacquer Italian design I found to be very impressive.

I constantly looked over my shoulder to make certain I did not get separated from my party; I glanced down the aisle I spotted my party moving away moving in the direction towards the elevator bank. I also saw a young woman a sales representative standing close by, so I asked her for a business card. I confirmed her card to be the high-quality manufacturer from the banner placed at the entry to the display OPPEIN the name of the manufacturer and quickened my pace to catch up with my party.

Later that night at dinner I told the team how I was impressed with the quality at one and only one kitchen cabinetry display. Keith asked who the manufacturer is. I reached in my pocket retrieving several business cards finally finding the correct one. I read the name on the card Oppein, Keith responded that's funny we are scheduled to visit their factory in the morning I heard good things about them.

We traveled by van early in the morning to the factory, I found a modern factory including a huge sales room displaying a dozen or so different cabinetry styles. The quality identical to what I witnessed the previous day at the Canton Fair.

I had an idea to change manufactures. I called Dianna, she said, oh my God, Jack. You have big balls. Are you certain this will work? I talked with

Melissa, and she said, I trust your judgment. Good luck with your decision. I called the EE Reed team back in Houston. That conversation was awkward. As you can imagine they were very concerned. In addition, now EE Reed would have to unwind the agreement with the Canadian factory.

All believed I was crazy… you see, I had David direct EE Reed to forward electronic set of drawings to the factory for pricing. To my great surprise in just one day the Chinese finalized the bid estimate three days later the shop drawings were completed. We, well … actually David Rendon and the young Chinese woman the sales representative who previously gave me here business card (she gave us her American name; unfortunately, I cannot remember her name now) immediately she and David began reviewing shop drawings for the next couple of days the two working tirelessly to make a purchase possible. We scrubbed the numbers doing our best to analyze the estimate for our cabinetry.

The date October 17, 2016 our schedule demanded the final product arriving to the jobsite no later than March 15, 2017. Overseas shipping required a six-week time line, so the final shipment must leave the docks no later than February 1, 2017 please be mindful in only 103 days China will close down all factories for two weeks due to the chinses New Year holiday January 28, 2017.

So, I knew I could purchase a more economical product from China, I did not know I could obtain a superior product. The price realized just $134 per unit additional cost, so I have 199 units total additional cost a mere $26,666. I pulled the trigger. I also scheduled another trip for David and our BGT team to return to China in mid-November to approve the mock up as well as confirm the factory was on schedule with production to meet our demand. It worked delivery was made on time, sometimes you have to take a risk to make something good…great.

Dianna's design notion included a waterfall quartz countertop, the cabinetry comprised two distinct finishes the bottom a grained light gray thermofoil and the top white lacquer finish. David approved the mockup which met our standards he was pleased.

David called me from China to advise of the good news and added Oppein has our mockup on the sales floor with their other products they believe the design will be found favorable and hope the profits commensurate. Jack Oppein named the lower thermofoil cabinetry Rendon collection and the upper white lacquer the Bousquet collection. We both laughed discussing how this to be a nice tribute.

So, while we scrubbed the estimate, simultaneously we continued touring factories. I was impressed with all the tile factories. While touring the last tile factory, we moved from the factory to the loading area. I walked into a huge storage facility housing several competition designer tiles in boxes stacked to the ceiling. For example, brand-name boxes of tile I witnessed being loaded in trucks for shipment, I saw box after box of designer tile from several countries for example Italy, Spain and yes, America. The print on the box (made in USA, others labeled made in Italy.)

I questioned this; the plant manager explained at first our competitors from other countries came here to see our product as we had copied their design. After a couple of meetings, they actually retained us to make their tile. At first, we shipped our product to them in plain boxes after time they negotiated a new contract they supply their boxes; we charge them an additional ten cents per box shipping the product directly to the desired destinations.

I learned the Chinese tile was very economical. Remember earlier I told you Melissa believed it best to cut my construction budget by $1.5M to make Kirby Collection attractive to the investors? In addition to using a lessor quality cabinetry for the residential tower I had to also make the decision to omit the tile at the sixth level plaza deck? We ran some numbers finding I could eliminate the colored concrete topping at the plaza deck replacing same with Chinese tile at no additional cost to my development. With that I made another change to reintroduce tile back to the sixth level plaza area.

I was happy very excited as now I could boast a top shelf development once more, this trip to China surfaced some creative options and we solved my concern with the residential kitchen and bath cabinetry also replacing the subpar colored concrete with the tile at the six level plaza I had hoped for in the first place, Life was good I was more than certain Kirby Collection will be a huge success.

HARVEY

Previously I told you during construction if something can go wrong it usually does. We always pay close attention to the weather I had three weather apps on my phone; I know what you are thinking, why three? Yes, that is silly ho-wever; one must pay attention to the weather forecast to navigate a project to the finish. One afternoon in early August 2017 Richard Milby and I started to discuss Hurricane Harvey a storm I was following. While talking we realized we both had been following the storm for three or four days. We began sharing our concern and with that conservation well I guess that was the start of plan-ning as well as casting the strategy to prepare Kirby Collection … in the event Harvey found landfall in Houston.

For a week to ten days our construction crews buttoned up Kirby Collec-tion. We elected to work overtime as the office tower roof was scheduled to commence in early September. Unfortunately, this was a mistake. You see the slopes in construction the slopes are called crickets they were cast when the concrete was placed, the roof drain lines completed early. As fate would have it time was not on our side the roofing material lacked about 10–12% of the area in three small locations one adjacent to the elevator shafts, the other two where the roof tied to the two stair shafts. These three relatively small areas a depression of 3–4 inches deep remained unprotected.

Harvey hit Houston directly. The skies opened up to rain, and my God, did it rain, so much rain that I never experienced before. Houston received over sixty inches of rain. The three depressions, those unprotected roof areas flooded and caused a stream to flow to become three distinct water falls drop-ping the rain precariously down our elevator and stair shafts.

So, we got lucky our Harvey hurricane damage found to be minimal. Lim-ited to the following, we replaced all elevator car electronic computer com-ponents locate on the roof the elevator cabs, we ran a maintenance cycle on all elevator cars including changing all oils, and repaired shaft damaged dry-wall. Our exposure was limited to relatively minor damages, so I often wonder; say we elected to not place the roof material coating the exposed area, as time most likely would not allow our construction crews to finalize same, leaving the roof footprint exposed would we have incurred leaks throughout the build-ing? I believe yes however as the slope and rood drains were already finished possibly that damage could have been less? Maybe more? I will never know.

I placed my car as well as Linda's on high ground to protect them from flooding. Houston received so much rain flooding the streets all this became water ways several freeways closed for over week under water.

Linda and I watched the streets flood from our third-floor apartment located less than a mile from my development. At times water shot into the air 2-3 ft. from the 3x3 foot square storm grates located in the street and apartment parking lot flooding the oversaturated ground even more. Please be mindful Harvey dumped over 60 inches of rain. Yes over 5 ft. of rain. We were located in the Houston Buffalo Bayou area our apartment actually on Buffalo Speedway. You see storm water in Houston dumps in bayous when the bayou system reaches capacity the water pressure flows in the opposite direction dumping huge gallons of storm water yield back on to the streets.

Around noon the next day in our area the water began to recede so I walked to my jobsite as I was curious actually rather nervous to see what I would find, along the way twice I was forced to walk through about a foot of water. I saw several abandoned cars siting precariously in the street median where the storm surge left the cars to rest as the water moved on to find the storm drains.

When I arrived at my development I stood and smiled as she looked fine. I noticed all the debris in a perfect line up on the grass lawns of the residential homes across the street from Kirby Collection, the debris sitting about twelve or fifteen feet from the street curb. The day Harvey arrived was trash day for this neighborhood. The high-level water surged pushing the trash containers previously in the street to flip over dumping the trash. The trash cans and the tops of the plastic lawn sprinkler control covers now created a distinct line on the residences front lawns.

I immediately quickened my pace to the parking garage the main gates were open so I knew someone from the construction team was already on site. I descended the stairs to the below grade parking level. At first all appeared to be perfect; however, as I moved to the far end from where I was standing, I found a small amount of water an inch or so around the sump pump pits at the north end.

I later was advised in this area the storm water had reversed similar to the storm water grates in the streets forcing storm water into my garage, they also advised the vertical spray reached the underside of the elevated garage deck just above the sump pits. That said my garage was now dry with the exception of a sizable puddle encircling the sump pits. I did a happy dance for a minute or so I must have been a sight, fortunately I was alone so no one could see my awkward exhibition.

As I walked up the ramp to return to grade well, I noticed a couple of workers cleaning up Kirby Collection from the storm at the residential valet drop-off area. In the distance I spotted Richard Milby. He took me up to the level six plaza area on our way Richard advised you are not going to believe this. Arriving at the plaza level I was shocked to see the residential swimming pool full of rain water. Please be mindful prior to the storm our swimming pool was empty.

Six construction workers all Mexican left their families returning to work. Richard was supervising; in addition, as I walked to greet them, I watched Richard working as well right beside these loyal construction workers.

Just a block away is the Pie House an upscale diner a restaurant the construction staff and my team often frequented for lunch. So, on this day I advised lunch is on Jack, I introduced myself to the workers as we walked to The Pie House, Lunch was the least I could do at the moment to show my gratitude. The city remained flooded several streets and neighborhoods under water as well as the freeways submerged in the murky remains from the rain.

I learned many from our extended Kirby Collection team were suffering from Harvey. Eleven from our team lost their homes so much water they escaped by gathering their family to the high point, sitting on their roof until first responders helped them to safety.

I learned of heroic stories from our team. One I would like to share a young construction worker in his mid-twenties lost his home and pickup truck his only possession a small flat bottom fishing boat. His friend another construction worker from our team decided to use his boat to rescue others. So these two brave compassionate soles motored for the next two days rescuing the needy to safety. All the while the people who he helped had no idea this young man a first responder had lost everything.

I was so proud to be living in Houston I witnessed so many heartwarming stories the volunteer grew the news reported over 50K volunteers were working at the convention center doing their best to assist the ones in need.

The following work day was Monday only one worker showed up, five the next day, twelve the day after. Houston was hurting, the city in many neighborhoods still under water. Houstonians everywhere began cleaning up immediately streets became lined with a collection of ruined water-soaked furniture, discarded carpet and damaged drywall.

One other sad deplorable thing… during the hurricane four thieves broke in to Kirby Collection they stole construction tools. The theft was recorded on video; unfortunately, the Houston police were not able to identify the thieves. Most of what they took was owned by the subcontractors these companies had insurance to replace same. Unfortunately, the thieves also stole personal tools from fourteen workers. Can you imagine taking the tools one uses to earn his lively hood? So, the EE Reed site supervision managers compiled a list of stolen personal worker tools. On behalf of Thor Equities, I made arrangements for the stolen tools to be replaced and delivered to the jobsite handed directly to the workers.

I called Melissa to advise Kirby Collection weathered the storm we received minimal damage $78K actually the cost for same was far less than our insurance deductible $250K. With Melissa's concurrence on behalf of Thor Equities we gave $1000 dollar gift cards to the eleven team members who found their homes flooded. In addition to show our team we care and support them I planned a BBQ lunch for the workers on site, similar to topping off construction BBQ. At the BBQ lunch each construction work was given a $100 gift card for the local HEB grocery. I wanted something that would immediately impact their family something to help them through the Harvey aftermath. $3,500 in HEB gift card showed compassion and thought. Our construction works returned to work we lost just a hand full of construction workers to other employment opportunities. Most amazing, productivity increased; Kirby Collection moved ever so smoothly to the finish line.

I am very fortunate, luckiest man … Lovely lady I live with has supported me always; she was on board for decades to pack up the kids and relocate our family to allow me to develop the next cool project of my dreams. In our most recent years, Linda continued her support here in Houston visiting back to California to stay close with our children and grandchildren who she misses dearly.

The development was approaching completion our days in Houston coming to an end. We, or should I say, I enjoyed our time in Houston as Linda missed our grandchildren and children dearly. She was so thrilled to be returning soon to California and back to our home.

I was very fortunate to work with a very talented team. I only pray to have an opportunity to work with them once more. Kirby Collection opened five weeks ahead of schedule, the cost of carry $26K loan interest per day. This would allow for a mortgage to be secured at a significant "cost of carry" savings. Unfortunately, Thor did not obtain a mortgage at constructions end, they waited for over a year missing the savings. In addition, what was most amazing a first for me none of the budget contingency was used for Kirby Collection's base building shell and core construction. To be clear we delivered her at the same cost budgeted to commence construction $135M. Not adding a single dollar. You see I was fortunate to buy out the contracts for $1.8M this savings offset the base building shell & core change orders. I held a 3% contingency. I did use contingency for legal fees to secure the loan, tenant improvement allowances to secure retail as well as office tenants. One year after completion Kirby Collection ... Office Tower realized 100% leased, Retail 90% leased and Residential 92% leased. We delivered her ahead of schedule under budget meeting our market demands. I miss our team.

I did assist Thor Equities for about six months on some insurance and operational issues from my home in California. Melissa was a princess among women, I enjoyed working for her, only wish I met Melissa earlier in my career.

I had the pleasure to work with smart and creative people, I made some good friends, I was ever so proud to lead Kirby Collection; my days there hold fond memories indeed, she was my final development a huge success. My team overcame so many daunting and difficult hurdles, I am proud of each and every one. One hell of a team, we had a great ride we created a most important development.

CHAPTER 28
NOT AGAIN, THE C WORD RETURNS [2018]

Around early August 2017 my tongue started hurting again not a lot. The pain was actually mild; sometimes I was not certain if I even felt any pain at all. My tongue was definitely swollen. When it gets swollen, I often make the mistake of biting my tongue that usually causes my tongue to swell more and I unfortunately find I bite my tongue over and over again. I think did I bite my tongue? I don't think so maybe something is wrong? Is that pain? Why is my tongue swollen?

Please be mindful, due to the previous cancer, I often look at my tongue in the mirror usually after I bush my teeth. Does it look okay, Jack? Do you see any lesions? The slight pain was coming from the very same location where the tumor was removed back in winter of 2007.

Interesting, I think and to me alarming. My mouth has that same odd metal taste identical to when I had a tumor on my tongue. However, I do not see any lesions. I touch the area with my fingers, but no increased pain was felt, and I touch the area once more carefully searching for a hard spot. Nope, no lesions, no hard spots, just a bad metal taste. Jack, is this in your mind? Well maybe, I think, however what about the metal taste? So, I look at my tongue again. I find an old tube of Orajel in the medicine cabinet; I place a dapple of Orajel on my tongue. Now my mouth is numb.

It is early morning. I put these cancer thoughts on the back burner. I return to the day at hand, say goodbye to Linda, and drive to work. In the back of my mind, I keep wondering is the cancer back, however, I cannot find any signs. After a week or so, now I am not certain my tongue is swollen … I think maybe the slight pain is in your head, Jack. Hell, I don' know. I am not sure.

I talk to Linda, sharing my fear. I already know what Linda will say, I am not a doctor, Jack. If you believe you have an issue, go see a doctor. She does not even glance at my tongue not even to appease me. Linda just saying mumbling, go see the doctor.

So, what do I do? I am doing my best to stop thinking about my tongue, but I cannot stop wondering, is the cancer back? Well, I hope not. I have to be certain. I cannot stop my thoughts as I find I continuously wonder is the cancer back?

What does my surgeon think?

So, to make certain, I make plans to see the doctor, actually, not just any doctor. I make plans to travel from Houston back to Los Angeles to see my surgeon Dr. Saadat.

Linda traveled with me. She will stay in Los Angeles for a while, maybe a week to ten days to visit with our children and grandchildren. I will remain for the weekend, returning to Houston as I must get back to work. When I finalized my contract with Thor Equities, I negotiated eight trips each year for Linda so she could stay close with our children and their families. These trips were great for Linda. She enjoyed her time back in California.

I was a little nervous when I walked into Dr. Saadat's office. I guess I could have seen a doctor in Houston. That certainly would have been more practical for sure. This way I can be certain, and I get to spend the weekend with our children and grandchildren. Dr. Saadat, after checking out my tongue, found nothing, no lesions no hard spots, no pain maybe a little swollen. He advised all appears to be fine. He went on to say, maybe you bit your tongue again, Jack? Well, now I thought maybe I did bite my tongue. I chew gum often. I guess I should stop doing that.

So, as you can imagine, I was happy, actually thrilled; no need to wonder no need to be concerned. Good news, after seeing my surgeon, Dr. Saadat, I can now relax and get on with my life. Spend a lovely weekend with my family in California, forgetting about cancer.

About fourteen months later, Kirby Collection opened. She looked gorgeous. My time in Houston had come to an end. With that, Linda and I moved back to our home in California.

Ashley steps up

After being away from family for five years, we were so happy to return to our home. While away we had our home remodeled. Dave the contractor had two years to finish the job. He and his family lived at our home during the process. His wife, Kelly, was a childhood friend of my daughter Ashley. Per the contract, work was scheduled to be complete February 2018.

Linda and I traveled back to our condo in California for Christmas of 2017; while visiting I made arrangements with Dave to see his progress.

The meeting was awkward. Dave's work was far from complete. You see, actually his work had just begun at several remodeling locations two of the three bathrooms and kitchen were still in the demolition phase. In addition, floors, painting as well as exterior improvements were lacking progress.

As you might imagine I was very disappointed. Returning to Houston, I was concerned the work will not be completed. I believed I made a huge mistake trusting my home remodel to Dave.

Got to love daughters. Ashely stepped up and took charge. Ash is an interior designer by education. She has a fine eye for detail and design. She advised Dave this is my parents' home; you will get his work completed as required. Ashley made any and all closing design decisions ensuring the progress to be complete. Unfortunately, this action caused a void between her and her childhood friend Kelly. The work was completed in March one month beyond the scheduled deadline. Linda and I moved back to our home later that spring. I am so thankful for Ashley's leadership and tenacity.

Future

I was not certain what I wanted to do next concerning work. Melissa advised Thor's sister company in Mexico, Thor Urbana has a great development just starting design in Belize, she believed a good fit for me. The project on paper was a dream of dreams. They owned an island. The island development included a Four Seasons hotel, golf course, runway for small airplanes, harbor for yachts and more than thirty parcels for sale where the rich could create vacation homes.

Before my trip, I was 90% certain I would accept. On my return home, I was 60% certain I would pass. I tried to contact Melissa several times as I wanted to give her a heads-up. Unfortunately we did not connect.

I was disappointed I would not be the lead, the role they had in mind being more like an Anna or David, a minor role and one not of interest for me. I could not imagine myself taking direction from another. I still wonder today was it a mistake to pass? With a limited role, I could skate, relax.

Fortunately, my planning and investment strategy-wise for retirement allowed me choices. I did not need to continue working; however, I was not sure retirement was what I wanted. I was also very fortunate to be able to put off any decision as Thor Equities requested that I work from my home for a few more months assisting with Kirby Collection insurance and operational issues.

I elected to set up my old consulting company again—Bousquet International Ltd. I also contacted several friends and previous colleagues to advise I returned back to California.

We enjoyed being back in California; retuning to our home, I found to be a welcomed pleasure. I so missed our family. I no longer had a defined schedule pushing my limits ten-plus hours each and every day, always having my phone handy in the event I need to be available and respond to a call at any and all hours of the day and night.

I found my day changed drastically. In a short time, I felt useless, I missed the challenge, I missed the pace, I missed the risk, I missed the competition, and I missed the team.

I did enjoy time with my grandchildren. Often my daughter, Ashley, or daughter-in-law Rachel would ask if I could pick up their children after school. I always replied absolutely. You must understand I was excited to see them. For me, this is a task of love. I was delighted and looking forward to the school day's end and picking a grandchild up at school.

On one delightful day, I believe my favorite moment for one of these occasions, I drove to Meadows Elementary School arriving, as usual, early to pick up Knox.

I stand with scores of mothers and the occasional grandparents. We line the fence on the public side of the school playground fence. After minutes waiting, I hear the bell ring and watch the children scurry quickly in all directions from their classrooms assembling by lining up in various groups in organized single-file lines, waiting for their teacher to walk to the head of each line. I keep searching for Knox's class, and then I see Knox to the right standing in his line about maybe three to four students back. I called out to Knox several times until he turned his head in my direction and we made eye contact.

The children are so eager to go home and I am surprised by the discipline to stand in a single-file line waiting for the teacher to make contact with the parent or, in my case, grandfather double-checking with each student to allow release of the student to run to the gate opening leaving school. Most times picking up a grandchild from school are uneventful however this particular day holds a fond memory for me.

After Knox heard me calling his name, when he saw me, he started jumping up and down in delight. About nine or ten lines to his left, his cousin, Taylor, also spotted me from her line. Taylor yelled, Are you also here to get me and Hayden?

I yelled back, No just Knox today. I instantly reached for my cell phone, placing a call to my daughter, Ashley, to see if I could get her children as well. Ashley was just pulling up to park.

When Knox saw me on the phone, he began yelling to Taylor, HE IS CALLING YOUR MOM!

I yelled back to Taylor, Your mom says yes you can go to my house. Hayden saw me and his teacher also released him. In seconds Knox, Taylor, and Hayden were giving me hugs happy to be together with their cousins.

Every day a flavored, shaved-ice-cone truck sits parked by the gate hoping for children to convince their parent for a cone. Of course, the four of us got in line. We drove back to my home and enjoyed the remainder of the afternoon. I cherish those moments with my grandchildren.

You see, things changed about a year and a half later. Drew and Rachel relocated to Coeur d'Alene, Idaho. So now Savi is in kindergarten and Knox third grade and live so far away. I still have Taylor and Hayden at Meadows. However, Scarlett lives on the opposite side of our valley, so I never have picked up Scarlett.

Today is December 3, 2020, so we are dealing with the COVID virus. None of the California grandchildren attends school. Well... at home by computer that is... yes things have definitely changed. I miss picking up grandchildren after a day of school. I miss seeing Knox and Savi dearly. The move to Idaho left a hole in in heart.

Yep, it's back

About five months later, after returning to California, unfortunately my tongue started to hurt again. It was early in the morning. I awoke, got out of bed, walked to the bathroom, and looked in the bathroom mirror. I stuck out my tongue as far as practicable.

Oh shit, damn what the hell, oh my God Jack do you see a lesion, look again. You know what; I think it must be your imagination, Jack, messing with you. Stop it, Jack. So, let's try this once more. I am scared. I open my mouth, I stick out my tongue. CRAP, yep, I have a lesion in the same location where the tumor was removed eight years ago.

I called my surgeon, Dr. Saadat's office. Fortunately, after a short wait he was on the call.

Hello, Jack what can I do for you? I told him my tongue was hurting. I continued to talk about the lesion. Our conversation continued for less than five minutes. Dr. Saadat advised he wants to see me today. Jack, can you come to my office this afternoon at two?

I responded, absolutely.

Driving to his office, as I am sure you can imagine, I was nervous, scared actually feeling a bit sick to my stomach. After entering his office, signing in, and a short time in the waiting room, my name was called I was taken to a room. I sat in a chair nervously waiting for Dr. Saadat to enter. My wait was a bit longer here. When he entered the room, we exchanged greeting pleasantries before he asked me to move to the examination chair.

Rather quickly upon examining my tongue, he advised, This does not look good, Jack. The doctor went on to say, This will hurt a little. I have to take a biopsy. The pain was quick and not terrible. However, my tongue was definitely hurting. I also experienced a slight, very slight difficulty talking, due to the two shots of Novocain.

When I walked to my car, as I opened the car door my phone rang. I was getting a phone call from Razie; she is Thor Equities risk manager; included on the line were two representatives from Lockton our insurance broker. I explain my speech, advising I just received a biopsy, and I apologized if my speech was difficult to understand. The conversation was short maybe fifteen minutes of discussion. I explained the contractor's intent and concern regarding an insurance issue. I advised per my previous conversation with the contractor that all should be in order now with this insurance issue behind us. The call ended.

A week later, my time working for Thor Equities came to a close. The Kirby Collection development was a good ride. We ended my association with Thor Equities. I enjoyed my time with Thor Equities. I definitely appreciate the time and experience working for Melissa. I hold Melissa in the highest regard.

My stroke did not define me. I fought, I challenged myself, I figured out a way to overcome. Kirby Collection is a great development. I made each and every decision from the concept to completion. I am happy I won. My stroke did not defeat me, cancer has not defeated me, and dermatomyositis did not defeat me.

I return for a checkup with my surgeon each year ... hell, just yesterday I was there. When I pull into the parking lot, I always remember that awkward moment participating on a business call minutes after a biopsy with cancer concern and fear on my mind.

I received a call the next afternoon from my surgeon's office. She advised my biopsy tested positive for cancer and the surgery date was scheduled. I needed to make arrangements quickly for a CT as well as PT scan so my surgeon could model the tumor and size of same. I hate those CT scans. I am claustrophobic.

While I was at his office, I talked to Dr. Saadat about my fear; he prescribed a Xanax pill. I was still worried and was very nervous to get in that CT tube headfirst.

That morning Linda drove me to get my CT scan. While she drove, Linda kept on saying, I can't believe you are scared and need something to relax you; this is not a big deal, Jack. You're acting like a little kid, a baby.

The PT scan I took the previous day was easy, lots of room between me and the top of the PT ring. That said the CT scan was not. I arrived to take my CT scan; I was directed to take my pill. About ten minutes later, I became relaxed and calm. Fortunately, I requested a pill as things soon turned out to be more complicated. I not only needed to enter that CT tube headfirst. While lying on my back the staff placed a tubular box frame over my face. All the time adjusting while advising the device is necessary to frame and focus on the area of concern, that being my mouth. The device extended up over my face, coming to less than a quarter inch of clearance to the CT tube surface once I entered the CT tube. While moving my body into the CT tube the technician all the while reminding me not to move most definitely "do not turn your head, Jack," with a final, Jack, if you have any concern or discomfort just push the button in your left hand and we will remove you from the CT tube immediately. So, fear strikes me instantly. I feel heat running through to my body, my mind begins to race, and I say to myself, jeez you are an idiot, Jack, a stupid idiot. Jack, you know you cannot trust your left hand why in the hell didn't you have them place the emergency button in the other hand the one who still likes you.

Are you okay, Jack? I hear on the speaker as my body is entering the CT tube.

Yes, I am fine; yep, all is Otay, I respond. The process lasted about forty-five minutes. I believe I was acting like a baby. Linda was correct; this was not difficult at all. That said, I will definitely request a pill again in the event I am ever required to enter a CT tube headfirst. YEP, for sure I will request a pill to relax me and take away my fear.

Later that same morning, close to noon, I received a call from my anesthesiologist's office. The woman on the call advised that the anesthesiologist scheduled for my upcoming tongue surgery would like to speak to me this afternoon. After I hung up, I told Linda about my call as I thought this to be odd. Linda thought not.

The anesthesiologist requested we meet at the surgery center, the exact same place I received my first tongue surgery as well as where I was scheduled in two days for my second tongue surgery. After a short time sitting in the surgery waiting room, I met the anesthesiologist in a very small meeting room. This room to me appeared to be about the size of a small walk-in closet, a make-shift quest office, just enough room for a small desk and two chairs. The anesthesiologist told he was my anesthesiologist for my first surgery. He asked how bad my pain was after that surgery. I told him it was unbearable. I felt like a truck had parked on my tongue; the pain was intense. How I had to do something to occupy my mind.... I told him that I refinished some furniture and next painted one of our bathrooms.

What he said next caught me by surprise. Jack, this upcoming surgery will be very difficult. This tumor is over ten times the size of the first surgery. I do not believe you should have the surgery done here. I believe you should have your surgery at the hospital. It will be safer there. One never knows what could go wrong. Your surgery last time was simple by comparison. This new surgery is complicated. He went on to say, I am fearful you may not be able to handle the pain. There is a relatively new anesthesia—micro beads. It works like a pain block and will last for seventy-two hours. This aesthesia is not yet approved for your surgery; however, I believe this to be what you need. So, I have planned to give you the micro beads. However I highly recommend you call your surgeon Dr. Saadat to request the surgery is administered at the hospital.

So, I told thank you and that I would absolutely call Dr. Saadat today. Will you still be my anesthesiologist with the surgery scheduled at the hospital?

He smiled and said, Of course I will.

I called Dr. Saadat as soon as I returned home. We discussed the anesthesiologist's concerns. He called me back later to advise all was fine. The micro bead sounded like a great idea and the surgery was now scheduled at the hospital in two days.

Early in the morning, Linda drove me to the hospital. I was pleased actually very happy to find my daughter, Ashley, was there waiting for us to arrive. She was standing outside, close to the entry doors. I quickened my pace calling, Good morning, Ashley thank you for coming. You'll be a great help for your mother and a nice surprise for me." I gave Ashley a big hug.

She whispered in my ear, all will be fine, Dad. It's going to be okay.

We entered the waiting room; Linda moved towards the front desk to sign me in. Ashley and I found a seat. Moments later a nurse entered the waiting room calling my name. We are ready for you, Jack. Can you please follow me?

When I stood, Linda and Ashley stood with me. We all hugged for one final moment. Next thing I remember, I was laying on my back in the operating room, several nurses scurrying around and Dr. Saadat leaning close to my face saying, we will be ready in minutes. You are looking good, Jack.

One of the nurses began hooking up a couple of IVs, when I notice a young man in the distance across the room begin to walk towards—yep, he is moving in my direction. As he approached me, he said his name and he went on to advise he was my anesthesiologist.

So, I immediately become scared, my mind racing. I begin talking to myself, what the hell where is my anesthesiologist? I try my best to compose myself. I say, Where is…? Unfortunately, today I cannot recall his name.

This guy responds, I was scheduled for your operation this morning. My mind is racing.

I say, Are you scheduled to give the micro beads anesthesia?

Yes, absolutely, he responded. I have it right over there. He turns his back and points to a counter across the room. Well, what do I do? Do I even do anything? With that hesitation, all in the room keep moving in a random dance when my new anesthesiologist leans in and says, Jack, I want you to start counting backward from 100. So, I start counting, I cannot stop wondering what happened. Why do I have a new anesthesiologist? I also start to question is this stuff even working 93, 92, 91….

I wake to find I am in another room. I see Dr. Saadat standing close to my bed talking with one of the nurses. Then the nurse says, He is waking, Doctor. She turns takes a step or two in my direction saying, all went well. How are you feeling, Jack?

Dr. Saadat added, You did well. The surgery is a success.

So, what do you think happened next? Yes, I went home… things were great I had absolutely no pain not any pain at all. The next morning, I woke and all was great; no pain. I thought, This is a miracle; nothing like my last tongue surgery. Why was I so concerned? This isn't a big deal at all.

That afternoon I wrote a thank-you note for the anesthesiologist. Yep, the first guy, the one who reached out to me to have the surgery at the hospital and make certain I received the micro beads. I drove to the outpatient clinic where we met earlier in the week. Unfortunately, he was not there. They told me he was working at the hospital this afternoon. I asked if they could get this note to him. I went on to say, It's a thank-you note. The woman at the desk smiled, saying, He is scheduled to be here in the morning, and that she would give my note to him. So, I never actually was able to thank him in person. I wanted to ask why he was not at the hospital, there for my surgery. Was there a schedule conflict? Did he and my surgeon have words? I do not know. However, I am so grateful he reached out to me. Interesting I cannot recall his name. Unfortunately, I searched my notes unable to find his name. However, I am so very grateful.

Holy crap that hurts

Well, I bet you know what I will say next. Yep, remember the micro beads only last for seventy-two hours? The moment seventy-two hours concluded, the pain was so intense; I thought I was going to go crazy. Dr. Saadat prescribed pain medicine; I took the pain pills, however they had little effect reducing the pain. They did not help, made me loopy, and caused constipation. The pain was unbearable, so bad that painting a bathroom or refinishing furniture would not be a distraction. The pain captured and occupied my thoughts, my mind, it was a pain I never experienced before.

Linda called Dr. Saadat and told him I needed something to relieve the pain. She asked if it was possible to get another shot of the micro beds. He told Linda he has a schedule opening after the weekend; she could take me to his office Monday.

So, I was excited. I could not wait for my appointment. Got to love Linda; she has spunk; she can make things happen. I love this woman. Linda definitely looks out for me. She can definitely argue like no other; however, yes, she cares and looks out for me.

So, let's jump to the moment … picture me sitting in an elevated patient chair in one of the doctor's rooms. Linda is with me, sitting on one of the side chairs, and Dr. Saadat is placing a gel on my tongue explaining this will help to numb my tongue prior to the shot. He is holding a needle in his hand saying, This is going to hurt very bad, Jack. Are you ready? I nod my head say yes. I am wearing blue jeans, so I hold on to the fabric of my jeans by the pockets with both hands as tight as possible. You see I need to occupy my hands. I can't take a chance that I may reach to stop him if the pain is out of control. I focus, preparing my mind for incredible pain.

He sticks the needle in my tongue, in the area just cut from surgery. He does this four or five times. I have to be strong; I have to be brave. HELL, my wife is sitting a mere five feet from me. I cannot act like a baby a Nance boy.

You can do this, Jack. Sure you can. Be strong, Jack. This will be over soon and you can take anything for a couple of minutes. Just like that, he stops. Dr. Saadat says I believe I got everything all in the area. I am thinking, Wow that was absolutely awful, the pain worse than I even had imagined.

Next, I hear the doctor say these shocking and disturbing words: We will let the Novocain be for ten or fifteen minutes. I will be back shortly to give you the micro beads. He leaves the room and closes the door behind him.

Oh crap, oh my God, what the hell, Jack, can you do this again, can you Jack? You bet I am conversing to myself now. How in the hell can I do that again? I do not think so, you have to, you can do it focus. Holy crap I have no choice I got to do this again....

Linda reaches her hand and touches my leg while asking, are you okay, Jack?

I respond, Yes. That said, I thought he was giving me the micro beds. I cannot believe I have to do this again.

Linda says, I know, honey. I also thought you were getting the micro beads. You can do it. It will give you another three days without any pain.

So, I sit there and I start to focus once more. I begin to prepare myself for more needles to be pushed into my tongue. Dr. Saadat returns about fifteen minutes. He asks if my tongue feels numb. I respond yes. I reach once again to grab my jean pocket in an effort to occupy my hands.

So wouldn't you think the Novocain would help? Wouldn't you think the Novocain would easy my pain? Hell, I did. Regrettably, I felt each and every pass as he stuck the needle in my tongue another four or five times. The pain so direct so intense I made a sound on the second time he pushed the needle in. Are you okay, Jack? Are you all right? he asked.

Yes. I responded. Hurry, please. Hurry. So it was awful, terrible, absolutely painful, but then it was over and in a matter of seconds upon his finishing, my excruciating pain disappeared.

I now felt a dull throbbing pain, nothing by comparison. My pain not that bad at all and then all pain, the strong as well as the mild pain vanished in a snap. I looked at Linda, her looking back at me asking, Is the pain gone. I smiled responding yes.

The doctor cleaned the blood on my chin. I believe now you can heal three more days will help you. Are you okay, Jack?

Yes," I responded. That was awful, but thank you. You are a prince among doctors. Thank you.

Three days later I felt pain once more, however, not intense. My pain was no longer a bother. I healed two months later. I was scheduled for a follow-up, and all was fine. I can talk; thank God I did not lose the ability to talk.

Next steps follow-up with Dr. Saadat each year counting to five as the fifth-year medicine believes the cancer is gone. I went eight years after the first surgery. I pray the cancer never returns. As I do not believe Jack can do this a third time. Actually, I am certain he cannot.

CHAPTER 29
NEXT [2021]

Not certain what to say yet. How about this?

Linda and I enjoyed returning to our home in California. We both missed our family dearly. I found such joy and pleasure spending time with our grandchildren. A highlight for me was picking up the kids after school. Hayden, Taylor, and Knox all attended the same elementary school. Scarlett lives on the opposite side of our valley and her family prefers isolation. Regrettably, we... well actually for all of us, it's a rare occasion to see Geoff's family; unfortunately, I never had the opportunity to pick up Scarlett after school. The following year Savi also attended Meadows Elementary School, so now I was fortunate to have four grandchildren nearby and I advised Ashley and Rachel, if you ever need help, if you need someone to get the kids, I am your man. I was pleased that they asked me to help; I only wish it could have been more often.

As I mentioned earlier Drew's family moved to Idaho in the fall of 2020. I miss them dearly. As crazy as this may sound, Drew still works as a Teamster here in Hollywood, commuting from Idaho. Yep, I also think he is crazy. When working, he stays at our home, usually here for four to five weeks at a time. Drew and Rachel wanted to provide a more favorable environment for their children enjoying the Coeur d'Alene lifestyle.

Back in the fall of 2013 when Linda and I moved to Houston, I decided to take one of my guitars with me. I am glad I did. I placed the guitar—a Yamaha acoustic—on a stand in the living room. She was a birthday gift from Linda back in 1973. My logic, you see I thought if the guitar was close and in sight, I was hopeful that I would often reach out to try and play again. My left hand definitely resisted. As I have told you earlier, my left hand is without feeling. My strategy worked. I found the guitar awkward at first. That said, with constant practice, I discovered I could play again.

Linda would travel back to California often for an extended stay, my alone time provided an opportunity to master my deficiency. I uncovered a way to play again. I found it fascinating that I could remember songs from my teenage days, however not the tunes learned later in life; I had to relearn those. Once I began getting on track, I enjoyed sitting out on our third-level balcony, appreciating the view of Buffalo Speedway and watching the cars fly by while playing the guitar.

I did try to sing, so many times I cannot even count. Unfortunately my stroke took any chance of singing from me. A silver lining without singing is I concentrated on leads. In some ways I got playing the guitar back; in other ways not. I do enjoy playing. I believe I drive Linda crazy sometimes.

Working from home and still employed by Thor, life was easy. For the first time in decades, I had time, lots of time, a new freedom for Jack, not being occupied or consumed by work. I could actually put my phone away; I no longer received a couple hundred emails each day. Well, maybe not as my phone seems always close at hand. I guess old habits are hard to break?

Returning home, I took all my guitars out of storage. It was a pleasure see the girls and have them close at hand again. I mounted the acoustic guitars off guitar hooks on a wall in the pool table room setting up the Les Paul and Rickenbacker on stands with their amps in one corner. I hung several photos of my developments from my previous lifetime on the walls. I also shipped the sofa that was in my Houston office and placed it in this game/music room.

This is my room, my special place. The windows look out to our swimming pool and the Santa Clarita Valley below. I still wake up early. I make breakfast, then step down to my place, the lowest of three levels, where I play guitar for a couple of hours each morning while Linda sleeps.

Galuska guitar

My dear friend from my previous lifetime Paul Galuska and his wife Lee moved to Santa Monica shortly after we relocated to Houston. I reconnected with my old friend upon our return to California.

It was so great to see Paul again, so much time in between. We caught up on our lives, our family, and our connection still apparent after so many years.

Then on April 9, 2017, I purchased one of his guitars. Paul has a little guitar shop where he creates handmade acoustic guitars. Earlier I looked at his Instagram page, and his guitars looked nice, very nice. Well, now Paul ... an old friend making guitars ... yep, I want one; what a great memento. Paul had four or five guitars to show me at his apartment. His shop just down the stairs. We met first at his shop. I was impressed as Paul talked about his passion. It was clearly evident Paul enjoyed his work. I selected a parlor guitar. She was gorgeous, small in size. I believed her to be perfect for the little hands of my grandchildren to learn how to play. I chose Galuska guitar #18.

When I returned home, I was shocked. You see #18, yes, gorgeous; however, I found her more than a beauty, more significantly she played with ease, her tone magical. Her string action better than my other guitars. Now, I was really impressed my friend Paul made her pretty, also great.

I thought, thank God I did not quit, thank God I took a guitar to Houston five years ago, and thank God I can play again. I told Linda how impressive I believed my Galuska guitar was.

That lovely lady I live with, Linda, knew I believe prewar dreads made of the best wood have the greatest tone, so for my birthday she commissioned a Galuska custom dread. What a lovely adventure selecting her materials, with Paul providing guidance and direction. She was ready January 22, 2018—Galuska #27. Paul made her with love. This girl was an absolute beauty, her math perfect, her action smooth, and her intonation enchanting. I keep her in one of two places on a guitar stand in my living room; I also hold a guitar hook the level below for her in my pool table/music room. She gets played most; I enjoy her best.

Retire or not, should I stay should I go

About a month before I discovered my tongue cancer returned, I reestablished my consulting company Bousquet International again. My plan was to set things up and seek opportunities. I called old business friends, scheduling lunch and or visits to their offices. I wanted to let everyone know Jack is back. That said, my thoughts changed when I recovered, when I got past the second tongue surgery a couple of months later. I did not find the same drive to pursue clients. Actually, I was certain I would not enjoy the work. I thought if I return to the working world, it must be an extraordinary development or some exotic location. I retained an attorney, Roger Doumanian, to terminate BI. Set up and closed, no work to display for the effort.

I was very close to returning back to work just before my cancer showed up again. It just did not work out, which I believed good as I also thought the opportunity an odd fit. I did not look for work. I was, however, fortunate in receiving several calls. I turned down the opportunities. Most were failing projects that required leadership. However, I knew the owners to be assholes, and that was why their projects were in trouble. I no longer wished to work with difficult people. I know one day my phone would stop ringing; that is fine. I had a great ride, many important developments for sure....

Then in late November, I was called again. This time for an opportunity back in Houston. The project required an additional ten levels added to an existing building in downtown Houston creating a W Hotel at the top with office below and retail at grade. The prize that interested me, this developer was also owner of a huge four-plus-acre site (two hotels, apartments, condos, office, and retail planned) just two blocks south of my Kirby Collection development.

So, I said I would take their offer only if both developments are included. We discussed what I wanted for compensation. I planned to secure an apartment at my previous development, Kirby Collection. I was looking forward to the opportunity and now I could enjoy the lifestyle I created at Kirby Collection. Linda, however, believed "let's be retired and enjoy life here in California."

No follow-up call ... I assumed they decided to find another to lead their developments. When to my surprise, Al Kashani called me again months later in the final week of February 2020. A meeting was scheduled Friday, March 13th for me to travel to Houston.

Though the COVID virus was not understood at the time, it did, however, hold my concern. So on Tuesday March 10th, I called to say I would not be making the trip. Interestingly, on March 11th, all sports games and events were canceled. The next day the financial world stopped spinning. That weekend Los Angeles commenced quarantine. I have a compromised immune system; thank God I canceled that trip.

Quarantine was not fun at all, life slow and boring. Fortunately, Linda and I as well as our family were safe; not one contracted the virus. Linda and I are lucky, very fortunate we are financially secure. However, many in the world were struggling and finding days uncertain. Life for all in America, including the world around us changed to a new normal, a sad most desperate existence. Linda suffers from depression on occasion. This time she struggles; I worry for her. I look forward to when the world starts spinning again. I look to travel, and I look to enjoying a great restaurant, attending a ball game … hell I look forward to seeing my friends and Connecticut family.

My stroke rendered me damaged; yes, I am damaged; however, I would not allow myself to be broken. I did not permit my stroke to define me. I beat my stroke I conquered my shortcomings.

I found confidence to believe I can rely on me to move on, to let Jack go. That said, I miss Jack. I do my very best to leave him behind, I try to forget him, not think about him. I guess I am content but not satisfied being this guy. Jack enjoyed life. He could have fun. Jack was happy, never a worry or doubt. Although he also had more of an edge, Jack demanded excellence. This poser is more forgiving … definitely not as fun.

CHAPTER 30
A LOOK BACK [2001]

Jack was better, yes he was. When were things the best? Well, certainly just before his stroke.

Worn down from life at times, my thoughts do wander, remembering Jack. Yes, I miss him. I usually reminisce about the moments prior to my stroke when he was retained to turn around the troubled and failing Hollywood & Highland development... one hell of a team. He just led his most challenging development to a successful completion. Started his own business with friends and colleagues, the future appeared promising. Our children in their teens with great highs and tragic lows. Life was good and we were living the dream.

Jack overcame his fight with dermatomyositis an incurable disease. Jack was sitting on top of the world, living the sweet-tasting, good life. That guy was confident, assertive, strong; Jack believed he could do anything. Looking back, as I recall, Jack, this causes me to wonder did I make a mistake letting him go, moving on, saying goodbye. I cannot say for certain if not, would I have gone insane? Could I have found Jack? Hell, I just do not know. Yes, I do—he could never return. But yes, I try to move forward. That said, I miss him. Jack was better, a much better man than me.

Looking back and recalling the summer of 1999, when I was retained to turn around the Hollywood & Highland/Kodak Theater development, the project in desperate trouble. About six months earlier, David Malmuth my boss from our previous DDC days, called and requested I come to his office. He advised the H&H project was failing, his confidence now lost to the Tri-

357

zec-Hahn executives. I got along well with David. I enjoyed my years with him as my DDC boss.

A meeting was scheduled at the Peninsula Hotel in Beverly Hills with Trizec President Lee Wagman. The interview positive, however, I did not receive a follow-up call for another five months. Laura and Doug from my DDC team employed a year earlier by Trizec-Hahn working on the Hollywood & Highland development. Laura responsible of the Renaissance Hotel design, Doug Curtis for the Kodak Theater. Not certain, however, I believe Laura and Doug responsible for my call from Trizec CFO Andy Blair?

I was surprised when Andy called. The next day I traveled to his office in San Diego. Lee joined our discussion; they offered me the position effective immediately based on one condition. Andy asked that I spend a day with his retail team another day split between his hotel and theater teams as he wanted to make certain I was well aware how dire and out of control the development had become. A year later one evening at dinner with Andy, I joked saying that I should have requested a home in Malibu, Andy replying at the time, Jack we may have granted you that wish.

You see, in addition to the schedule being a huge bust, the budget was substantially out of control. For example, on two consecutive occasions, the Trizec team would value engineer say $5M from the cost, then reprice the development only to find the cost now up another $20M due to other previous unforeseen factors. They could not get the budget to pencil, so they added a third level of retail as this would increase income, believing that should cover the cost burden. They liked that notion so much they went a step further and added a fourth level to the retail. Second-story retail is a challenge ... the third and fourth levels created a whole new set of problems and concerns, certainly this notion was not the best of ideas.

It gets worse; Kodak finalized a naming rights agreement to pay $75K each year for a ten-year term. The city's redevelopment agency so excited for AMPAS with the Academy Awards return to Hollywood the city providing $95M in development cash incentive to Trizec for the below grade parking / Kodak theater. Yes, the City of Hollywood owns the parking garage and Kodak Theater.

AMPUS in severe internal disagreement some believed the Kodak choice good while others believed Kodak choice terrible, thinking AMPAS sold out having the awards at a mixed-use development one that included that awful grouping of stores called retail. Key AMPAS executives speaking out saying the awards will be at K-Mart. Trizec threatened weekly by AMPAS saying they might terminate the agreement. If so, the Kodak and city redevelopment funds would certainly disappear.

Needless to say, morale within the Trizec team was low. I was also shocked to find the General Contractors McCarthy retail and theater contractor as well as Matt Construction the hotel contractor morale dismal, the contractors believing Hollywood & Highland development out of control. The design was a work in progress with no leadership to steer the direction. They all lost hope had no confidence in the owner Trizec to lead the effort.

For two days I met with the Trizec teams. Andy did not sugarcoat; it was clear Hollywood & Highland was definitely in trouble. I thought what the hell, I cannot make this any worse; this development will receive national attention, due to the Kodak Theater world attention. I always believed if it is difficult or impossible I want to lead it. I believed I could make a difference, I knew ... hell Jack was certain he could turn her around.

Decision day

My agreement stipulated, after a month on the job, I was scheduled to travel to Toronto to meet with Peter Munk. Wendy from Andy's financial team joined me on the trip. You see, Mr. Munk was curious; he needed conformation he could not afford another issue. Trizec doing poorly in Eastern Europe, struggling in Vegas. I was given a question before hired ... can I do it, can I turn this aircraft carrier around in a small stream?

Construction had already commenced digging the six levels below-grade parking, design now in progress, the theater and retail in the Design Documentation phase for the hotel in the Schematic Design phase. What I found interesting is that Mr. Monk wanted the truth. For example, if I were to say no, this is impossible, I would receive three years' salary. He would reverse construction, fill in the hole, cancel the design; he would abandon, yes, close down the development.

That day at his conference room table Mr. Munk asked, can you do it, Jack? I replied I know you are having difficulties with other developments most notably Eastern Europe. I do not believe your shareholders and stakeholders can take another hit. The proforma for H&H does not make sense. For example, the rents assumed I do not believe can be realized as they are commensurate with Rodeo Dr. Hollywood is not Beverly Hills.

I stood, looking Mr. Munk in the eye, and I told him ... I can do it. I can turn this ship around. However, Mr. Munk only you can decide if you can live with a lower profit than stated in the proforma, you must decide do you believe me. As you do not know me, I say it's a flip of the coin. I reached into my pocket retrieving a silver dollar my mom gave to my daughter Ashley as a First Communion gift. I placed the coin in Mr. Munk's hand.

He smiled asked again; you believe you can do this? Absolutely, I replied. Jack, do you have a schedule that works can you show it to me, when and how H&H will be completed, do you have a date? I answered I do not have a schedule yet that makes any sense, I will figure this out, I guarantee H&H will open in time for the academy Awards. I just can't show you how yet. That coin is for you to choose, it is a flip of the coin decision.

One more time Mr. Munk questioned me however this time his question more positive, Jack can do it? Yes, I can. Heads we move forward. He flipped the coin in the air caught the coin and placed the coin in his hand. I could not see the coin I had no idea heads or tails. I asked heads? With that Mr. Munk flipped the coin again; this time he let me see the coin... and HEADS it was.

Mr. Munk went on to say you will not see me again until H&H is completed. I will send a letter to Lee and Andy advising you are in charge no one can overrule you; well, that is only with the exception of me. Be smart Jack.

My first day, I arrived at the door on Hollywood Blvd. to the El Capitan offices the Trizec Hollywood team occupied above the El Capitan Theater located across the street from H&H site. I did not have a key for the door. A young woman arriving seconds before standing in front of me she in the process to unlock the door. She turned and said can I help you? I responded this is my first day unfortunately I do not have a key. You must be Jack Bousquet; I am Lisa Vigil your secretary nice to meet you I am new too I started last week.

Lisa pretty a very young woman, on my second day she confided to me, this being her first time as a secretary; she was scared fearful to miss the mark… Lisa worked hard she grew into her position I enjoyed working with her. About three months before opening Lisa stepped into my office to advise she accepted a marketing position with Trizec, she fearful I would be angry. I gave Lisa a hug told her congratulations I knew she would be great. A couple years later, Lisa was hired for Disney Concert Hall marketing team. I was very proud of Lisa. The last time I saw Lisa, she a lovely bride was at her wedding.

Court

Two weeks after I started, our attorney Jerry Newman stopped in my office. He needed my assistance. Trizec did not own all the property necessary for the development. His plan, take by eminent domain the parking lot of an apartment tower located where Trizec required access to the Kodak Theater's loading lock. In return Trizec purchased an adjacent property; we would demo the structure on same property construct a replacement parking lot for the apartment tower in its place.

So how do we do this I asked? Jerry responded you will tell the judge this is necessary as the only way to ensure safety for the construction workers. Yep, I also thought his idea thin. Jerry continued to say don't worry Jack we will be in the judge's office I will be with you. I studied the idea to make sure I was ready. Remember I still do not know what I do not know. H&H is a massive $650M development extremely complicated.

Can you see where this is going? That day with no warning we ended up in court not in the judge's office, I on the witness stand. The opposing attorney, hell I did not even know an opposing attorney existed, I did not know the adjacent property owner angry he harbored deep concerns with our development. The opposing attorney questioned me for over forty-five minutes. At one point my mouth so dry I thought my tongue was sticking to the roof of my mouth. I remained calm I did my best to sell our story. That said driving home that night I was very down, hard on myself I thought I could have done better. . The next afternoon Jerry called to advise we won; you did a good job, Jack.

Team

Laura was already working on the hotel, Doug the theater. I called Kevin my first month, who at the time working in Dallas for the past couple of years he joined our team looking after the retail. Kevin commuted from Dallas arriving Monday morning returning home Thursday night an apartment came with the position. Shortly after I convinced Carla to join our team, she responsible for looking after area development (everything in-between the structures for example landscaping, hand rails, stairs exterior lighting floor surfaces). About a year later, when Laura went on maternity leave for her second child Gus Files joined our team as construction manager reporting to Laura working on the hotel. In the final year of construction, Rob Fleming, a brilliant engineer added to our team to master the New Media Initiate, we could not get the video boards to work. Rob was a godsend (content displayed on the video boards) Jack Illes found Rob at a Malibu party. Jeanne Roccapriore joined as assistant for my team. In the final months, I hired two additional staff to assist with closing construction issues. Unfortunately, I cannot recall their names.

Morale

I knew my team could weather the storm; my concern was with the contractors and consultants. I called an all hands on deck meeting at McCarthy' site office including consultant's contractors and primary subcontractors the room full standing room only.

I talked about the morale, I talked about team, I advised, I do not care how smart anyone is I need a team. If you cannot work in the team, I do not need you. I next asked one question each in the room to respond, this took over two hours it was painful. That said it worked they became a team we stopped fighting. It not perfect by any means many problems remained to solve, we began to move forward as a team.

I asked each and everyone in the room to respond to my question I began with John Moffatt our superintend for the theater-**what do you think is wrong, what will you do to change it, not your company... what will you do how can you make a difference**? I knew John form a previous development he was the superintendent for Disney Feature Animation building at

Disney Studios. John very outspoken I was certain he would speak his mind. YES John got the ball rolling.

So yikes, like I said the next two hours very painful. All spoke their mind the plan working, I was however surprised when Carla stood saying she believes the problem to be fees we should pay the consultants more money. If looks could kill, my eyes would have shot lasers at Carla. After the meeting, Carla was concerned. She asked Kevin, do you think Jack will fire me? Kevin gave me a heads up so I stopped in Carla's office I explained her comment not the best thing for that meeting as I was trying to build, have them forget earlier days, we are moving forward together. Years later 2019 Linda and I enjoying a vacation in Playa del Carmen, Carla and her husband Lynn joining us, Carla told the story to Lynn we all laughed.

I did make one significant change the mechanical engineer Levine Seegel Associates failing terribly. I did not fire them that said I limited their role to shop drawing review; we entered into an agreement with mechanical subcontractor ACCO for theater mechanical on a design/build basis. ACCO did one hell of a job.

Global problems

Hollywood & Highland most definitely a cluster fuck, significant issues encountered substantial global problems hurting our schedule causing delays and cost to correct same spiraling, a heroic endeavor. For example, we found a momentous structural connection issue. The 6 levels of below grade parking structure a precast concrete design was not coordinated with the above grade structural steel design, in far too many locations no connection apparent for the steel to tie to the precast causing a huge schedule problem. Kevin and Carla performed a recon investigation to find the missing connections in advance allowing the engineers to rectify the problem and mitigate the issue.

Construction

Hollywood &Highland tested all of McCarthy's engineering and building skills. Over three years, McCarthy excavated 650,000 cubic yards of dirt from a seventy-five-foot deep hole, poured 72,000 cubic yards of concrete, and installed 12,000 tons of structural steel and 3,265 pieces of structural precast. The team met developer Trizec-Hahn's goal for a November 2001 grand opening by working overtime, seven days a week. At peak, 900 workers were on the job site.

Matt Construction employed another 300 workers for the hotel; Hopkins Construction employed seventy-five workers for Wolfgang Puck's Ball Room/ Catering Center In addition dozens of retail contractor's constructing the retail and restaurant interiors.

After two years of predevelopment and nine months of construction I took over the effort leading her to completion. At the time, the below grade excavation in progress, the below grade parking precast structure in fabrication. Below grade design complete unfortunately not coordinated, above grade design still in progress. By area the theater and retail in Design Development phase the hotel design in the Schematic phase.

My first two decisions I added back cost to the Theater I also delayed the hotel schedule start. Remember my mission get the budget and schedule under control?

Just prior to my arrival in an effort to get H&H budget under control the Trizec team stripped the Kodak Theater of her finishes for example they omitted the cherry millwork, fused glass panels, removed floor finishes leaving polished concrete in its place. I believed this a mistake; I believed David Rockwell's design magical. My first decision; I gave direction to the architects to put the finishes back. Lee stopped by my office he thought this a mistake as my first directive added dollars back. I advised the Kodak Theater is the prize, the H&H development would fail if we left her naked, and Lee concurred. I told him don't worry we are going to get there we have the team to make it happen.

The only other time Lee had a comment I believed his idea great. Lee was concerned with the street view of the hotel, his idea in Lee's words; he said he had an epiphany let's add a water wall fountain on the hotel side with plant material covering the wall to the street side. I thought this idea great, the wall closed the hotel arrival area the wall made a huge difference and it gave us the perfect location to place the hotel flag (her name in stainless steel lite on the wall).

I was surprised Trizec started construction while the design still in progress. I understood a parallel effort must coincide however I believe they pulled the start trigger far too soon the construction documents crappy problems throughout the drawings. Plans were set to start the hotel construction (blow grade) in similar manor. The Renaissance Hotel in a T shape the stem of the T an old Holliday Inn we demoed back to her structural frame. We added a new structure creating the top of the T, literally sewing the two structural components old and new superstructures together to finalize the T shape.

I saw a problem I believed it wise to wait to postpone the start of the hotel construction. The Trizec hotel team and retail team never coordinated their respective designs. I was fearful tie backs for the parking garage which extended into the hotel site may be in jeopardy. So, in my first month I called another all hands on deck meeting again in the McCarthy site conference room this time Matt Construction, Englekirk our structural engineer, WATG hotel Architect, Ehrenkrantz, retail designer Alton & Porter retail architect of record. We started the meeting confirming the garage tie backs as they were not placed in coordination with the hotel new foundation is it possible, that tie back cable might be damaged? The answer yes, well that is alarming, that's not good. So, I asked how many tendons it would take damaged to cause the garage tieback wall to fail. The engineers responded two maybe three?

If the garage ties back wall fails could the existing Holiday Inn structure slip in the hole? Yes, the engineer's response. One last question is it possible to construct a portion of the precast garage structure to keep us safe… to be clear what must be constructed to ensure we do not cause the retaining wall to fail? After a couple of minutes, the engineers had concurrence advising McCarthy must build to the K line. I stood and steeped over to the opposite side of the conference room table to see exactly where the K line located. Walking back to my seat the team discussing schedule for same. I said we will not start the hotel construction until McCarthy constructs to the K line, I believe that will also coincide allowing the hotel designers to complete the hotel construction documents.

As I recall this the only coordination meeting Paul Matt attended. Paul got up from his seat walking to the door, stopped as his path found me. Paul leaned in to say, I am glad you are here; we will be okay now. Our meeting continued closing out protocol between adjacent McCarthy/ Matt construction zone.

Later in the course of construction while building the interior partitions things not going well at all the Issue, dimension busts causing problems everywhere.

Chris the homeless photographer

One afternoon while I was walking the jobsite checking up on our progress, I saw what appeared to be a homeless man walking around taking pictures. As you can imagine with well over thirteen hundred workers several cranes carrying materials overhead I was concerned for his safety, we could not afford an accident this guy did not belong on my construction site. One of the McCarthy superintendents was standing nearby I pointed to the homeless guy and advised let's get him out of here. The superintendent said jeez this is crazy how in the hell did he get here.

A couple of days later after attending a meeting in the job trailer I saw 5 or 6 photos siting on a desk. The photos were absolutely amazing the photographer captured an intimate humanistic depiction not merely a construction photo he captured the construction workers essence at their making. For example, rod busters were hanging on at elevated heights tying up reinforcing cages or iron workers placing steel at heroic elevations. The photos concentrated focus on the construction worker most often the construction worker's face. I was immediately impressed, I asked where did you get these who is the photographer. Young project engineers said remember that homeless guy you ran off, its him he is selling the photos.

So, I asked Laura to track this guy down I want to meet him, tell him I would like to see his photos. She found him; his name is Chris he stays a flop house for men called the Mark Twain at the other end of Hollywood.

The next afternoon Chris arrived at our office he was scared very meek fearful man dressed in greasy tattered shabby clothes. I introduced myself he told me his name is Chris. He thought he was in trouble fearful that I would take his photos and call the police. I learned Chris is basically homeless he lives in Michigan during the summer where he mows lawns when he can; he travels to Hollywood for the winter

I told him not to worry I went on to advise how impressed I am with his photography. To make a complicated story short I hired Chris to take photos for me. After many questions I made sure he would receive a sizeable profit for his services.

You see each month I send a progress report to the shareholder and stake holders. I include three or four construction photos in the body of the report.

I made arrangements with McCarthy to give Chris a hard hat get some proper shoes and teach Chris basic protocol for construction safety. Chris was scheduled to weekly appointments checking in at the jobsite trailer where a project engineer would accompany Chris while he took photos of our progress. Chris's photos were fantastic; I kept four or five for myself. So, nope, the Chris story does not end here, I have more to tell you.

The designers created a graphic for the two entries into the parking garage, one at the Highland Ave entrance the other at Orange Street entrance. I was not impressed with the graphic notion advising come on guys we can be more creative than this. We tried to find a more creative solution nothing really caught my attention. I think it was Kevin who said people are driving into the parking a garage let's make it appear as if they are driving into a theater.

With that thought we came up the idea to purchase a photo of people in a theater, blow up the image and apply same to the wall. When one enters the parking garage, they pass by all the people watching a movie... entering the show by car. Then I thought rather than purchasing a photo, let's create our photo with the audience comprised of architects, engineers, construction personnel, and city officials all who are the collective team responsible for the Hollywood & Highland development. When people come here, their children can say, look that is my mom or there he is, that is dad on the wall right over there. A tribute for all who were responsible for making Hollywood & Highland happen.

I told my team I wanted Chris to be the photographer. Let's hire a comedian to stand on the stage at Grauman's Chinese Theater that will provide the focus for all to be looking in the same direction and hopefully laughing for the photo.

It worked the images provided the perfect idea also everyone so very thrilled and gracious to be invited for the photo opportunity. I was however surprised to find Laura also retained another photographer as she was concerned the event might be too difficult for Chris. I was pleased to see Chris was able to participate. For me I enjoyed Chris having a team role with H&H.

Unfortunately, years later when I returned to Hollywood & Highland for an evening at the Kodak, I was surprised to find a Buick advertisement covered our images at the Highland entrance, fortunately the Orange Street. Image remains as we placed it.

Fruit salad

Lots of budget busts however what I will tell you next will make you wonder how we were able to continue. McCarthy packaged two disciplines in one bid package, interior drywall combined with exterior plaster. The lowest bid of three a freighting $38M overrun. YES $38M, I pride myself, I never lose my cool never show a temper. That said, upon hearing this news when the final bid opened, I tossed a chair, the legs penetrating the conference room wall. Ron Hall McCarthy's estimator and I mixed words. Ron began by saying he is not a magician, his attitude his smart-ass comment is what pushed me over the edge.

After three weeks we reduced the overrun by $16M mind you still a $22M problem however a major step and accomplishment (42%). The solution logical yet a bit bold on the design side.

First, we split the bid package as we learned subcontractor's risk to high when multiple disciplines combined. This resolved 25% of the problem. H&S awarded the interior drywall discipline, HKS&S the exterior plaster discipline. Second working with HKS&S, I planned a trip to Vegas inviting McCarthy and architect Ehrenkrantz to join Kevin and me. I knew HKS&S was the contractor for Desert Passage a retail center at the time in the final days of construction (Trizec development) and the Paris Hotel open and operating. I was certain we must change the exterior skin design and I needed clear and completed documents for the schedule to work. So, this trip provided a plethora of existing options as dozens of plaster skin types /designs could be found at Desert Passage and the Paris Hotel. I was hopeful we could lift the detailed construction documents for same.

Imagine a small group of people touring both completed Vegas projects. When I would come across a skin type I believed pleasing, we would stop, Elaine Nesbit, architect caring a Polaroid camera taking a photo, HKS&S advising the cost per square foot to construct. Greg Schooner, contractor records the cost/sf on the back side of the photo. At days end Kevin holding a couple dozen Polaroid photos. Our contractor previously tallying the seventeen different areas of H&H skin. Now we obtained all necessary information to make a decision we know each area we apply cost of same for existing buildings providing an impeccable mockup and complete architectural drawings for reference.

I joked this is like having guests for dinner, your wife wants a fruit salad so you price the fruit options. For example, grapes yes that will work bananas and apples yes another economical fruit. KIWIS, nope too expensive NO don't even think about Densuke watermelon.

Exterior elevations three to four stories our team now must engineer the exterior skin. Nope no engineered drawings in the construction documents can you believe it? I have no idea what Alton & Porter were thinking ... skin drawings weak only including architectural concept information no details and nothing for structural that information not available at the time. Hell, all the drawings were weak.

The theater our critical path... we started at the theater running clockwise around the project. Kevin led the effort meeting with the consultant team sometimes I found Kevin actually running with the drawing to the field subcontractor teams to keep the schedule. At one end of the construction conference room the engineering commenced, approved at the opposite end, HKS&S now in receipt of construction documents for that particular section. Next the consultant team commences engineering for the adjoining skin section lifting a copy of the architectural model details chosen from our Vegas trip, and so on.

It worked; in time we got caught up, yes things improving. However, to make the budget bust reverse we had to buy out the job trades significantly below targets to realize a savings. Typically, the owner looks to the general Contractor to buy out the job (hire subcontractors) within the first ninety days. I developed a buy strategy in the opposite approach. I stretched the schedule giving us time opting to buy when we believed we found the most economical subcontractor. All along concentrating on fixing the poor quality Alton & Porter construction documents, clear drawing beget a better price. It worked, for example we opened to the public Nov, 2001 McCarthy's GMP (Guarantee Maximum Price) not finalized until June just five months earlier. This worked well; my team got her back in budget.

The hotel much simpler she under budget with a great buyout from the start as we had a great set of drawings the preconstruction process made the hotel a success. Our schedule assumed a November opening we were ready actually a couple of weeks ahead of schedule however due to 911 the hotel market crashed, we elected to open the day after Christmas December 26, 2001. We used that time to train the hotel employees. For example, serving free meals breakfast and lunch to the management consultants/contractors teams with waiters doing everything with the exception of collecting money.

I watched McCarthy who I believed stretched beyond their capacity, Wolfgang Puck ball room was falling behind. I hired Hopkins Construction to assume the Ball Room/catering center construction responsibilities removing the responsibility from McCarty's contract... Initially McCarthy field team cause friction to Hopkins however in short time that issue was addressed,

Roto-Rooter

Two inspectors employed working on sight responsible to look after the subway construction. Previously, about a year earlier the subway tube was constructed by LA Metropolitan Transportation. In accordance with city conditions Trizec responsible to construct the subway station. McCarthy just commenced drilling the caissons a deep foundation system to support the station.

Please be mindful, I was hired to stop the bleeding my, responsibility to get the budget and schedule back on track. Foolish inspectors, shortly after I guess about three weeks from my meeting in Toronto with Mr. Munk, I got a huge surprise.

McCarthy set up operations at the lowest level of the below grade parking garage to drill caisson foundations for the subway station at a depth of 60 feet underneath the already excavated 6th level below grade parking. When the spoils from the drill auger reviled a small piece of waterproofing material about the size of a pack of cigarettes the inspectors shut down the job. Yep, all construction stopped. The inspectors believed the auger scored the subway tube damaging the waterproofing membrane. The inspectors advised construction is not able to commence until we fix the damaged area or prove the damage did not occur.

I asked how long to dig down and find the problem I asked how much will it cost? The response I received from McCarthy 3-4 weeks maybe longer at least $1M maybe more, maybe twice that?

Hell, three weeks of lost time will cost a million maybe more; this problem is huge this will kill the development this will side track my efforts to lead H&H. We were sitting in the conference room my thoughts spinning. I saw the yellow pages sitting on a book shelf on the opposite side of the room. I walked to the book shelf opening the yellow pages (yellow pages- how one found things before google) I saw a full-page ad for Roto-Rooter. I called the number I got his wife; she said her husband was on a call cleaning out potato peels in a garbage disposal in West Hollywood. She gave me her husband's cell phone number.

I called immediately he answered my call, everyone in the room that is with the exception of the McCarthy team shaking heads believing I was crazy, this guy is calling Roto-Rooter, some laughed. McCarthy guys understood. I asked about his camera equipment he advised he could run the camera maybe a quarter mile make video on the spot. He went on to say he was tied up on a difficult job; however; he could come to the jobsite in a couple of hours, saying he knew the location; it's that big construction site at Hollywood & Highland. -McCarthy made arrangements for him to enter the site he would call me upon his arrival.

Once he arrived, he was directed to drive down the dirt ramp to the bottom of the hole. A couple minutes later, we met him at the bottom. I walked him to the caisson hole I showed him the small piece of waterproofing, he knew what I wanted, he said you want me to drop a light and camera down the hole and film it? Exactly and I need three copies (technology at the time those big black VCR cassettes) he advised it will take a half hour I gave him my business card I advised when you are done call me.

Less than twenty minutes later he called. I asked will I be happy? He responded you will be mighty happy. I walked cross the street I joined him we watched the video in his truck, now I could smile; I called the others to join us. Our team including the two inspectors watched the video. One of the inspectors said, so what there is dirt all around the caisson hole? I replied we did not score the subway tube as all you can see all the camera views is dirt, this piece of waterproofing is merely trash that got pushed in when the subway contractor backfilled. Now I could be all that an a bag of chips: I said I need smart people working here you guys shut us down hell that caused a couple hundred grand today, if you can't think smart I need you to leave.

I asked the Roto-Rooter guy how much I owed him? How about a thousand dollars he responded. I said I am not going to pay you a thousand dollars for a couple of minutes work. I thought he was going to grab my tie and smack me. I am sure he thought me an asshole. I turner to Greg and said I believe you have the authority to sign up to ten thousand dollars for petty cash? I do not want this man to wait I would like him to be paid now. With that I thought the Roto-Rooter guy was going to kiss me.

Hell, this guy just saved us millions we can get back to work things can move forward again. I was happy I was smiling. I shook his hand and said today is Friday, I know you have a wife as I spoke with her earlier. For tonight only take her out to dinner, get a bottle of wine, get two, and take a limo if you have kids get a babysitter. Do you want to have dinner at Spago? We can get you a table we are building Wolfgang's catering center. Hell, go to any restaurant you want. You do not know me however trust me; this is my project I will pay for everything…a night on the town on me.

Unfortunately I never heard from him. The guys think he did not want to tell his wife he got ten thousand dollars. Maybe he wanted a boat? I wish he had taken me up on my offer. I wish he sent me the bill. I never heard a peep from those two inspectors again, they became invisible.

Two strikes

We incurred two strikes that hurt the schedule, both strikes being judicial grievances. Because the redevelopment agency contributed development funds the unions payed close attention. The first strike lasting over a month was due to an issue concerning who can drive a fork lift. Can you believe that? Not a worthy cause like greater pay or insurance benefits.

Typically, when a forklift is operating twenty hours or less in a week the role can be shared between the carpenter and operators union. The carpenters caused the strike trying to make a point. More than twenty hours the operators call jurisdiction. I worked the protocol channels meeting with government officials, attorneys and union representatives getting nowhere trying my best to end the strike. Fortunately, many continued to work however no carpenters crossed the gate. We set up separate gates (strike protocol one gate union the other gate open shop). For example, the inspectors belong to the operators' union; they did not show up. Fortunately, the management staff put on work-pants and maned the site. Finally, the strike ended.

Not too long after maybe ten months or so the second strike occurred. Again, the carpenters called for a strike over another flippant jurisdictional issue.

Iron workers have rights to place the end cap a piece of angle metal at the metal desking slab's edge. However, if a correction is required the Carpenters have right to correct same. Again, the carpenters wanted to make a point believing they a super union should have the right to install that edge condition in the first place. Please be mindful the carpenters did not sign the Project Labor Work Force Union Agreement as they believe carpenters should cross typical boundaries, H&H being a city funded project gives the Carpenters attention.

This time I chose a different tact, instead of seeking city government intervention and assistance I employed this strategy. After a couple of dead end days listening to both union representative teams whine and complain we scheduled an early morning meeting between the Carpenters and the Iron Workers.

I was certain they could not meet together; I was certain that would cause drama. Out of sight a block or more apart Kevin addressing the Iron Workers at the Burger King parking lot located on Highland Ave. I was addressing the Carpenters at the Chinses Theater parking lot just off Hollywood Blvd. I called Kevin's cell phone both he and I on speaker phone, my solution as we need four workers to fix the areas in question, I propose two separate teams one composed of two Carpenters and the other composed by two Iron workers. McCarthy lead superintendents will make certain the work commensurate. With that we had an agreement just minutes after my proposal however not this day they agree to come back the following morning. Sometimes it's the little things in life make me smile. This strike was solved in a week and a half; I only wish we came up with the notion sooner.

911

Similar to the day John F. Kennedy was killed, everyone remembers this morning. One just knows one can recall where they were and what they were doing. The morning of September 11th, 2001 I was in Hollywood working on the

Kodak Theater at the Hollywood & Highland complex. 900 McCarthy workers wanted to go home; I asked to talk with them first. So, they all assembled at the Kodak Theater loading dock drive area. I addressed the workers standing on the loading dock with the theater behind me.

I introduced myself, I gave a speech…. I know what it is like to miss a day's pay. However, if you sign out with your foreman today, and return tomorrow I will make sure you are paid. I had to make certain they would come back. Hell, it was a Tuesday I did not want to lose the rest of the week.

Please be mindful knowing the cost and this notion being my burden I knew the price tag to be well over a hundred thousand dollars to shut down for the day, which I believed well worth me the money.

I continued on to tell the workers …great things will happen at this Theater, the world will watch shows from this theater. It is a privilege for you to work on her, you all should be proud, your families should be proud. We are behind schedule no one believes we can make it. It isn't the architects or engineers that will turn this around, it's you the plumber, the electrician the painter … no one believes we can do it …. I believe you can do it. Help me prove them wrong.

So help each other, work smart when you return, put in the effort, when you see someone who needs help, well help them. Take pride in your work; let's show them what you can accomplish.

A young project engineer approached me from behind he taped my back and handed me a large paper bag. I glanced inside the bag it was full of stick-on American flags, hundreds of flag stickers. I am thinking WHOA where did these come from, timing is everything this is great. I moved to the edge of the loading dock and placed handful of flags in several workers hands, please pass the flags back I want to see an American flag on everyone's hard hat. Be proud you are building the Kodak Theater, be proud to be an American, be strong.

Does anyone have a question or want to say something? So, one guy who looks like John Candy yells out there isn't any toilet paper in the johns someone keeps stealing the paper. Greg, the project executive, with McCarthy, the theater contractor, takes the bullhorn from my hand and says he will make sure the paper is taken care of; the worker next to the John Candy look-a-like yells the graffiti is disgusting. I take the bullhorn back I call out I will have the inside of the johns painted and asked does anyone have a question that doesn't involve taking a dump. They all laughed. One guy yells out: let's have a moment of silence!

After that moment, I advise GO HOME to your families, remember to sign out with your foreman I will see you in the morning. While they departed, about thirty-five of the 900 construction workers made a line to shake my hand.

The next day production increased and morale was high. When I toured the site, many reached out to say thanks. They delivered the project 2.5 weeks early, and she was perfect.

I felt like I was in a made-for-TV movie. A terrible day for our country a sad day for all… that said I bet most likely not a memory you assumed from me concerning 911?

Sunday breakfast with the police

Hollywood city noise restrictions limited our construction activities to the following conditions; no work prior to 7:30 A.M. no work after 6:00 P.M., no work allowed on Sunday.

September of 2001 the final months of construction I found McCarthy struggling the schedule was close, however they were definitely behind, I was fearful any unforeseen situation will certainly cause the schedule to be missed. I was fearful we may not make our schedule.

I wanted to provide overtime on Sundays. As construction activities focused on the interior work, I believe noise would not be a concern.

I was certain Hollywood & Highland with her Kodak Theater was ready as the Academy Awards were seven months away scheduled for March 24th, 2002. The hotel was actually weeks ahead of schedule. I was also concerned with the Governors Ball Room Hopkins Construction was on schedule however the roof mechanical equipment yet to be placed troubled me.

Six months earlier to ensure a strong Christmas sales experience I chose November 11th as our grand opening date for the retail, I was fearful that date may slip. We cannot miss that opening date, retail stores and restaurants all set for the magic day with ceremonies reserved and scheduled with government officials, AMPAS executives, and of course Hollywood dignitaries.

November 9th a party for Jeffrey Katzenberg prior to opening was scheduled as a soft opening event to give the project notable press. I must be in receipt of the Occupancy Permit prior to November 9th. The finish trades behind schedule totaled about 100 workers I needed to work overtime on Sundays.

I directed McCarthy to provide overtime on Sundays. A group of mothers who lived on the adjacent hillside neighborhood would meet at the jobsite at 7:15 with cameras in hope we started construction prior to 7:30. The women enjoyed complaining, I knew they would show up if we scheduled additional work for a Sunday.

So, in the fall of 2001 every September and October Sunday I arrived at the jobsite at 7:00 A.M. to make certain I would be standing at the entrance gate greeting the workers for the day. Two police officers arrive each Sunday maybe ten to twelve minutes after I arrived.

Imagine this scene, as the construction workers entered the construction gate two police officers gave the construction workers a ticket. I, on the construction side of the gate, asked for the workers' tickets, telling the workers not to worry; I will pay the ticket fee. I look forward to seeing you guys again next Sunday. The first Sunday I was fearful the police may elect to arrest me. The cost of the ticket was a pittance of about $50, however, the number of tickets each Sunday cost the development just over five thousand dollars a cost I chose to bear. For example, construction loan interests, the cost of carry $85k per day, plus just think of the associated cost burden if we opened late. My decision easy…

On the second Sunday after all the workers entered the site, me standing with another huge handful of tickets, I asked the police officers if they would like to join me for breakfast on me at Hamburger Hamlet, a restaurant just across the street.

While the construction workers were passing through the gate, I introduced myself to the police officers. I struck up a conversation of small talk. I told them I come from a family including several uncles and cousins who proudly wear the badge serving their communities. For the next seven Sundays, I bought breakfast for the officers. We got to know each other. I enjoyed Sundays talking with them.

In late October, Kevin and I were at court, I in the back, Kevin pleading our case with the judge. I wanted to close Hollywood Blvd. one block in front of our construction site for two consecutive weekends. The plan to erect a crane to lift mechanical equipment for the Governors Ball room and roof top mechanical equipment for the Kodak Theater, we wanted to shut down the street Friday night at 9:00 P.M. open Monday morning at 6:00 A.M. Kevin gave a compelling story unfortunately the judge denied his request. Judge saying son you cannot close Hollywood Blvd. Kevin answering the judge it will be closed for weeks each year to set the complex for the Academy Awards. The judge was not reconsidering.

To my surprise the two police officers, the same guys who join me every Sunday for breakfast, tapped my shoulder, and as I turned to face them, they said that sucks what are you going to do, Jack? I was surprised they were in the room in the audience here for a Hollywood theft incident that occurred a couple of blocks north of my project.

I told them I was out of ideas. I need a crane to lift the equipment as there is no other choice for placement. I must get a permit to close Hollywood Blvd. Well, come with us, Jack. Eric Garcetti has his office upstairs in this very building. At the time Mr. Garcetti was a member of the Los Angeles City Council and represented the 13th district Hollywood.

So, with little hope and no other choice I followed the officers in the elevator moments later we were meeting with Eric Garcetti in his office. One of the police officers introduced me to Mr. Garcetti saying, this guy is a good egg. He is doing great things for Hollywood; he needs your assistance, Mr. Garcetti. I explained my debacle how I needed a permit for two consecutive weekends to ensure Hollywood & Highland with her Kodak Theater to be ready and poised for opening. Moments later I left the building with the necessary permit.

All went well Hollywood & Highland opened big and we opened on time obtaining the Temporary Occupancy Permit a week earlier. We received the Occupancy Permit in record time.

Names displayed proudly on the bathroom walls

I wanted our team to be remembered, I wanted to leave our mark. This is a tradition I learned from my Disney days. For example, at Disneyland along the pre-ride entry point, as quests file in waiting to access the Star Tours ride you will find overhead metal baskets move in unison holding what appears to be small parts. Each basket has an identification number. The numbers represent the last four digits of an imaginer's phone number each basket signifies the imaginer who worked on this project. Every imaginer's number posted proudly on one of the hundreds of baskets. The Haunted Mansion holds the most important and distinctive mark, just as a guest is ready to access one of the ride cars the guest will see a woman's head in a glass jar with her hair standing straight up. The woman who was the designer for this ride made a cast of her mother's head/face to be displayed in the jar. The night before the ride opened to the public at the cast party, she showed this image to her mother. I could go on however I believe you have the idea.

The six Hollywood & Highland retail restrooms are designed in black and white tiles included random accent tiles placed in line about 5 feet from the floor. The accent tiles depicting turn of the century business displaying the business names. Laura, Carla, and I changed the names listed on the tiles to include all Trizec-Hahn employees who were working on the Hollywood & Highland development....

On November 9th, two days prior to our grand opening the development hosted a huge Hollywood Star Studded party for Jeffrey Katzenberg in the Wolfgang Puck Ballroom.

My secretary, Lisa Vigil, while in one of the ladies' rooms, happened to find her name on the wall. Then she noticed so many others. She brought several ladies back to see her discovery. No longer was my surprise a secret, the cat now out of the bag. Employee's gift tiles were scheduled for recipients to receive on opening day November 11th, 2001. I believe the gifts were appreciated I did however receive five lovely thank-you letters from women saying how proud they are to have their name listed on the bathroom walls.

When I returned from my five-year assignment in Houston one evening, I met friends at H&H for diner. Unfortunately, I found five of the six retail restrooms had been remodeled. Our mark now regrettably lost.

I was fortunate to have an awesome team, Hollywood & Highland I believe to be my most challenging and difficult endeavor. We made the impossible a reality, my team accomplished above and beyond. I have fond memories indeed.

I still miss him however with time I find his thought has diminished. When on occasion where my mind wanders back to Jack... yes Hollywood & Highland days are how I recall him... was he better... absolutely. That said this guy is good enough, I have become content, happy, YES, I am gratified; you see I am extremely fortunate being the other.

I believe if you wake up each morning ready to sacrifice, if you are willing to work actually put in the time... deciding what you want to give verses what you are going to get. You can make your dream a reality. With just half a brain you can still accomplish your dreams. You can make anything happen it is merely up to you... go and find success in spite of your limitations.

Everything you want in life is on the other side of hard; I do not take my second chance lightly Hope is a good thing...I believe maybe the best of things.